D1264023

DEVELOPMENTS IN INORGANIC POLYMER CHEMISTRY

SOLE DISTRIBUTORS FOR THE UNITED STATES AND CANADA
AMERICAN ELSEVIER PUBLISHING COMPANY, INC.
52 Vanderbilt Avenue, New York 17, N.Y.

DEVELOPMENTS IN INORGANIC POLYMER CHEMISTRY

EDITED BY

M. F. LAPPERT

Senior Lecturer in Chemistry

AND

G. J. LEIGH

Lecturer in Chemistry

both at the Manchester College of Science and Technology, University of Manchester (England)

ELSEVIER PUBLISHING COMPANY

AMSTERDAM – LONDON – NEW YORK

1962

Library of Congress Catalog Card Number 62–10362

With 25 illustrations and 14 tables

PRINTED IN THE NETHERLANDS BY
DRUKKERIJ MEIJER, WORMERVEER AND AMSTERDAM

CONTRIBUTORS TO THIS VOLUME

PROFESSOR DR. MARGOT BECKE-GOEHRING
Anorganisch-Chemisches Institut der Universität, Heidelberg (Germany)

PROFESSOR H. J. EMELÉUS
C.B.E., M.A., Ph.D., D.Sc., A.R.C.S., F.R.I.C., F.R.S.
Department of Inorganic Chemistry, University of Cambridge

J. S. HUGHES, B.Sc., F.R.I.C.
Midland Silicones, Ltd., Barry, Glamorgan

J. IDRIS JONES, M.Sc., D.Sc., F.R.I.C.
National Chemical Laboratory, Teddington, Middlesex

C. N. KENNEY, M.A., Ph.D.
Research Department, Alkali Division, Imperial Chemical Industries, Ltd., Winnington, Cheshire
Present address:
Department of Chemical Engineering, University of Cambridge

M. F. LAPPERT, Ph.D., D.Sc., F.R.I.C.
Department of Chemistry, Manchester College of Science and Technology, Manchester

N. L. PADDOCK, B.A.
Department of Chemistry, Faculty of Science, University of Manchester

J. M. C. THOMPSON, M.A., B.Sc., D.Phil., F.R.I.C.
Research and Development Department, Nobel Division, Imperial Chemical Industries, Ltd., Stevenston, Ayrshire

PREFACE

This book largely stems from a course of postgraduate lectures on "Inorganic Polymers", held in The Department of Chemistry, of the Manchester College of Science and Technology, in the autumn of 1960. The response from the large audience to these lectures persuaded us that many chemists unable to attend them would also welcome access to the material there presented. We were further encouraged by the wide and rapidly growing interest, both in academic and in industrial circles, and by the lack of any previous source book of information.

Accordingly, this volume represents a summary (together with the cited references to review articles) of the knowledge currently available in the major areas of inorganic polymer research. A particularly valuable aspect, we believe, is the substantial bibliography, much of it, such as Patent specifications, Government reports, and the extensive Russian literature, not commonly accessible. The scope of each chapter is defined by its author. In the field of silicones, it was not practicable to present a comprehensive account, because it would have destroyed the balance of the book, because of the numerous existing monographs, and finally because of the difficulty of one man covering this vast field. However, Mr. J. S. Hughes' lecture, on "Some Recent Advances in Silicone Chemistry", was received here with such interest, that we wished to make its substance available to a wider public and we prevailed upon him to make his contribution to this book. In fairness to him it should be emphasized, however, that his chapter represents only a selection of topics of recent interest.

The field of Inorganic Polymers is still at a very early stage in its development. As regards production of technologically-useful materials, progress has been very limited, except with the silicones. On the other hand, much interesting new chemistry has already been discovered, and we hope that this book will provide added stimulus for further researches. Having a summary of the major advances makes it possible to see at least some of the areas in which fresh endeavours are needed. It seems to us that particular effort is required in the fields of structural chemistry, polymer technology, evaluation, and testing, and general physical chemistry, especially from the aspect of the correlation of structures and physical properties.

In conclusion, it is a pleasure for us to thank the contributors for their cooperation. We are also grateful to those who gave permission to reproduce various figures, as acknowledged in the text.

M. F. LAPPERT

Manchester, 1962 G. J. LEIGH

CONTENTS

1. INORGANIC POLYMERS, A GENERAL SURVEY
by H. J. Emeléus
1. Introduction 1
2. Polymers based on homoatomic structures 3
3. Polymers based on heteroatomic structures 10
References 18

2. POLYMERS CONTAINING BORON AND NITROGEN
by M. F. Lappert
1. Introduction 20
2. Addition polymers of borazens 22
3. Addition polymers of borazins (condensed system) 26
4. Addition polymers of borazins (fused system) 29
5. Autocomplexes 31
6. Polycondensates having only boron and nitrogen in the main chain 33
7. Polycondensates having only boron, nitrogen, and elements other than carbon in the main chain 38
8. Polycondensates having boron, nitrogen and carbon in the main chain 40
9. Polymers derived from isocyanates 42
10. Evidence for π-bonding in 3-co-ordinate boron-nitrogen systems 44
11. Hydrolytic susceptibility; hydrolysis and some other nucleophilic substitution reactions of 3-co-ordinate boron-nitrogen compounds 49
12. Summary and Conclusion 51
References 52

3. OTHER BORON-CONTAINING POLYMERS
by J. M. C. Thompson
1. Introduction 57
2. Materials containing B–B bonds and their derivatives. . 58
3. Boric esters of di- and poly-hydroxy compounds 59
4. Boronic esters 63
5. Boroxoles 70
6. *p*-Vinylphenylboronic acid and related substances 70
7. Si–O–B-containing polymers 71
8. B–O–P-containing polymers 75
9. Polymers containing B–P bonds 76
10. Compounds with B–As bonds 82
11. Compounds with B–S bonds 83
References 83

4. PHOSPHORUS-NITROGEN POLYMERS
by N. L. Paddock

1. Introduction 87
2. Preparation 88
3. Theoretical aspects 92
4. Comparison with experiment 96
5. Resistance to high temperatures 100
6. Flexibility 102
7. Acceptor properties of phosphorus 105
8. Conclusion 107
References 108

5. POLYMERIC SULPHUR AND PHOSPHORUS COMPOUNDS
by Margot Becke-Goehring

1. Introduction 110
2. Sulphur compounds 111
(i) Sulphur imides and nitrides, 111 – (ii) Thionyl imide and derivatives, 113 – (iii) Trithiazyl chloride and derivatives, 115 – (iv) Sulphanuric chloride and derivatives, 116 – (v) Sulphuryl isocyanate and derivatives, 117 – (vi) Sulphamide, sulphamic acid, and derivatives, 119
3. Phosphorus compounds 121
(i) Polyphosphates and polyphosphinates, 121 – (ii) Phosphoryl amides and derivatives, 127 – (iii) Phosphonic acids, phosphonic amides, and derivatives, 129 – (iv) Phosphonitrilic imide and derivatives, 132 – (v) Polymers with phosphorus in a lower oxidation state, 135
References 136

6. SOME RECENT ADVANCES IN SILICONE CHEMISTRY
by J. S. Hughes

1. Introduction 138
2. Structure, preparation, and properties of silicones 138
3. Production of chlorosilane intermediates 141
4. Thermal properties of silicones 144
5. Silicone rubbers 148
6. Silicone fluids 151
7. Silicone resins 155
8. "Carbon functional" silicones and copolymers 156
9. Future aspects 159
References 159

7. POLYMETALLOSILOXANES. PART I. INTRODUCTION AND SYNTHESIS OF METALLOSILOXANES
by J. Idris Jones

1. Introduction 162
2. The synthesis of metallosiloxanes 167
3. Alkali metal silanolates 167

4. Organosiloxymagnesium compounds 170
5. Organosiloxyaluminium compounds 172
6. Organosiloxytitanium compounds 174
7. Organosiloxyboron compounds 179
8. Organosiloxytin compounds 182
9. Organosiloxyarsenic compounds 182
10. Organosiloxyphosphorus compounds 185
11. Organosiloxysulphur compounds 187
12. Other organosiloxymetal compounds 189
References 195

8. POLYMETALLOSILOXANES. PART II. POLYORGANOMETALLOSILOXANES AND POLYORGANOSILOXYMETALLOXANES
by J. Idris Jones

1. Introduction 200
2. Silicon–oxygen–aluminium polymers 201
3. Silicon–oxygen–titanium polymers 213
4. Silicon–oxygen–tin polymers 219
5. Silicon–oxygen–arsenic polymers 222
6. Silicon–oxygen–boron polymers 225
7. Silicon–oxygen–phosphorus polymers 229
8. Silicon–oxygen–sulphur polymers 233
9. Silicon-oxygen–antimony polymers 234
10. Silicon–oxygen–germanium polymers 235
11. Silicon–oxygen–chromium systems 236
12. Miscellaneous polyorganometallosiloxanes 238
13. Structure and general properties of polymetallosiloxanes 239
References 252

9. METAL CHELATE POLYMERS
by C. N. Kenney

1. Introduction 256
2. Synthetic methods 257
(i) Linking of ligands with ions, 258 – (ii) Polymer formation in the presence of metal, 261 – (iii) Incorporation of metal ions in a preformed polymer, 262 – (iv) Reactions with chelates containing functional groups, 264 – (v) Ferrocenes, 266
3. Chemical and physical properties 267
References 273

Author Index 275

Index of Compounds 286

Subject Index 302

Chapter 1

Inorganic Polymers, a General Survey

by

H. J. EMELÉUS

1. Introduction

The concept of a polymer as a substance with moderate or high molecular weight and containing a recurrent structural unit is familiar to all chemists. Such structures are very common among natural organic substances and a wide range of synthetic organic polymers is also known. The purpose of this series of articles is to review the extent to which comparable inorganic polymeric substances exist. The line of demarcation between the two fields is not always very clear but most organic polymers are based on a framework of carbon—carbon bonds, with oxygen and nitrogen atoms as the chief additional structural units. Such polymers may often be tailored to a considerable extent, so as to endow the resulting macromolecule with special properties, but all such compounds have inherent limitations which arise chiefly from the ease with which they undergo pyrolysis and oxidation. Thus there are few purely organic compounds which are stable in air at temperatures in excess of 300°. Other limitations become apparent in considering the resistance of organic polymers to attack by chemical reagents such as acids and bases, or to solvents. It is the existence of these limitations which has given an impetus to the search for inorganic polymeric compounds of higher resistance to heat and oxidation, or with new combinations of properties which are not encountered in the organic field. The amount of recent

References, p. 18–19

research on inorganic polymers has been very great and it must be admitted that at present many of the results obtained have been disappointing from the point of view of improved technical products. The subject is being studied on a very broad front, however, and, as this monograph will show, a fuller understanding of principles is rapidly emerging which may ultimately lead to further technical progress and, even now, constitutes a major advance in the academic study of the field.

Before considering the types of polymer which are encountered among inorganic compounds it may be pointed out that many common inorganic substances are polymeric in character, though the degree of polymerisation is usually excessive. The silicates, for example, all contain a skeleton of linked silicon and oxygen atoms, with varying degrees of cross-linking. Thus, starting from the ion SiO_4^{4-}, which has a tetrahedral distribution of its four oxygen atoms around the relatively small silicon atom, condensed anions are formed by sharing oxygens between the tetrahedra, leading to discrete anions such as (I) and (II). If the structure (I) is

$[O_3Si—O—SiO_3]^{6-}$

(I)

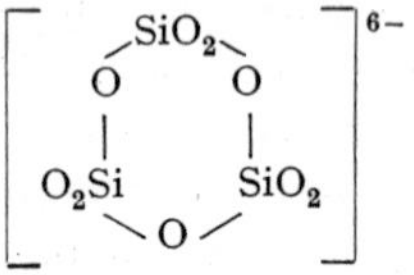

$$\left[\begin{array}{ccc} & SiO_2 & \\ O & & O \\ | & & | \\ O_2Si & & SiO_2 \\ & O & \end{array}\right]^{6-}$$

(II)

extended, a chain-like metasilicate anion results, while further cross-linking leads in turn to the union of two such chains into a band or an anionic sheet. Only when cross-linking is complete is the neutral structure of silica itself produced. Similar condensed anions are encountered in a great many other cases (*e.g.*, in the borates and polyphosphates). We find similar oxygen cross-linking also in such neutral molecules as the orthorhombic form[1] of P_4O_{10} and the cubic form of antimony trioxide. Other examples of familiar

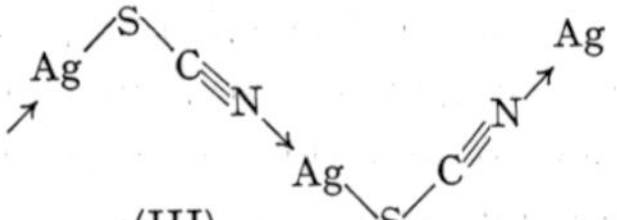

$$\nearrow Ag—S—C\equiv N \rightarrow Ag—S—C\equiv N \rightarrow Ag$$

(III)

$$\nearrow Pd\begin{smallmatrix}\swarrow Cl \searrow \\ \nwarrow Cl \nearrow\end{smallmatrix}Pd\begin{smallmatrix}\swarrow Cl \searrow \\ \nwarrow Cl \nearrow\end{smallmatrix}Pd\swarrow$$

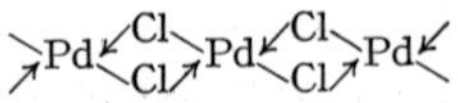

(IV)

inorganic substances which have typical polymeric structures are silver thiocyanate, (III)[2], and palladous chloride, (IV)[3].
These random examples are typical of a very large group of known structures, involving both metals and non-metals. The task which confronts the inorganic chemist is to select from the array of elements those which, when bonded together into a polymeric structure, will give a material with chemical and thermal stability. He must, in some cases, seek means of limiting the degree of polymerisation of a given structural unit, so as to endow his product with solubility in certain types of solvent, or a reasonably low melting point. Quite often, too, organic radicals are built into a framework which is essentially inorganic in character. This is done, for example, in the silicones, which combine the stability of the $\geqslant$Si—O—Si$\leqslant$ framework found in the silicates with water repellancy and other properties, associated with hydrocarbons. Of paramount importance, however, is the fuller understanding of the basic principles which determine the stability of bonds between atoms of various sorts.

Several approaches to the classification of inorganic polymers are possible. It is proposed here to divide them into two groups, those with a skeleton of atoms of the same sort (homoatomic) or of different sorts (heteroatomic). Examples will be given to illustrate the range of possibilities in each group and such generalisations as seem justifiable by our present knowledge will be pointed out.

2. Polymers based on homoatomic structures

The search for inorganic polymers based on a homoatomic structural unit needs no further justification than the fact that many polymeric carbon compounds are of this type. As will be seen, the conclusion reached is that catenation is very much less pronounced among compounds of other elements than it is in carbon, a fact which calls for some explanation. Atoms of the more positive metallic elements do not combine with one another in their compounds because the latter are ionic in character. This phenomenon is found to be restricted to the less positive metals. Covalent bonds between metallic elements occur in a few cases as, for example,

References, p. 18–19

in the alkyl and aryl derivatives of tin and lead of the type M_2R_6, but the metal-metal bond is weak.

Non-metallic elements other than carbon combine together to a limited extent. In the case of boron, the halides of the type B_2X_4 have a B—B bond and in B_4Cl_4 there are four boron atoms arranged tetrahedrally, each associated with a single chlorine atom[4]. The crystal structures of a number of metallic borides have also been determined[5] and they reveal a marked tendency for boron atoms to link together to form anionic chains, layers, or 3-dimensional networks. In the boride AlB_2, for example, the boron atoms are arranged in layers, as in graphite, with interspersed layers of aluminium. It seems that the bonding between the boron atoms is often, though not invariably, covalent in character and this raises the very interesting possibility that other boron compounds may in time be found in which there is extensive catenation. It should be noted that boron atoms in boron hydrides are often bonded by hydrogen bridges and that these, as well as covalent B—B bonds, have a low hydrolytic stability.

Catenation of silicon is encountered to a very limited extent in saturated silicon hydrides, which have been characterised up to Si_6H_{14}. It also occurs, one must suppose, in "unsaturated" silicon hydrides of the type $(SiH_2)_n$, which are formed in the cracking of higher silanes or in the hydrolysis of certain silicides. When silicon tetrachloride is cracked in an inert atmosphere at 1100° it also gives chlorides of high molecular weight, among which $Si_{10}Cl_{22}$ has been identified. Also, a polymeric iodide, $(SiI)_n$, is obtained in the thermal decomposition of Si_2I_6. In certain silicides (*e.g.*, $CaSi_2$) each Si atom is also linked to three others to form a layer, in which the Si—Si bonds are of much the same length as in elementary silicon. A major limitation to the formation of homo-atomic polymers with chains of silicon atoms is the very limited extent of the analogy between carbon and silicon as far as the formation of multiple bonds by silicon is concerned. It seems also that the Si—Si bond is inherently unstable to hydrolysis. This is because the maximum co-ordination number of silicon is six, whereas that of carbon is four. The behaviour of germanium is like that of silicon in certain respects (*e.g.*, the formation of hydrides with chains of germanium atoms) but it seems to offer even less prospect for the formation of useful homoatomic polymer structures.

Phosphorus exhibits catenation in the tetrahedral P_4 molecule and also in crystalline black phosphorus, which is made up of corrugated layers of phosphorus atoms, each of which is bonded to three neighbours. The P—P bond is also encountered in the hydride P_2H_4, the halides of the type P_2X_4, and probably also in ill-defined solid hydrides. The metallic phosphides, many of which have been subjected to a detailed structural analysis[6], show little evidence of covalent bonding between phosphorus atoms.

Two unusual phosphorus compounds deserve mention at this point, because of their high thermal stability. They are $P_4(C_6H_5)_4$, (V), and $P_4(CF_3)_4$, (VI). Phosphobenzene, (V), is a yellow powder (m.p. 149°) and was first prepared in 1877 by the interaction of phenyldichlorophosphine with phenylphosphine:

$$2\,C_6H_5PCl_2 + 2\,C_6H_5PH_2 \longrightarrow (C_6H_5)_4P_4 + 4\,HCl\,.$$

The ring structure (V) has not been fully established, but is highly probable[7]. A very similar compound, (VI), has been prepared by

$$\text{(V)}\quad \begin{array}{ccc} H_5C_6\diagdown & P—P & \diagup C_6H_5 \\ & |\quad\; | & \\ H_5C_6\diagup & P—P & \diagdown C_6H_5 \end{array} \qquad\qquad \begin{array}{ccc} F_3C\diagdown & P—P & \diagup CF_3 \\ & |\quad\; | & \\ F_3C\diagup & P—P & \diagdown CF_3 \end{array}\quad \text{(VI)}$$

reaction of mercury with diiodotrifluoromethylphosphine or by pyrolysis of bistrifluoromethylphosphine or tetrabistrifluoromethyldiphosphine[8]. A pentamer is formed at the same time and, in the last two reactions, also some material of higher molecular weight. The tetramer is stable up to 300° and the pentamer is only a little less stable to heat. This unexpected strengthening of the P—P bonds, which are normally of the σ-type, may be explained by π-bonding, involving the lone pair of electrons on the phosphorus atoms and $3d$-orbitals on adjacent phosphorus atoms. This type of interaction will be referred to again later in connexion with such compounds as the phosphonitrilic halides (Chapter 4) and is of considerable importance in producing molecules with high thermal stability.

References, p. 18–19

The only other example of an element with a strong tendency to catenation is sulphur and in this case there is fortunately much structural evidence available. The S_8 ring, with a puckered crown form, occurs in the crystal of orthorhombic α-sulphur and in β-sulphur, while, in liquid sulphur up to 160°, the same molecular unit also predominates. As the temperature is raised, chain-like units of considerable length are formed and, in plastic sulphur, there are roughly close-packed helices of linked sulphur atoms together with S_8 rings[9]. A modified eight-membered sulphur ring is found in heptasulphur imide, S_7NH, and X-ray studies of several polysulphides[10] have shown the presence in the solid of unbranched chains of sulphur atoms forming extended helices. Sulphur chains also occur in the polysulphur hydrides and halides, two groups of compounds which have been extensively studied by Fehér and his co-workers. There is again no evidence of branching in the sulphur chain and the same is true of a number of organic polysulphides and the polythionate anions. There are indications that bonds between bivalent sulphur atoms in some instances possess some (p_π-d_π) bond character. A few related selenium and tellurium compounds are known, but catenation is very much less frequent for these two elements, notwithstanding the occurrence of crown-shaped Se_8 rings in the α- and β-modifications of selenium, and of infinite helices of linked atoms in hexagonal selenium and tellurium.

One further point may be made in relation to homoatomic polymer types. It concerns the special position of fluorocarbon polymers, such as polytetrafluoroethylene. These are organic derivatives and, as such, would lie outside the scope of this monograph. On the other hand they differ greatly from their hydrocarbon analogues and owe so much to their fluorine content that it is proposed to discuss them briefly here. The fluorocarbon polymers possess outstanding thermal stability which, as a rule, is combined with high resistance to chemical attack and insolubility in the majority of solvents. These properties have already resulted in numerous applications, particularly in the cases of polytetrafluoroethylene and polychlorotrifluoroethylene.

The simplest polymeric fluorocarbon is carbon monofluoride

which is formed when graphite is heated at 420°–460° in a stream of fluorine[11]. It is a solid which varies in colour from gray to white, the colour being darker the more deficient it is in fluorine. Thus, the material $CF_{0.92}$ was gray[11]. Later preparations varied in composition from $CF_{0.68}$ to $CF_{0.995}$, the latter being white, and transparent in thin layers[12]. It was found that the electrical conductivity decreased with increasing fluorine content and was almost zero for the white preparations. Carbon monofluoride is unreactive chemically, being unattacked by concentrated acids or alkalis, and unwetted by water. It does, however, deflagrate when heated rapidly, forming a mixture of carbon and fluorocarbons, among which carbon tetrafluoride predominates.

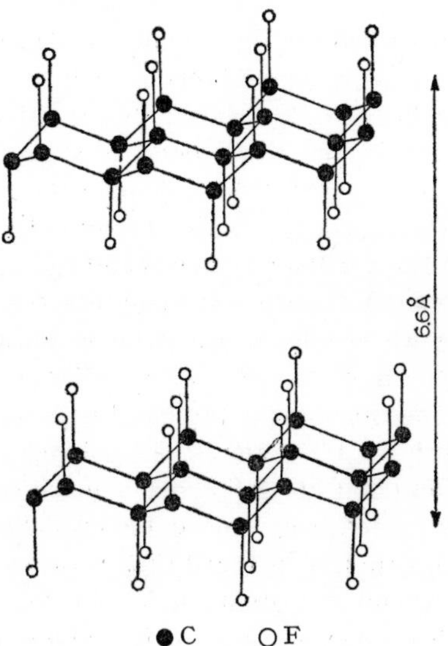

Fig. 1. Crystal lattice of carbon monofluoride. [Reproduced, with permission, from W. RÜDORFF, *Advances in Inorganic Chemistry and Radiochemistry*, Vol. I, Ed. H. J. EMELÉUS and A. G. SHARPE, Academic Press, New York, 1959, p. 232].

The structure[13] of carbon monofluoride is shown in Fig. 1. It is a homopolar compound with C—F bonds like those in a fluorocarbon. This important fact is inferred from the infrared absorption spectrum, which shows a broad band at 1215 cm^{-1}, attributable to a C—F stretching vibration. The structure is made up of puckered layers, with sp^3 hybridisation round the carbon, and with an inter-layer distance of 6.6 Å, compared with 3.34 Å between the planes of ordinary graphite. The change in the type of bonding of the carbon atoms also explains the loss of electrical conductivity. Treatment of graphite with fluorine and hydrogen fluoride at room temperature gives a second product, the composition of which varies in the range C_4F–$C_{3.6}F$, depending on the conditions of preparation. In this, it is believed that every fourth carbon atom is covalently bonded to fluorine. It is again very inert, though the electrical conductivity of graphite is partly retained.

The best known fluorocarbon polymers are those derived from aliphatic fluoro-olefins. Their stability is high compared with that of their hydrocarbon analogues and this is attributable to two main factors. Firstly, the C—F bond is strong and, secondly, replacement of hydrogen by fluorine removes one of the chief points of chemical attack (*e.g.*, in oxidation). The fluorine atoms are also somewhat larger than hydrogen and thus may form a more effective shield round the carbon chain. Polytetrafluoroethylene, $(CF_2{\cdot}CF_2)_n$, is a white solid which is made by polymerising the tetrafluoroethylene monomer in the presence of aqueous persulphate, the monomer itself being produced by cracking CF_2HCl at ca. 800° ($2CF_2HCl \rightarrow C_2F_4 + 2HCl$). The polymer is thermoplastic. It has a transition point at 327° above which it can be fabricated. It is stable in air up to about 300° and is insoluble in all solvents. Polychlorotrifluoroethylene, $(CF_2{\cdot}CFCl)_n$, is rather similar, though its thermal and chemical stability is a little lower. Its electrical properties are also somewhat inferior to those of polytetrafluoroethylene. Various other fluorinated vinyl-type polymers have been synthesised with the aim of improving on polytetrafluoroethylene, the processing of which is difficult. Thus a copolymer of tetrafluoroethylene with hexafluoropropylene, with the formula

$$(CF_2{\cdot}CF_2{\cdot}CF_2{\cdot}\underset{\displaystyle CF_3}{\underset{|}{CF}})_n$$

has a melt viscosity which is low enough to allow processing by normal means. Polyvinylidene fluoride, $(CH_2 \cdot CF_2 \cdot CH_2 \cdot CF_2)_n$, has also been introduced recently. It behaves as a normal thermoplastic resin but, as would be expected, has a lower chemical and thermal stability. It is, however, soluble in strongly polar solvents. It is evident that, by using partially fluorinated compounds, it may be possible in time to obtain useful products with properties intermediate between those of the hydrocarbon and the fluorocarbon polymer types.

Another interesting development is the production of elastomers[14]. Typical of these are the copolymers of vinylidene fluoride and hexafluoropropylene. Variation in the monomer ratio and method of polymerisation gives a range of products, but there are two features in the structural unit,

$$(CH_2 \cdot CH_2 \cdot CF_2 \cdot \underset{\displaystyle CF_3}{\underset{|}{CF}})$$

which are significant. The methylene groups introduce flexibility into the backbone of the structure and the pendant $—CF_3$ groups reduce the tendency to crystallise. The methylene groups also provide a point of attack when cross-linking is desired. Copolymerisation of vinylidene fluoride with chlorotrifluoroethylene gives comparable products. These rubbers have already found applications in the aircraft industry and the *Douglas DC-8* is said to contain 28 lbs. of fluoro-elastomers. They have excellent resistance to oils, fuels, and solvents, up to quite high temperatures. Their chemical resistance is also high, though not as high as that of polytetrafluoroethylene.

Fluoroaromatics, the chemistry of which is just beginning to be elucidated, offer the possibility of still further developments in this general field. The first fluoroaromatic polymer, polytetrafluorophenylene[15], was made by the route shown below:

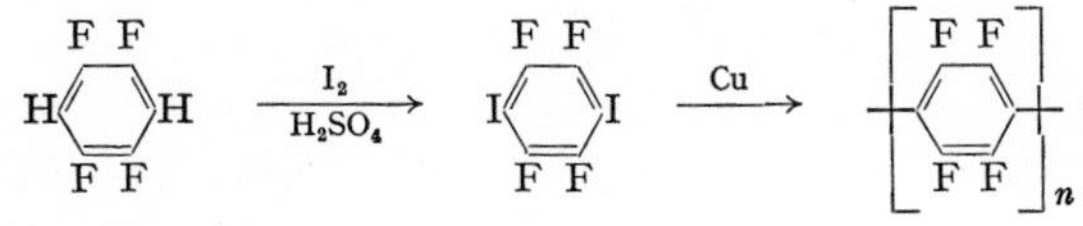

$$H-C_6F_4-H \xrightarrow[H_2SO_4]{I_2} I-C_6F_4-I \xrightarrow{Cu} \left[-C_6F_4-\right]_n \quad (n = 3\text{—}11)$$

References, p. 18–19

No technical products have yet emerged in this new field. It is, however, quite clear that, as our knowledge of fluoroaromatics increases, there will be an increasing effort to extend their possible applications into the polymer field. Perfluorostyrene, $C_6F_5 \cdot CF:CF_2$, is as yet unknown but is typical of the desirable monomers. Equally important would be the synthesis of highly-fluorinated polyesters and polyamides. They would certainly be substantially different from their hydrocarbon analogues and, as in the case of the fluorine-containing polymers already mentioned, their special properties would be likely to be directly attributable to the presence of fluorine.

3. Polymers based on heteroatomic structures

From the above, it is clear that catenation of atoms of one kind is, except in the case of carbon, not a promising route to the production of useful polymeric materials. When, however, backbone structures which include atoms of different kinds are considered the situation is quite different. Atoms of the majority of the non-metallic elements, and of some of the less electropositive metallic elements, combine in a variety of ways to form strong covalent bonds. The main problem is to devise a backbone structure containing these bonds which has the requisite thermal and chemical stability and, particularly, to limit the degree of polymerisation and cross-linking. Many of the possible systems will be discussed in detail in subsequent chapters, but it seems appropriate at this point to refer to some examples and to point out, where possible, some of the salient features.

$$(CH_3)_2SiCl_2 \longrightarrow (CH_3)_2Si(OH)_2 \longrightarrow -\underset{\underset{CH_3}{|}}{\overset{\overset{CH_3}{|}}{Si}}-O-\underset{\underset{CH_3}{|}}{\overset{\overset{CH_3}{|}}{Si}}-O-\underset{\underset{CH_3}{|}}{\overset{\overset{CH_3}{|}}{Si}}-$$

The most important group of polymers of this class is the silicones, in which the backbone structure is based on the strong bonds between silicon and oxygen, which occur in silica and the silicates. Their formation may be illustrated by considering the hydrolysis of dimethyldichlorosilane to the unstable $(CH_3)_2Si(OH)_2$. The latter loses water intermolecularly. The result is a mixture of linear and cyclic polymers.

Terminal groups may be provided by using trimethylchlorosilane, and, if cross-linking is required, it can be provided either by methyltrichlorosilane or silicon tetrachloride. It is possible in this way, and by varying the organic groups, to tailor the silicones to a considerable extent and so to suit them to a variety of technical uses.

Attempts have been made in recent years to improve the silicones by incorporating fluoroalkyl groups. This is done by first making a fluoroalkylchlorosilane, by the addition to a fluorinated olefin of a silyl hydride; *e.g.*,

$$SiHCl_3 + C_2F_4 \longrightarrow CHF_2{\cdot}CF_2{\cdot}SiCl_3$$

$$SiHCl_3 + CF_3{\cdot}CH{:}CH_2 \longrightarrow CF_3{\cdot}CH_2{\cdot}CH_2{\cdot}SiCl_3$$

Aqueous hydrolysis of the products of such reactions leads directly to the fluorinated silicones. One would expect such materials to combine some of the desirable properties of the fluorocarbons with those of the silicones. In fact, however, the simple fluoroalkyl radicals when attached directly to silicon are readily hydrolysed by alkali if the fluorine is in the α- or β-position relative to silicon (*i.e.*, as $R_{(F)}$—Si$\lessgtr$ or $R_{(F)}{\cdot}CH_2$—Si$\lessgtr$). Only when fluorine is in the γ-position is hydrolytic stability achieved. This, combined with excellent thermal stability, has led to useful technical products. A polysiloxane of the type $(CF_3{\cdot}CH_2{\cdot}CH_2{\cdot}SiO_{1.5})_n$ is not decomposed by 40 per cent alkali and is thermally stable up to about 400°. A silicone rubber ("Silastic LS-53"), in which the methyl-3,3,3-trifluoropropyl group is incorporated, has a working range from —68° to 205°.

The outstanding successes in the silicone field have led to a considerable amount of research on related backbone structures, such as B—O—Si, Al—O—Al, Al—O—Si, and Sn—O—Si (see Chapters 7 and 8). Elements such as boron, aluminium, titanium, and tin share with silicon the property of forming condensed acids by elimination of water from their hydroxides and yield structures, the bond strengths of which are comparable with those in the

References, p. 18–19

silicates. This class of compound may be exemplified by the products formed by partial hydrolysis of titanium ortho-esters. Among the simpler condensation products are molecules such as (VII) and (VIII). Similarly, using mixed titanium and silicon esters, compounds containing the Ti—O—Si bond may be obtained.

$$(RO)_3Ti—O—Ti(OR)_3 \quad \text{(VII)}$$

$$(RO)_3Ti—O—Ti(OR)_2—O—Ti(OR)_3 \quad \text{(VIII)}$$

(VII) (VIII)

The introduction of nitrogen into the basic polymer structure opens up a wide range of further possibilities. The most familiar compounds of this type are the phosphonitrilic chlorides and their derivatives, which will be discussed in detail in Chapter 4. When phosphorus pentachloride is heated with a small excess of ammonium chloride in refluxing *s*-tetrachloroethane (b.p. 146°), a product is obtained which is a mixture of an oil and crystals. The greater part is soluble in petroleum ether and is made up of cyclic polymers of low molecular weight, with the empirical formula $(PNCl_2)_n$. These may be separated and entities with molecular weights corresponding to values of n from 3 to 6 can be identified. A substantial part (*ca.* 25%) of the product is of higher molecular weight. That part of the original product which is not soluble in petroleum ether has the constitution $(PNCl_2)_nPCl_5$ and is thought to contain chain-like polymers of the type $PCl_4(PNCl_2)_nCl$.

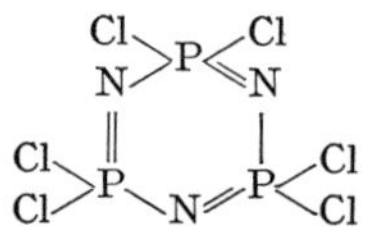

$$(Cl_2P{=}N)_3 \text{ (cyclic)} \qquad —P(Cl_2){=}N—P(Cl_2){=}N—P(Cl_2){=}$$

(IX) 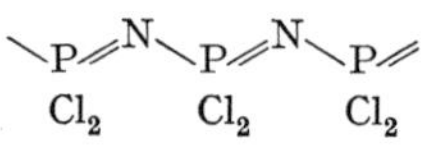 (X)

The structures of the simpler petroleum ether-soluble polymers have been established by X-ray crystallography and may be exemplified by the trimer, shown above (IX). The chain-like polymers may be represented by (X).

Though the trimer is depicted as a structure with alternating double and single bonds, the P—N bonds are in fact all of the same length and are shorter than would be expected for a single bond. The bonds have partial double bond character, which suggests an analogy with aromatic systems. It is explained by the fact that each nitrogen atom in the ring has a lone pair of electrons, while the phosphorus atoms have vacant *d*-orbitals. This leads to π-bonding, with a resultant strengthening of the structure. The compounds are moderately stable to heat and the P—Cl bonds also undergo hydrolysis less readily than in the simple phosphorus halides. A great many variants on the phosphonitrilic chlorides are possible. Thus, for example, the corresponding bromides and fluorides are known and alkyl, aryl, or alkoxy groups may replace the halogens. No major applications of these various products have yet been reported, but the field is one which still offers very considerable scope for further exploration. The phosphonitrilic halides themselves are sufficiently reactive towards a variety of reagents to allow derived polymers to be tailored to a certain extent.

Closely related to the phosphonitrilics are the so-called 'PON' polymers[16], which have phosphorus atoms linked through nitrogen, with oxygen atoms attached directly to phosphorus. The simplest

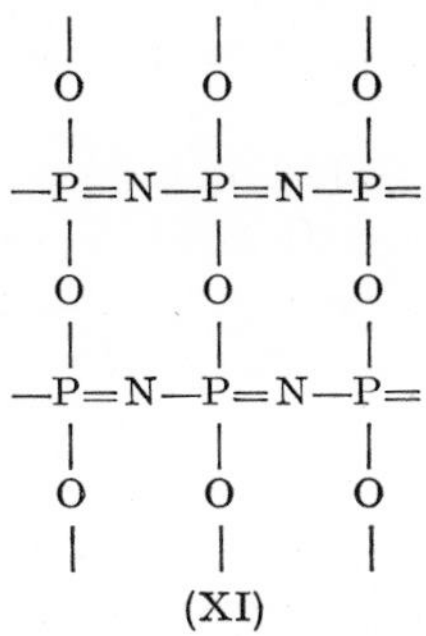

(XI)

compound of this type is phosphorus oxynitride, $(PON)_n$, which was made in 1846 by Gerhardt by heating phosphoryl imidoamide to red heat in absence of air. It is a high-melting solid which is stable

References, p. 18–19

to heat and also moderately stable to chemical attack. The structure has not been elucidated but may involve both the P—O—P and the P=N—P bond as shown in (XI), in which case $d\pi$—$p\pi$ bonding occurs between the phosphorus and the nitrogen atoms, as in the phosphonitrilics. Further details may be found in Chapter 5. The possibility of making polymers based on this sort of structure may be illustrated by considering the reaction of monosubstituted phosphorus oxychloride with, say, an alkylamine.

$$\mathrm{Cl{-}\overset{\overset{\displaystyle O}{\|}}{\underset{\underset{\displaystyle R}{|}}{P}}{-}Cl} + 2\,\mathrm{R'NH_2} \rightarrow \mathrm{\underset{\underset{\displaystyle R'}{|}}{NH}{-}\overset{\overset{\displaystyle O}{\|}}{\underset{\underset{\displaystyle R}{|}}{P}}{-}\underset{\underset{\displaystyle R'}{|}}{NH}}$$

$$\downarrow$$

$$\mathrm{\underset{\underset{\displaystyle R'}{|}}{NH}{-}\left[{-}\overset{\overset{\displaystyle O}{\|}}{\underset{\underset{\displaystyle R}{|}}{P}}{-}\underset{\underset{\displaystyle R'}{|}}{N}{-}\right]_n{-}H} + \mathrm{R'NH_2}$$

In principle, such a polymer could be cross-linked by a P—O—P bond, and there is also considerable scope for varying the nature of R and R′. The meagre information on such compounds suggests that they have reasonably good thermal, oxidative, and hydrolytic stability.

The reaction of non-metallic chlorides with ammonia or amines occurs readily and one would expect a wide range of polymeric materials to be produced by this means, since the simple amides formed initially usually condense quite easily to form products in which nitrogen bridges the two non-metallic atoms. The main difficulty in such cases is to limit the degree of polymerisation. Thus silicon tetrachloride in its reaction with ammonia or amines readily gives highly condensed products. It remains a very challenging problem to devise effective methods of restricting the extent of polymerisation and in many cases also of eliminating hydrolytic instability. This tends to be greater in the atoms of higher co-ordination number.

Borazole and its derivatives constitute a further group of polymers in which the strong bonds formed by nitrogen with other non-metallic elements contribute to the stability of the backbone structure. Borazole itself, $B_3N_3H_6$, was first prepared by heating the diammoniate of diborane or by heating the boron hydride itself with ammonia. It forms a six-membered ring of alternating BH and NH groups, with all the B—N bonds equivalent. The unshared electrons on each nitrogen atom go into the ring and endow the structure with a pseudo-aromatic character. Many substituted borazoles are known, *e.g.*, those with alkyl or aryl groups, replacing the hydrogen atoms linked to boron and nitrogen. Halogenated borazoles are also readily made from such reactions as that between ammonium chloride and boron trichloride. Borazole and its derivatives are rather readily hydrolysed by alkali and this is an inherent difficulty in the further development of this class of polymer. Two aspects of borazole chemistry are of special interest at the present time. The first is the possibility of fusing borazole rings or linking them together by suitable groups. The second is the problem of preventing ring formation and so obtaining chain-like polymers based on the B—N—B backbone.

To illustrate the first of these problems, reference may be made to the condensation of aminoborazoles (Chapter 2, Section 6). *B*-Trichloroborazoles with ammonia and amines give the corre-

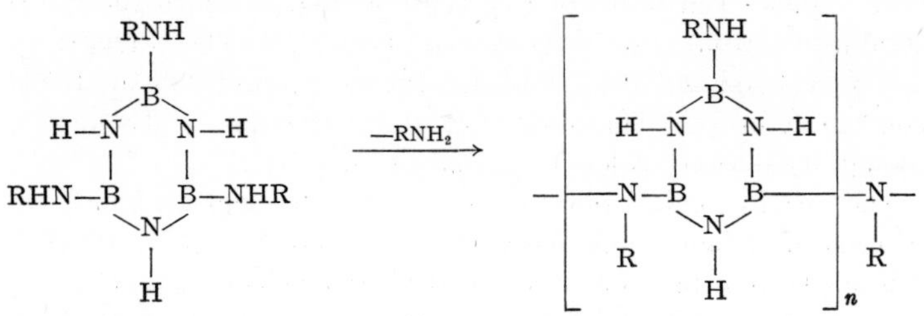

```
        RNH                                    ┌        RNH         ┐
         |                                     │         |          │
         B                                     │         B          │
       /   \                                   │       /   \        │
    H—N     N—H          —RNH₂               │    H—N     N—H     │
      |     |           ————→                  │      |     |       │
RHN—B       B—NHR                            ——│—N—B       B———————│—N—
       \   /                                   │  |    \   /        │  |
         N                                     │  R      N          │  R
         |                                     │         |          │
         H                                     └         H          ┘n
```

sponding *B*-aminoborazoles. Polycondensation of the initial products occurs by heating, giving products which are thermally-stable, but infusible and insoluble in organic solvents. The type of condensation occurring is illustrated below. If it could be controlled, it could conceivably lead to useful materials.

References, p. 18–19

The second point may be illustrated by the condensation of certain aminoborazens (see also Chapter 2, section 6), such as $PhB(NHBu^n)_2$. This loses butylamine when heated but, instead of condensing to a ring, it is believed to form linear polymers of comparatively low molecular weight of the type shown in (XII). Failure to form a ring is attributed in this case to a steric effect arising from the presence of the comparatively large *n*-butyl group. This approach to the tailoring of inorganic polymers has, as yet, been little used and it seems to offer considerable scope for further exploration.

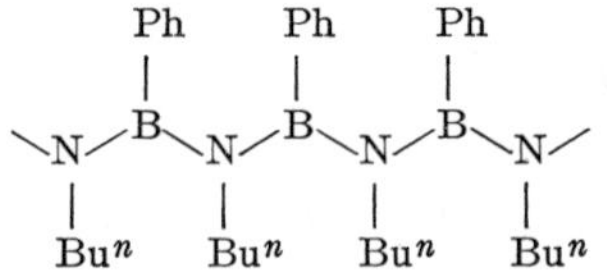

```
        Ph        Ph        Ph
        |         |         |
  \N/    B\    N/   B\    N/   B\    N/
   |          |          |          |
  Bu^n       Bu^n       Bu^n       Bu^n
```

(XII)

It is convenient at this point to refer to the cyclic products obtained from the adduct formed by dimethylphosphine with the borine radical, $Me_2HP \rightarrow BH_3$, at 150° (for further details, see Chapter 5). Hydrogen is lost and a cyclic trimer, $(Me_2P \cdot BH_2)_3$, is obtained, with a smaller amount of the tetramer. The trimer is hydrolysed slowly by aqueous hydrochloric acid at 300° and is thermally-stable up to about 400°. This unexpected stability has been explained in terms of $B \rightarrow P$ π-bonding, in which the B—H bonding electrons enter *d*-orbitals of phosphorus. This strengthens the B—P bond and also diminishes the susceptibility of the B—H bond to hydrolysis. The compound $[(CF_3)_2P \cdot BH_2]_3$ is also known, though its stability is less than that of $[Me_2P \cdot BH_2]_3$.

The various combinations of the non-metallic elements which can be used in forming inorganic polymers include a number which it will not be possible to mention in this brief survey, though all are of interest at this early stage of the development of the subject. I will refer only to two further systems, namely those in which nitrogen is bonded to sulphur, and a comparatively new group with the semi-inorganic backbone —N—O—C—C— or —C—N—C—N—. The nitrogen–sulphur polymers, which will be discussed later in detail in Chapter 5, have been known for a long time. The simplest member, S_4N_4, formed by the reaction of sulphur chloride, of approximate composition SCl_3, with ammonia in an inert solvent such as carbon tetrachloride, forms an eight-membered ring, which is cradle-shaped. Nitrogen and sulphur atoms alternate and all the bonds are of equal length. This substance has an interesting chemistry. It can, for example, be reduced very readily to $S_4N_4H_4$, in which the hydrogen atoms are bonded to nitrogen. Chlorination gives a six-membered ring, $S_3N_3Cl_3$, with S—Cl bonds. On controlled pyrolysis, a dimer, S_2N_2, is produced. The latter polymerises readily to a chain-like polymer, $(SN)_n$. There is also a range of related compounds, some of which contain different proportions of sulphur and nitrogen atoms in the ring (*e.g.*, S_7NH). So far there is little indication that substances in this class possess the necessary thermal stability and resistance to chemical attack, especially by hydrolytic reagents, to be of potential technical value. They do, however, offer a very interesting field for fundamental research and it is not impossible that as our knowledge of their chemistry grows we may be able to modify the basic structures, so as to increase their stability.

The second system may be introduced by considering the reaction of fluoroalkyl nitroso-compounds, $R_{(F)}NO$, with fluoro-olefins. If trifluoronitrosomethane, CF_3NO, reacts with tetrafluoroethylene,

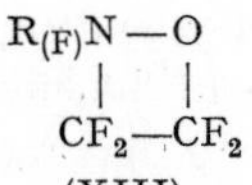

$$\begin{matrix} R_{(F)}N & — & O \\ | & & | \\ CF_2 & — & CF_2 \end{matrix} \qquad \left[\begin{matrix} —N\cdot O\cdot CF_2\cdot CF_2— \\ | \quad\quad\quad\quad\quad \\ CF_3 \quad\quad\quad\quad \end{matrix}\right]_n$$

(XIII) 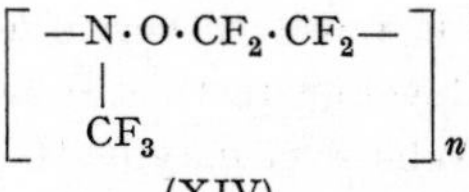 (XIV)

for example, there are two products. The first, (XIII), is an oxazetidine and the second, (XIV), a 1:1 copolymer. The yields of these two types of product may be varied by controlling the conditions, and the nature of the polymer can also be modified by the choice of olefin and reaction conditions. It is possible to obtain oils, waxes, or elastomers[14].

Polymers based on the —C—N—C—N— structure are well known, but those with C—F bonds would be expected to exhibit unusual stability, and this has in fact been observed recently.

References, p. 18–19

Polymerisation of trifluoronitrosoethylene, CF_2:CFNO, leads first to a structure believed to be (XV).

```
          O—CF₂            O—CF₂
          |   |            |   |
—CF—N—CF—N—CF—N—CF—N—
  |            |   |            |
—CF₂           O—CF₂            O—
```

(XV)

This loses carbonyl fluoride when heated, yielding a solid in which there is probably a chain of the type =CF—N=CF—N=.

The present state of our knowledge of inorganic polymers is such that it is exceedingly difficult to draw any general conclusions. The examples discussed deal with only a limited section of the field and it is quite clear that a very wide variety of products is possible. If the problem is taken to be the production of materials which have special properties complementary to those of conventional organic polymers, present indications are that the number of candidate compounds will be small. This is because of such defects as excessive polymerisation and lack of solubility and, in some cases, lack of resistance to chemical attack. The most promising leads at present seem to be provided by inorganic compounds in which organic groups are incorporated, or by fluorocarbon derivatives. The subject is, however, very much in its infancy and one may hope that, as it develops further, some of the present difficulties will be overcome. Whatever may be the outcome from the practical point of view, the large effort which is now being directed to this field is certain to lead to a far better understanding of its basic chemical aspects.

REFERENCES

[1] See A. F. WELLS, *Structural Inorganic Chemistry*, 2nd ed., Clarendon Press, Oxford, 1950, pp. 485, 496.

[2] I. LINDQVIST, *Acta Cryst.*, 10 (1957) 29.

[3] A. F. WELLS, *Z. Krist.*, 100 (1938) 189.

[4] M. AJOTI and W. N. LIPSCOMB, *J. Chem. Phys.*, 21 (1953) 172.

[5] See Ref. 1, p. 593.

[6] See J. R. VAN WAZER, *Phosphorus and its Compounds*, Vol. I, Interscience, New York, 1960, p. 123.

[7] W. KUCHEN and H. BUCHWALD, *Chem. Ber.*, 91 (1958) 2296.
[8] W. MAHLER and A. B. BURG, *J. Am. Chem. Soc.*, 79 (1957) 251.
[9] J. A. PRINS, J. SCHENK and L. H. J. WACHTERS, *Physica*, 23 (1957) 746.
[10] See O. FOSS, *Advances in Inorganic Chemistry and Radiochemistry*, H. J. Emeléus and A. G. Sharpe, Vol. II, Academic Press, New York, 1960, p. 240.
[11] O. RUFF, O. BRETSCHNEIDER and F. EBERT, *Z. anorg. Chem.*, 217 (1934) 1.
[12] See W. RÜDORFF, *Advances in Inorganic Chemistry and Radiochemistry*, H. J. Emeléus and A. G. Sharpe, Vol. I, Academic Press, New York, 1959, p. 230.
[13] W. RÜDORFF and G. RÜDORFF, *Z. anorg. Chem.*, 253 (1947) 281.
[14] The information in this section is derived from a paper presented by R. E. BANKS, J. M. BIRCHALL and R. N. HASZELDINE at the *Symposium on High Temperature Resistance and Thermal Degradation of Polymers* organised by the Plastics and Polymer Group of the Society of Chemical Industry, London, 1960; see S.C.I. Monograph No. 13, London, 1961, p. 270.
[15] M. HELLMAN and A. J. BILBO, *J. Am. Chem. Soc.*, 75 (1953) 4590; M. HELLMAN, A. J. BILBO and W. J. PUMMER, *ibid.*, 77 (1955) 3650.
[16] See paper presented by P. R. BLOOMFIELD at the Symposium mentioned in Ref. 14; S.C.I. Monograph No. 13, London, 1961, p. 89.

Chapter 2

Polymers Containing Boron and Nitrogen

by

M. F. LAPPERT

1. Introduction

Several types of compounds containing boron–nitrogen links as the sole, or principal, units in the polymer skeleton are known. These may broadly be classified according to the headings of Sections 2–9.

Borazens, (I), *i.e.*, open-chain compounds, in which both boron and nitrogen have co-ordination number three, are both isoelectronic and isosteric with corresponding olefins (II). This point is particularly emphasised by the canonical form (Ib).

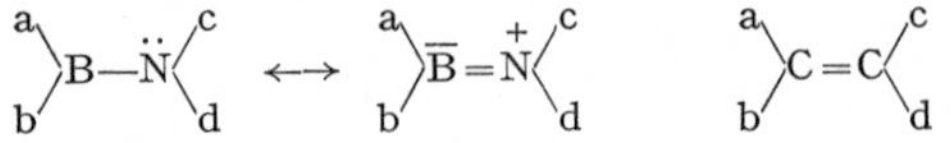

$$\begin{matrix} \text{a} \\ \text{b} \end{matrix}\!\!>\!B-\ddot{N}\!<\!\!\begin{matrix} \text{c} \\ \text{d} \end{matrix} \quad \longleftrightarrow \quad \begin{matrix} \text{a} \\ \text{b} \end{matrix}\!\!>\!\overline{B}=\overset{+}{N}\!<\!\!\begin{matrix} \text{c} \\ \text{d} \end{matrix} \qquad \begin{matrix} \text{a} \\ \text{b} \end{matrix}\!\!>\!C=C\!<\!\!\begin{matrix} \text{c} \\ \text{d} \end{matrix}$$

(Ia) (Ib) (II)

As olefins, especially α-olefins, are an important class of monomers for organic polymers, the idea that borazens might offer corresponding routes to B—N polymers has provided some impetus for research in this field. Reviews have dealt specifically with the physical and chemical basis for the analogy between borazens and olefins, borazoles (III) and aromatic compounds, and the borazole precursors ($YB=\ddot{N}X \longleftrightarrow Y\overline{B}\equiv\overset{+}{N}X$) and acetylenes[1]. Such analogies are somewhat superficial, as is clear, for example, from the characteristic substitution (and not, generally, addition) behaviour of the borazens (see, *e.g.*, Ref. 3). Nevertheless, they have been extremely valuable in stimulating later work and one aspect of boron-nitrogen chemistry, which has been particularly influenced by these concepts, is that of heteroaromatic compounds, such as 9-aza-10-boraphenanthrene (IV)[2]; evidence for its aromaticity rests largely on the similarity of its ultraviolet spectrum to that of the isoconjugate compound phenanthrene.

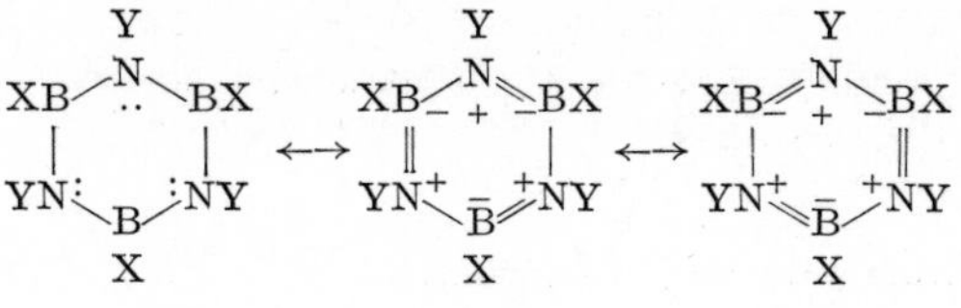

(III)

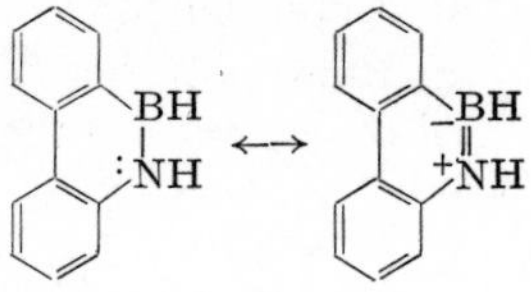

(IV)

The extremely high melting point of boron nitride, the structural similarity of the normal allotrope to graphite, and the existence (see Section 4) of a cubic modification, "borazon", said to be even harder than diamond and unattacked by air at 2000°, have all added further substance to the view that B—N polymers might prove realisable and that they might have high thermal stability. Another reason for exploring the potentialities of the boron-nitrogen system in a search for inorganic polymers, is that here catenation and ring-formation might be expected to be highly developed, since these elements show almost predominantly covalent behaviour and are of course, neighbours on either side of carbon in the Periodic Table.

Polyborazens and polyborazoles, which share the common property of having both boron and nitrogen atoms in the three-co-ordinate state, might, in addition, be expected to be more

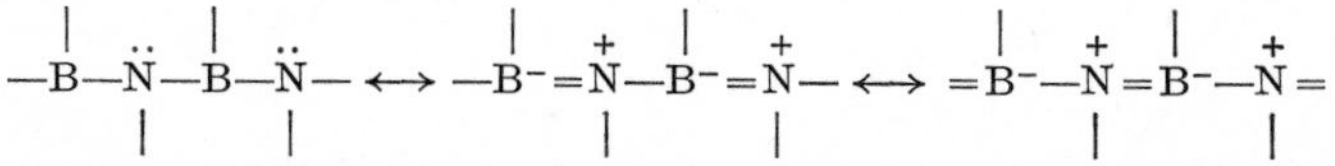

$$-B-\ddot{N}-B-\ddot{N}- \longleftrightarrow -B^{-}=\overset{+}{N}-B^{-}=\overset{+}{N}- \longleftrightarrow =B^{-}-\overset{+}{N}=B^{-}-\overset{+}{N}=$$

(V)

thermally-stable than conventional organic polymers, providing that the B—N bonds have appreciable π-character (V). Evidence for π-bonding in simple model B—N compounds will be considered in Section 10; certainly the B—N bond strength is high[4,5].

Three-co-ordinate boron compounds, which have an adjacent atom having a lone pair of electrons (*e.g.*, nitrogen, oxygen, halogen, or sulphur), are almost invariably readily hydrolysed, frequently even by brief exposure to the atmosphere. This is clearly a relevant problem to possible utilisation of B—N polymers and is considered in Section 11.

An attempt has been made to provide a comprehensive survey of the field up to the early part of 1962.

2. Addition polymers of borazens

Compounds included in this section are those which may be considered as derived from reactions of type:

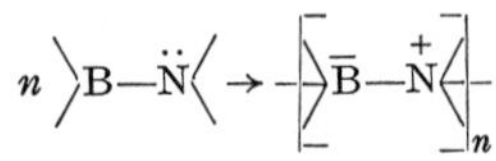

$$n\ \rangle B{-}\ddot{N}\langle \rightarrow \left[-\rangle\bar{B}{-}\overset{+}{N}\langle- \right]_n$$

Each structural unit is thus joined to the next by a co-ordinate link and it is this type of system which is truly analogous to the addition polymerisation of olefins. Only in a very few examples are both the monomer and a polymer known as stable entities and thus the *process* of addition polymerisation in borazen chemistry is uncommon.

In six types of borazens, $R_2N \cdot B(Hal)_2$, $R_2N \cdot BH_2$, $Me_2N \cdot BHMe$, $H_2N \cdot BR_2$, $MeNH \cdot BR_2$, and $o\text{-}C_6H_4O_2B \cdot NRR'$, monomeric, as well as dimeric, (VI), forms are known.

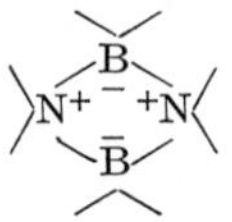

$$\rangle\overset{+}{N}\langle{}^{\bar{B}}_{\bar{B}}\rangle\overset{+}{N}\langle \qquad \text{(VI)}$$

Dimethylaminodichloroborane, $Me_2N \cdot BCl_2$, was the first of these substances to be studied[6,7]. When first formed, it is monomeric, but dimerises slowly at room temperature, or more quickly if heated. The dimer was reconverted to the monomer by sublimation[8].

The cyclic structure, (VI), for the dimer[7] was confirmed, by its chemical inertness (in contrast to the monomer) both to electrophiles (*e.g.*, hydrogen halides) and nucleophiles (*e.g.*, water), its low dipole moment[9], and its low B—N stretching frequency (932 cm^{-1}, compared with 1515 cm^{-1} for the monomer)[10a]. The tendency for dimerisation to occur with higher homologues has been shown to be related to steric factors[11]. Thus, dimers are formed with $R_2N \cdot BCl_2$ when R_2 = Me_2[6,7], $(CH_2)_4$[11], $(CH_2)_5$, $—CH_2CH_2OCH_2CH_2—$, but not when R_2 = Et_2[12,13], Pr^n_2[11], Bu^n_2, $—CH(Me)(CH_2)_4—$. Dimethylaminodifluoroborane was originally thought to be dimeric[8], but later was shown to be monomeric[14]; dimethylaminodibromoborane exists in both forms[15].

Aminodimethylborane, $H_2N \cdot BMe_2$, is dimeric at low temperature[16], but dissociates above 30°[17]; dipole moment[18] and spectroscopic (Raman and infrared)[19a] measurements confirm these structures. Aminodiphenylborane, $H_2N \cdot BPh_2$, on the other hand, exists only in the dimeric form[19b]. Monomeric methylaminodimethylborane, $MeNH \cdot BMe_2$, dimerises on cooling[20a]. Methylaminodiphenylborane, $MeNH \cdot BPh_2$, slowly changes from monomer into dimer at room temperature[20b]. Dimethylaminomethylborane, $Me_2N \cdot BHMe$, is almost wholly monomeric in the vapour; in the liquid state the dimer rapidly forms in high proportion, and the pure dimer is a solid at room temperature[20c].

Dimethylaminoborane, $Me_2N \cdot BH_2$, is dimeric at room temperature and atmospheric pressure, but dissociates into the monomer on heating *in vacuo*[15,27]; the entropy of formation of the dimer has been calculated[21a]. Like dimethylaminodichloroborane, the dimer is unreactive, whereas the monomer hydrolyses easily and reacts with hydrogen bromide[15]. Other lower primary alkyl homologues ($R_2N \cdot BH_2$; R = Et or Pr^n) are also dimeric solids at room temperature and are rather unreactive, whereas di-isopropylaminoborane is a monomeric liquid, which reacts vigorously with water[23].

Dimeric dimethylaminoborane has further been converted into the trimer, $(Me_2N \cdot BH_2)_3$, by reaction with pentaborane-9 at 100–110°[21b]. The trimer was shown to be cyclic (like VIII) by ^1H nuclear magnetic resonance and also by X-ray diffraction[21c], which also revealed it to be in the chair conformation.

References, p. 52–56

Compounds $o\text{-}C_6H_4O_2B \cdot NRR'$ were dimeric, unreactive, white solids, when sterically possible (RR'=MeH, EtH, Pr^iH, PhH, or Me_2)[85a]; monomeric compounds (RR'=Bu^tH[85a], Et_2[85b] or Bu^n_2) were reactive liquids.

The concepts of (i) steric factors affecting dimerisation, and (ii) dimer unreactivity, have been utilised in an attempt to prepare high-molecular-weight materials containing the four-membered ring, (VI), in the repeating units[22]. It was hoped to prepare polymers

$$\left[\begin{array}{c} Cl_2 \\ \bar{B} \\ ^+N \quad \bar{} \quad ^+N \\ \bar{B} \\ Cl_2 \end{array} \begin{array}{c} H_2 \quad H_2 \\ \\ \\ H_2 \quad H_2 \end{array} \right]_n \qquad \text{(VII)}$$

such as (VII) from piperazine and boron trichloride, and similar materials from the trichloride and 4,4'-dipiperidyl or *N,N'*-dimethylhexamethylenediamine, which might be hydrolytically-stable. These expectations proved unfounded, since easily-hydrolysed, salt-like products were obtained.

Only one example appears established of converting a low-molecular-weight borazen to a high degree of polymerisation. Thus, dimeric dimethylaminoborane was subjected to 3000 atmospheres pressure at 150° and afforded an amorphous, insoluble, and infusible polymer, which appeared to be stable to hydrolysis but not to heat and after a few months at room temperature reverted to the dimer[23]. This reversion could be inhibited, but not completely stopped, by stabilisation of the end-group with ether. It appears that the dimer is thermodynamically favoured at atmospheric pressure, and analogy can be drawn with some organic ring-chain polymerisations. Also, polymerisation by use of high pressure recalls the high pressure polymerisation of ethylene.

Methylaminoborane, $MeNH \cdot BH_2$, exists only as the trimer (VIII); X-ray diffraction analysis showed it to be isosteric with 1,3,5-trimethylcyclohexane[24].

Aminoborane, $H_2N \cdot BH_2$, normally exists in polymeric form, (IX), as a white, reasonably thermally-stable solid. It has been obtained by several methods, as indicated in Fig. 2, but originally by electrolysis of diborane in liquid ammonia[25a]. A trimeric form, similar to (VIII) has recently been obtained[25b] from borazole by hydrochlorination and subsequent reduction with sodium borohydride.

```
              H2
              B
           /  -  \
     MeHN+       +NHMe
        |          |            (VIII)
      H2B-   +   -BH2
            >N<
           H    Me
```

Three derivatives of polymeric aminoborane are known; these are (i) a co-polymer of $Me_2N \cdot BH_2$ and $(Me_2N)_2B \cdot H$; (ii) $[(H_3Si)_2N \cdot BH_2]_n$; and (iii) $[CH_3 \cdot CH{:}N \cdot BH_2]_n$. Reaction of monomeric dimethylaminoborane, $Me_2N \cdot BH_2$, with bis(dimethylamino)borane, $(Me_2N)_2B \cdot H$, at room temperature slowly produced needles, which could be sublimed on heating *in vacuo* to afford a white solid, formulated as the 1:1 co-polymer in (X)[26]; it was later regarded as having an approximately 10:1 molar ratio of the two monomers and was thermally unstable[27].

Di(silylamino)borane dimer polymerised irreversibly on heating to produce a non-volatile glass, formulated as the poly(*N*,*N*-disilyl) derivative of (IX), and the monomeric dichloro-derivative behaved similarly, although the product may have been a polycondensate, since hydrogen, silane, and dichlorosilane were identified among the volatile products[28]. The preparation of the starting materials is illustrated by the following equations.

$$2\,(H_3Si)_3N + 2\,B_2H_5Br \rightarrow [(H_3Si)_2BH_2]_2 + 2\,H_3Si \cdot Br + B_2H_6$$

$$(H_3Si)_3N + BCl_3 \rightarrow (H_3Si)_2N \cdot BCl_2 + H_3Si \cdot Cl$$

Pyrolysis of the nitrile-borane ($CH_3CN \cdot BH_3$ and $C_2H_5CN \cdot BH_3$) molecular addition compounds ultimately gave *N*-trialkylborazoles as principal products; compounds (XI; R = Me or Et) were regarded as intermediates, and evidence for their structures was obtained from infrared spectra and modes of hydrolysis[29]. Formation of *N*-ethylborazole from acetonitrile had previously been demonstrated[30].

References, p. 52–56

$$RC{\equiv}N{\cdot}BH_3 \rightarrow 1/n(RCH{=}N{\cdot}BH_2)_n \rightarrow (RCH_2N{\cdot}BH)_3 + (RCH_2N{\cdot}BH)_{4-5}$$

(XI)

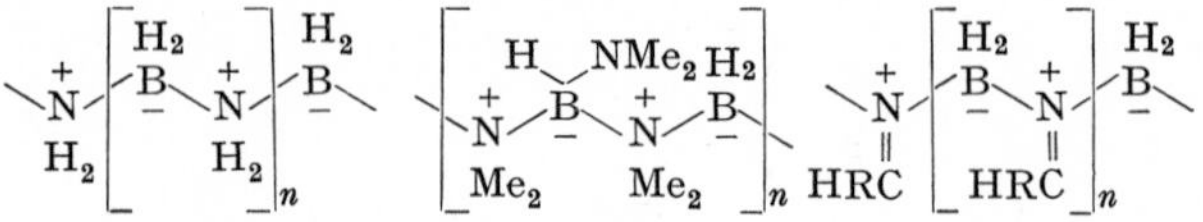

(IX) (X) (XI)

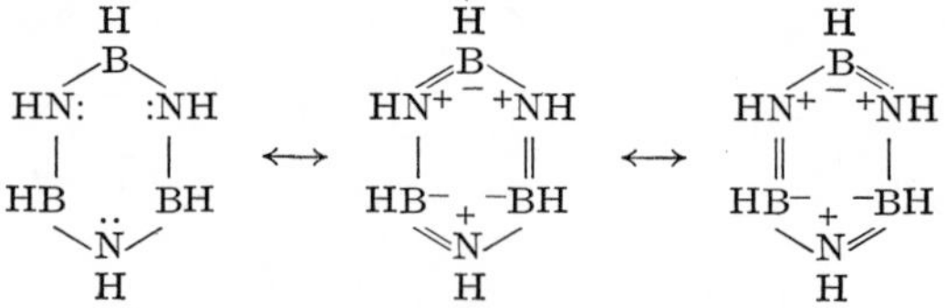

(XII)

3. Addition polymers of borazins (condensed system)

Compounds included in this section are those which may be considered as derived from hypothetical reactions of type:

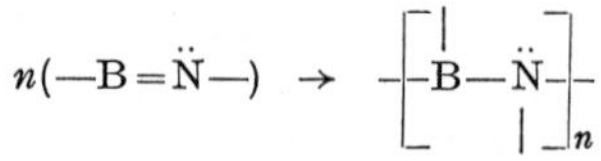

$$n(\text{—B}{=}\ddot{\text{N}}\text{—}) \rightarrow \left[\text{—B—}\ddot{\text{N}}\text{—}\right]_n$$

Each structural unit is thus joined to the next by a covalent link.

The trimers—*i.e.*, borazoles [derivatives of (XII)] have been studied extensively and will not be discussed, but recent reviews are available[47].

A series of cyclic tetramers, the borazocines (XIII), has recently been obtained[33a,48]. Whereas adducts, RNH_2,BCl_3, of primary amines and boron trichloride normally afford borazoles, $(RN{\cdot}BCl)_3$, on dehydrochlorination, those from highly-hindered primary amines, such as *t*-butylamine, give the borazocines. The tetrameric structure was established by analysis, molecular weight determination (ebullioscopic and cryoscopic), and from the mass-spectrum of (XIII; X = NCS, Y = Bu^t). Tetra-*B*-chloro-tetra-*N*-*t*-butylborazocine (XIII; X = Cl, Y = Bu^t), m.p. 247–248°, has been investigated most extensively. It is rather soluble in organic solvents and is

```
       Y  X                      Y  X
      ╱N—B╲                     ╱N=B╲
  XB   ··    :NY           XB⁻   +  ⁻  ⁺NY
   |          |     ⟷       ‖           ‖
  YN:        BX            YN⁺        + ⁻BX
      ╲B—N̈╱                     ╲B̄=N╱
       X  Y                      X  B
                    (XIII)
```

relatively stable to hydrolysis. It does not react with lithium borohydride, or Grignard reagents; with methylamine, partially *B*-substituted methylamino-derivatives were obtained, but with potassium thiocyanate in acetone, complete replacement was achieved, to give the *B*-tetra-isothiocyanato-derivative. On the basis of the low reactivity and low dipole moment, a strain-free

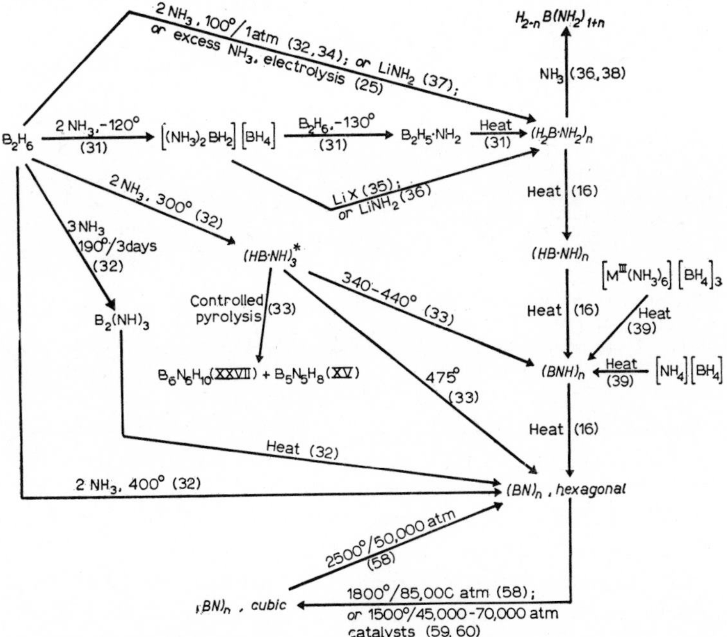

Fig. 2. The diborane–ammonia system. The numbers in parentheses are references; "polymeric" products are italicised. *For more convenient methods of preparing borazole and its derivatives, see Ref. 47.

boat-form of (XIII) is likely, as in cyclo-octatetraene, and this is consistent also with its great ease of sublimation and its high molecular depression constant (greater than that of camphor).

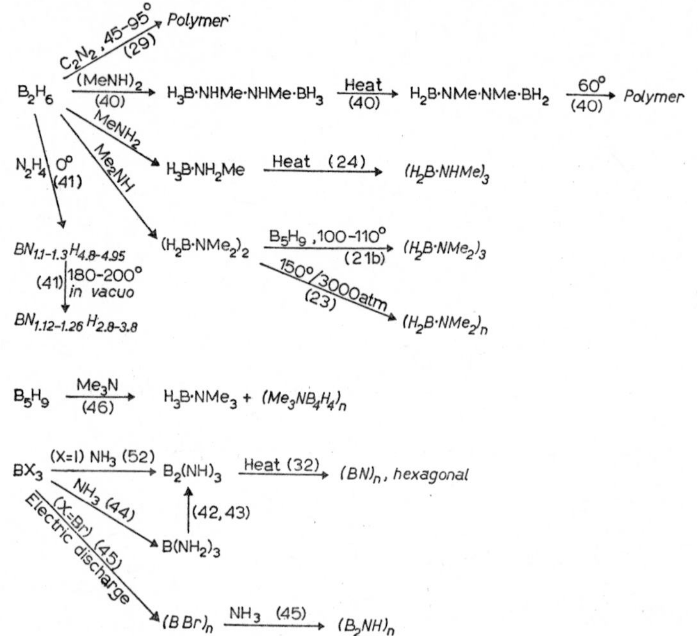

Fig. 3. Reactions related to the diborane–ammonia system. Numbers in parentheses are references; "polymeric" products are italicised.

As already indicated, pyrolysis of the nitrile-borane complexes gave *N*-alkylborazoles as principal products[29]; however, compounds of formulae $(RN{\cdot}BH)_4$ and $(RN{\cdot}BH)_5$ were also obtained and, although not characterised, may have been the cyclic tetrameric and pentameric borazins.

Acyclic materials are also known. The parent material would be $(HN{\cdot}BH)_n$, (XIV), and this was pictured as an intermediate in the pyrolytic dehydrogenation of polymeric aminoborane, $(H_2N{\cdot}BH_2)_n$, into boron nitride[16] (see Fig. 2). Three derivatives of (XIV) have been reported: the *N*-methyl-*B*-fluoro-, $(MeN{\cdot}BF)_n$ (and not the trimer, as originally thought[49]), obtained by pyrolysis of dimethylaminodifluoroborane, $Me_2N \cdot BF_2$[14]; the *N*-methoxy-, $(MeON \cdot BH)_n$, obtained as an unstable intermediate in the dehydrogenation of *O*-methylhydroxylamine-borane $(MeO \cdot NH_2 \cdot BH_3)$[50]; and the *N*-butyl-*B*-phenyl, $(Bu^nN \cdot BPh)_n$ (see Section 6)[51].

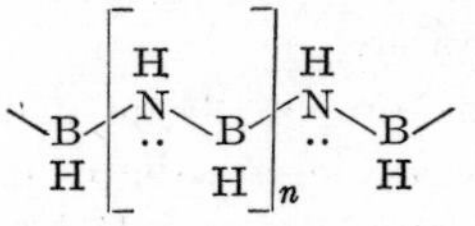

(XIV)

The monomeric borazins probably do not exist as isolable species, despite reports to the contrary. Thus, methanolysis of borazole gives $(HN \cdot BH)_3 \cdot 3MeOH$, which on heating to 100° was said[34] to form *B*-methoxyborazin, MeOB:NH; reinvestigation[53] has shown this to be the trimer.

$$(HN \cdot BH)_3 \cdot 3MeOH \xrightarrow{100^\circ} 3H_2 + B(OMe)_3 + (HN \cdot BOMe)_3 + \text{polymer}^*$$

(HN·BOMe)₃ → prolonged heat → non-volatile solid

* [intermediate between $(BN)_n$ and $(HN \cdot BOMe)_n$]

Likewise, the *B*-methyl-*N*-phenyl derivative[54], MeB:NPh, was later shown to be the borazole, $(MeB \cdot NPh)_3$[55].

4. Addition polymers of borazins (fused system)

Compounds included in this section are polycyclic and may be considered as derived from reactions of type:

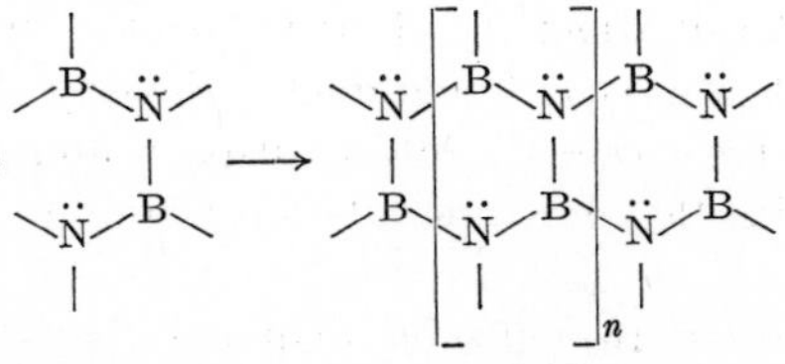

(XVI)

Each structural unit is thus joined to the next by two covalent links—*i.e.*, to make a fused system. The simplest compound of this type is the naphthalene analogue (XV), m.p. 27–30°, obtained, as shown in Fig. 2, by controlled batch pyrolysis of borazole in a hot-cold apparatus[33]. Its structure, like that of (XXVII), was confirmed by chemical analysis, infrared and mass spectra, and X-ray powder photography.

Structure (XVI) was proposed[16] for a material of composition $(BNH)_n$, regarded as an intermediate in the dehydrogenative pyrolysis of polymeric aminoborane, $(H_2N \cdot BH_2)_n$, which produces

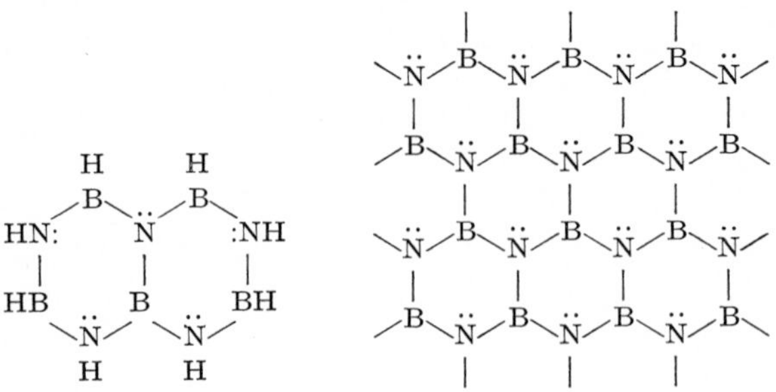

(XV)

(XVII)

ultimately the graphitic form (XVII) of boron nitride (see Fig. 2). The pyrolysis of borazole in all-glass cells has been studied in detail[33]; at 340–440°, the non-volatile product corresponded to an empirical formula $BNH_{0.8}$, and at 475° to $BNH_{0.3}$.

Boron nitride, in the hexagonal or "white graphite" form, was first obtained[32] by the pyrolysis of diborane-ammonia at 400°. Its structure (XVII) has been established by X-ray diffraction[56]. Hexagonal boron nitride differs from graphite in the important respect that localisation[57] of electrons on the nitrogen atoms of boron nitride leads to a different mode of layer packing, with boron atoms in one layer directly under nitrogen atoms in another. In accordance with this, hexagonal boron nitride is a poor electrical conductor.

Boron nitride, in the cubic or "diamond" form ("borazon"), was first obtained[58] by subjecting the graphitic form to a very high temperature and pressure (1800° at 85,000 atm); at 2500° and 50,000 atm it was reconverted to the hexagonal form. "Borazon" has also been made[59] from a mixture of graphite and the hexagonal modification at 70,000 atm. Alkali and alkaline earth metals, or their nitrides, are effective catalysts for the conversion of hexagonal into cubic boron nitride[60]. The pressure and temperature varies with the catalyst, but a minimum pressure of about 45,000 atmospheres at 1500° has been found to be optimum at the present time. "Borazon" was shown[58] to have a zinc blende structure and to be unaffected by heating twice *in vacuo* at 2000°. It is not attacked by the common mineral acids, and is only slowly oxidised in the atmosphere at 2000°. It is a good electrical insulator and hard enough to scratch diamond.

5. Autocomplexes

Compounds included in this section are those, (XIX), which may be be regarded as derived from monomeric units (XVIII) by intermolecular co-ordination and have other atoms as well as boron and nitrogen (*i.e.*, not polyborazens; see Section 3) in the main polymer

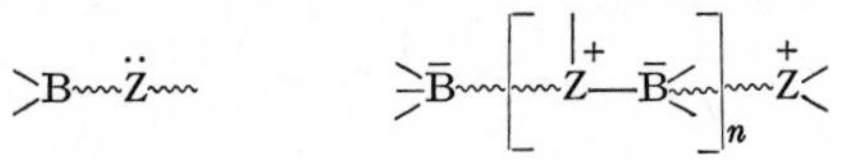

$$>B\sim\ddot{Z}\sim \qquad (XVIII)$$

$$>\bar{B}\sim\left[\sim\overset{|+}{Z}-\bar{B}\lessgtr\sim\right]_n\sim\overset{+}{Z}< \qquad (XIX)$$

chain. The monomeric species are thus substances which possess both acceptor (three-co-ordinate boron atoms) and donor [indicated as Z: in (XVIII)] sites. The boron pseudohalides tend to form autocomplexes. When boron trichloride and silver cyanide were left in contact with one another at room temperature in a sealed tube for forty years, monomeric white boron cyanide, $B(CN)_3$, was formed; however, by heating the two reactants together, darkening rapidly occurred and this was attributed to polymerisation[61]. Curiously, the infrared spectrum of this boron cyanide revealed no absorption in the 1800–2300 cm^{-1} range[62] (the C≡N stretching frequency in nitriles is generally at about 2250 cm^{-1}).

Both silyl and trimethylsilyl cyanides formed complexes

References, p. 52–56

($H_3Si\cdot CN,BH_3$ and $Me_3Si\cdot CN,BH_3$) with diborane; these underwent Si—C cleavage [*cf.*, behaviour of RCN,BH_3 (p. 26)] when heated to afford polymeric cyanoborane, (XX), and the appropriate silyl hydride[63]. The polymeric cyanoborane, which is a clear, glassy solid was characterised by its infrared spectrum (C≡N and B—H stretching frequencies). It was not hydrolysed by cold water, but on heating with water, hydrogen cyanide and hydrogen

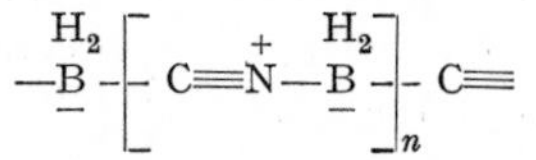

$$-\overset{H_2}{\underset{-}{B}}-\left[-C{\equiv}\overset{+}{N}-\overset{H_2}{\underset{-}{B}}-\right]_n-C{\equiv} \qquad \text{(XX)}$$

were formed. Pyrolysis behaviour was variable; rapid heating frequently resulted in explosion, but gradual heating led merely to some dehydrogenation at 200–350° and discoloration, presumably accompanied by reduction of the cyano-group, since hydrolysis of the pyrolysed material produced ammonia.

Polymeric di-*n*-butylboron cyanide, $(Bu_2B\cdot CN)_n$ ($n = 20$, as judged by cryoscopy in benzene), was obtained from di-*n*-butylboron chloride and either trimethylsilyl cyanide or silver cyanide[64a]. It was only slowly hydrolysed by 10% aqueous sodium hydroxide, whilst pyrolysis at 300–330° rapidly produced butane. The white, crystalline polymeric diphenylboron cyanide, $(Ph_2B\cdot CN)_n$, was also remarkably stable to hydrolysis and heat[64b]; it was obtained from the chloride and silver cyanide and was depolymerised as a result of its exothermal dissolution in pyridine to form $Ph_2B\cdot CN$,py.

Tri-*B*-cyanoborazole, $(NCB\cdot NH)_3$, has been obtained by heating tri-*B*-chloroborazole and silver cyanide in acetonitrile[65]; *o*-$C_6H_4O_2B\cdot CN$ has been made similarly and has the C≡N stretching frequency at 2210 cm^{-1} (see Ref. 101). These compounds proved difficult to purify.

Autocomplexing of monomeric boron cyanides, rather than small ring-formation, is inevitable, due to the BCN angle being presumably 180°, because of the *sp*-hybrid orbitals of carbon.

A number of monomeric boron isocyanates have been prepared and some of these tend to polymerise. Dimethylboron isocyanate, $Me_2B\cdot NCO$, prepared from the bromide and silver cyanate, is monomeric in the vapour, dimeric [probably (XXI)] in the liquid, and polymeric [probably (XXII)] in the solid; structures were based on the infrared spectra[66]. Six other isocyanates [$(BuO)_2B \cdot NCO$; $BuO \cdot B(NCO)_2$; $(Me_2N)_2B \cdot NCO$; $o\text{-}C_6H_4O_2B \cdot NCO$; $Ph_2B \cdot NCO$; $(HN \cdot BNCO)_3$] polymerised far less readily[67]. Corresponding monomeric isothiocyanates of boron, prepared from appropriate boron halogen compounds and a metal thiocyanate (Na, K, Ag, or Pb salt), were even less prone to polymerise[67].

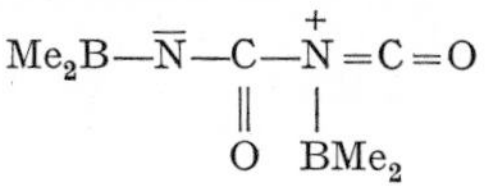

$$Me_2B—\overline{N}—\underset{\underset{O}{\|}}{C}—\underset{\underset{BMe_2}{|}}{\overset{+}{N}}=C=O$$

(XXI)

$$\left[\begin{array}{l} \quad\;\; \backslash\overset{+}{N}=C=O \\ Me_2\overline{B}\langle \;\; + \\ \quad\;\; /N=C=O \\ Me_2\overline{B}\langle \end{array}\right]_n$$

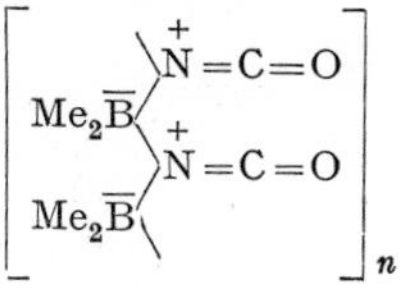

(XXII)

It is possible that the polymerisation, or oligomerisation, of boron isocyanates and isothiocyanates arises simply from the nature of the polarisation in the functional group, *i.e.*, $—N=C=O(S) \rightarrow —\overline{N}—\overset{+}{C}=O(S)$, giving rise to structures such as (XXI) and also to cyclic or polymeric ones, *i.e.*, without boron atoms in the main chain.

6. Polycondensates having only boron and nitrogen in the main chain

The preparation of the compounds described in this section stems largely from the recognition of the generality of the amino-borane-amine elimination reaction[68]:

$$2 \rangle B \cdot NHR \xrightarrow{\text{heat}} \rangle B \cdot N(R) \cdot B \langle + RNH_2.$$

This provides a means of joining two boron atoms through a nitrogen bridge. It was first demonstrated[68] in the course of the synthesis of the borazole (XXIII; $R = Et$) from tris(ethylamino)borane, $B(NHEt)_3$. From the borazole, polycyclic compounds and ultimately, the completely cross-linked material (XXIV) were obtained.

The polycondensate (XXIV; $R = Et$) was shown to be a poly-

References, p. 52–56

borazole, because its infrared spectrum showed absorption maxima at ~ 1470 cm^{-1} (B—N stretching frequency[69,70]), ~ 2930 cm^{-1} (C—H stretching frequency), and a doublet at ~ 741 and ~ 720 cm^{-1} (borazole ring out-of-plane bending frequency[68,71]). It was only slowly attacked by cold water but was hydrolysed by hot water to afford boric acid and ethylamine.

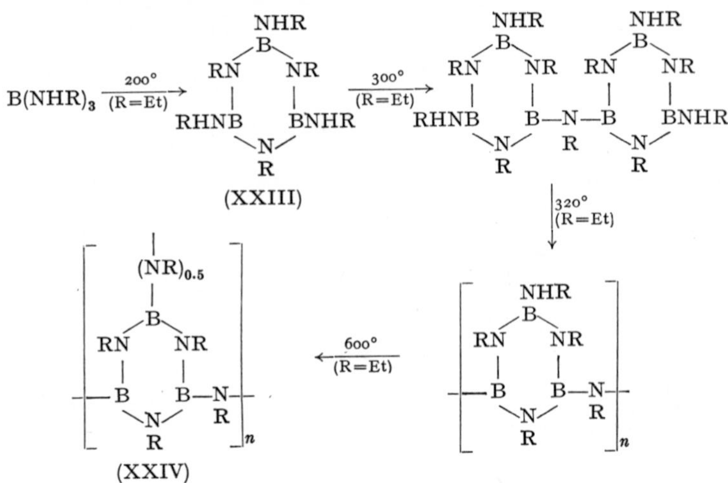

Other tri-*B*-aminoborazoles (XXIII; R = Me, Pr^i, Bu^n, Bu^s, Bu^t, C_6H_{11}, $PhCH_2$, and Ph) have similarly been synthesised[72] and on pyrolysis afforded in every instance, except for the *t*-butyl derivative, a dark brown, non-thermoplastic, brittle resin (XXIV). The resin (XXIV; R = Et) was insoluble in inert organic solvents, was evidently highly cross-linked, and appeared to be stable up to at least 600° in dry air. The borazole (XXIII; R = Et) was a viscous, colourless liquid, which during pyrolysis gradually darkened, increased in viscosity, changed to a light brown rubber (mobile liquid when hot), and eventually to the infusible resin. A polymeric borazole, obtained as a distillation residue by redistilling (XXIII; R = Et) was elastomeric, insoluble in organic solvents, and unaffected by boiling water, but hydrolysed by concentrated hydrochloric acid. Similar infusible and intractable polyborazoles have been obtained by polycondensation of other *B*-aminoborazoles [$(BuNHB \cdot NH)_3$ and $(H_2NB \cdot NH)_3$; each obtained from *B*-chloroborazole and amine or liquid ammonia][51].

It is clear that the production of technologically-useful polyborazoles will depend, in the first instance, on the availability of bifunctional starting materials, so that the indiscriminate and extensive cross-linking found in compounds of type (XXIV) be avoided. Unsymmetrical borazoles have been obtained mainly by stepwise *B*-alkylation or *B*-arylation methods. Thus, *B*-methylated borazoles ($MeH_2B_3 \cdot N_3H_3$, $Me_2HB_3 \cdot N_3H_3$, as well as $Me_3B_3 \cdot N_3H_3$) were obtained from borazole and trimethylborane[73], whilst reaction of Grignard or organo-lithium reagents with *N*-trimethyl- or *N*-triphenyl-borazole gave partially, as well as completely, *B*-alkylated or *B*-arylated borazoles [$R_2HB_3 \cdot N_3Ph_3$, $RH_2B_3 \cdot N_3Ph_3$, $R'_2HB_3 \cdot N_3Me_3$, and $R'H_2B_3 \cdot N_3Me_3$; R=Me or Ph; and R' = Me][74]. From some of the partially *B*-methylated *N*-triphenylborazoles, further unsymmetrical compounds ($Me_2Bu^nB_3 \cdot N_3Ph_3$, $MeEtHB_3 \cdot N_3Ph_3$, and $MeEtPr^nB_3 \cdot N_3Ph_3$) were prepared. Similar stepwise *B*-alkylation of *B*-trichloro-*N*-trimethylborazole [to afford $RCl_2B_3 \cdot N_3Me_3$ and $R_2ClB_3 \cdot N_3Me_3$; R = Bu, but not Et] has also been achieved[75]. The *B*-alkyl-*B'*,*B''*-dichloroborazoles may prove particularly valuable, for example for synthesis of *B*-alkyl-*B'*,*B''*-bisaminoborazoles and hence for substantially linear polycondensates, and for this purpose, *B*,*B'*-dihalo- and *B*-halo-borazoles, obtained by bromination of borazole[34], or by reaction of borazole with boron trihalide (Cl,Br)[76], may also be of interest, although they readily disproportionate[76]. A further method[10b] for preparing unsymmetrical borazoles makes use of the observation that steric factors (see Section II) predominate in displacement reactions of three-co-ordinate boron compounds[77], *e.g.*, the relative displacement tendencies of groups X and Y are OH > OR > NH_2 > NHR > NR_2 > SR in:

$$\rangle B{-}\ddot{X} + H\ddot{Y} \rightarrow \rangle B\ddot{Y} + H\ddot{X}\,.$$

For example, unsymmetrical *B*-alkylaminoborazoles [$(RO)(R'NH)_2B_3 \cdot N_3R''_3$ and $(RO)_2(R'NH)B_3 \cdot N_3R''_3$ from $(R'NH)_3B_3 \cdot N_3R''_3$

and ROH, and $(R_2N)(R'NH)_2B_3\cdot N_3R''_3$ and $(R_2N)_2(R'NH)B_3\cdot N_3R''_3$ from $(R_2N)_3B_3\cdot N_3R''_3$ and $R'NH_2$] have been prepared and, although the diphenylmethane analogues, (XXV), were obtained from some of these by condensation reactions[10b], the polycondensates have not yet been investigated. It is also of interest that compounds such as $EtNH(Et_2N)_2B_3\cdot N_3Et_3$ are potentially capable of producing linear polymers as a result of a two-stage propagation sequence; the first, elimination of ethylamine [*e.g.*, to give (XXV; X = Et_2N)], and then substitution of one NEt_2 group by NHEt (*e.g.*, to give XXV; in which three of the groups X are NEt_2 and the fourth NHEt).*

B,B'-di-isocyanato-*B''*-chloro-and *B*-isocyanato-*B',B''*-dichloro-borazoles were obtained from trichloroborazole and silver cyanate, in the appropriate stoicheiometry[101]. An unusual synthesis[33b,48] of the unsymmetrical borazoles (XXVI; R = 2,6-dimethylphenyl; Y = H; X = Cl, OH, OMe, OPh, OCH_2Ph, NHC_2H_5, or NMe_2) was based on the fact that the adduct of 2,6-dimethylaniline and boron trichloride surprisingly gave, under controlled conditions, the chloride (XXVI; Y = H; X = Cl); such an adduct would normally have been expected to form the symmetrical borazole, $(RN\cdot BCl)_3$, on dehydrochlorination. The structures of compounds (XXVI) were confirmed by analysis, molecular weight determination, infrared spectra [ν(B—H) at ~ 2500 cm^{-1}], and evolution of hydrogen with aqueous sodium hydroxide. The hydroxide, (XXVI; Y = H; X = OH), was reasonably resistant to hydrolysis.

The dimethylamino-derivative (XXVI; Y = Ph; X = NMe_2) was converted into a soluble polymer by reaction with benzidine. The polymer was presumably a linear material composed of units (XXVI; Y = Ph; X = $(NH-C_6H_4-NH)_{0.5}$). This provides a further example of the idea[77] that the relative displacement capacities of amino groups are NHR > NR_2.

The diphenyl-like compound (XXVII), m.p. 59–60°, was one of the products of controlled batch pyrolysis in a hot-cold apparatus of borazole[33] (see Fig. 2), and the product obtained by pyrolysis of

* *N,N',N''*-unsymmetrical borazoles have been prepared by first obtaining *N*-lithio-derivatives from *N*-hydrido-borazoles[67a].

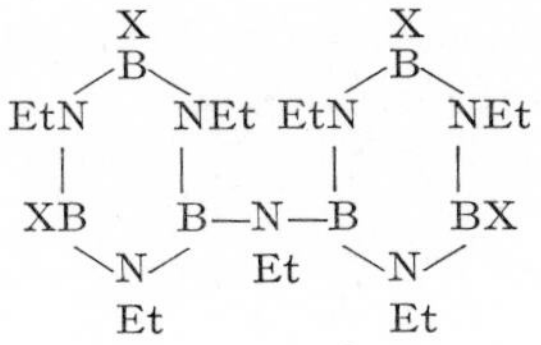

(XXV; X=Bu^nO or Et_2N)

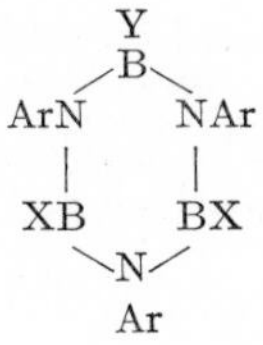

(XXVI; Ar = 2,6-dimethylphenyl; Y)

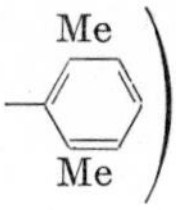

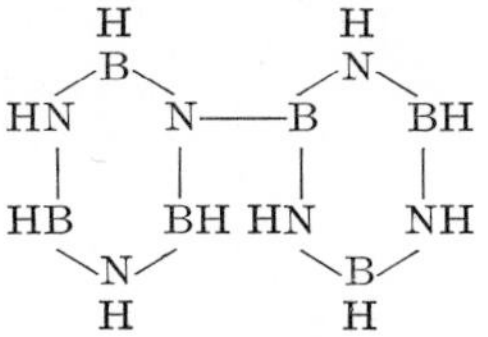

(XXVII)

B-tris(diethylamino)borazole, $(Et_2NB \cdot NH)_3$[51,51a] may well prove to be a polyphenylene analogue:

$$\rangle B \cdot NEt_2 + H \cdot N\langle \longrightarrow \rangle B—N\langle + Et_2NH.$$

The *B*-penta-*n*-butyl derivative of (XXVII) has recently been obtained, in small yield, from *B*-tribromo- or trichloro-borazole and the *n*-butyl Grignard reagent[80b].*

Pyrolysis of bis(amino)boranes, $X \cdot B(NHR)_2$, has also been investigated and borazoles have been obtained in a number of instances [$(PhB \cdot NPh)_3$[78], $(Am^iB \cdot NBu^i)_3$[79], $(Am^iB \cdot NPh)_3$, $(PhB \cdot NEt)_3$[80a], $(p\text{-}TolB \cdot NPh)_3$, and $(Bu^nOB \cdot NEt)_3$[68,72]]. Anomalous behaviour was, however, observed with some other compounds [R = Bu^n, Bu^i, or Bu^s in $Ph \cdot B(NHR)_2$] and condensation led first to linear dimers, and then to polymers $[PhB \cdot NR]_n$[51]; the degree of polymerisation was estimated [20 (R = Bu^i) and 40 (R = Bu^n)] from viscosity measurements and the preference for linear condensation may be due to steric hindrance to formation of borazoles.

* The *B*-pentamethyl-*N*-pentamethyl derivative was prepared from *N*-lithio-pentamethylborazole and *B*-chloro-pentamethylborazole[67b]; polymeric species were similarly obtained.

References, p. 52–56

7. Polycondensates having only boron, nitrogen, and elements other than carbon in the main chain

Compounds included in this section are those, in which successive B—N units are linked together through oxygen, sulphur, or phosphorus.

Polymers derived from hydroxylamine, *N*-methyl-, or *N*,*N*-dimethyl-hydroxylamine and diborane, are white solids, insoluble in inert organic solvents, and probably of structure (XXVIII) (R = H = R′; R = Me = R′; or R = H, R′ = Me). They were obtained from the molecular addition compounds, $RR'NOH,BH_3$, by dehydrogenation at 25°, and decomposed when heated[81].

(XXVIII) $-O\left[\overset{H_2}{B}-\overset{+}{N}RR'-O-\right]_n\overset{-}{B}H_2-$

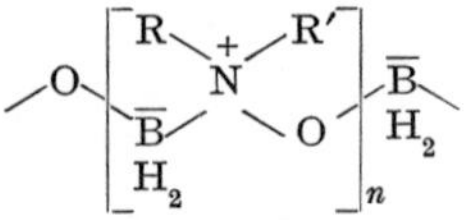

A polycondensate (XXIX), of tris(methylamino)boroxole, $(MeNHB\cdot O)_3$, was prepared[77] as follows:

$$B(NMe_2)_3 + B_2O_3 \rightarrow (Me_2NB\cdot O)_3 \xrightarrow[(-Me_2NH)]{MeNH_2} (MeNHB\cdot O)_3 \xrightarrow[(-MeNH_2)]{heat}$$

(XXIX) $\left[B_3O_3 \text{ ring bearing } (NMe)_{0.5},\ -B\ \text{and}\ B-N(Me)- \right]_n$

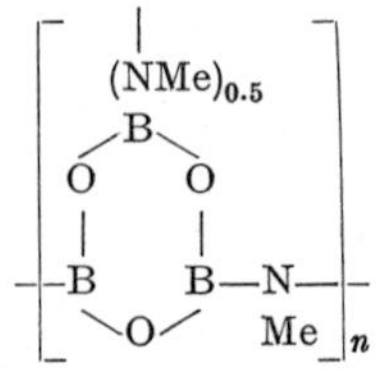

The polycondensate (XXIX) (see also Ref. 82) was a white, crystalline solid, identified as a polyboroxole from its infrared spectrum. It was thermally, but not hydrolytically stable, and was evidently highly cross-linked since it was not thermoplastic. A similar polyboroxole (XXX) was thought to be the product of equimolar reaction between trimethyl borate, $B(OMe)_3$, and aniline, whilst under less forcing conditions (XXXI) was formed[83]. The mechanism of these reactions may involve methyl metaborate, $(MeOB\cdot O)_3$, formation, substitution of *B*-methoxy- by *B*-phenylamino-, and condensation. Amines, including tertiary amines such as pyridine, are known to react with metaborates, but give polycondensates (XXXII) [$4(ROB\cdot O)_3 + 3py \longrightarrow 3(ROB_3\cdot O_4\cdot py) + 3B(OR)_3$], in which nitrogen is not in the main chain[84].*

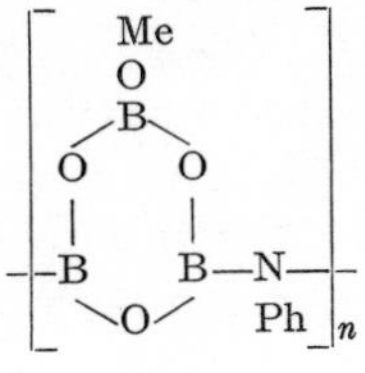

(XXX) 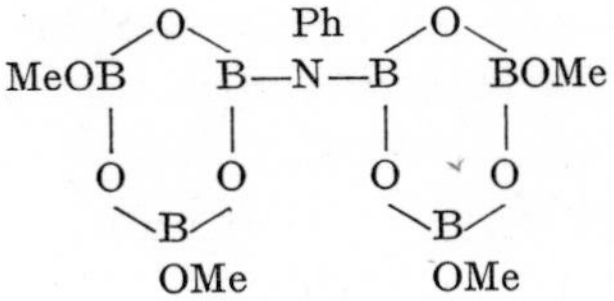 (XXXI)

Linking of two B—N units, through sulphur as bridging atom, has as yet only been achieved in a low molecular weight compound (XXXIII), obtained from sulphamide, $SO_2(NH_2)_2$, and *o*-phenylene chloroboronate, $C_6H_4O_2B\cdot Cl$[85a].

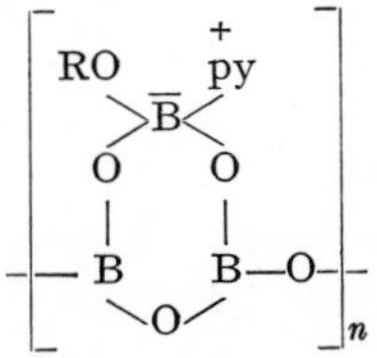

(XXXII)

B-Trichloroborazole formed complexes with trialkyl phosphates[86], including tri-isobutyl phosphate[51], probably (infrared spectra[86]) by

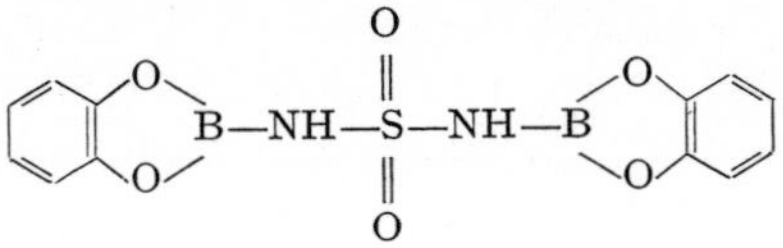

(XXXIII)

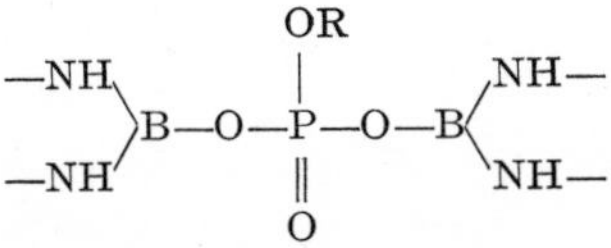

(XXXIV)

* Hydrolysis of *B*-chloro-pentamethylborazole afforded a bimolecular species with the two rings joined >B—O—B<[67b]; the same method has been used for higher-molecular-weight polymers.

means of hydrogen-bonding, $[ClB \cdot NH \cdots O{:}P(OR)_3]_3$; these at 100° gave alkyl chlorides and probably *B*-phosphatoborazoles, $[(RO)_2P({:}O)OB \cdot NH]_3$[51,86]. The isobutyl compound at 200°/0.5 mm gave tri-isobutyl phosphate and an organic solvent-insoluble resin, which only hydrolysed slowly and which may have been a polycondensate in which boron atoms were joined as shown in (XXXIV); it decomposed progressively at 450–800° to produce a substantially inorganic, solvent and acid resistant, hard, brittle product[51]. Tri-*B*-chloro-tri-*N*-alkylborazoles similarly afforded *B*-phosphatoborazoles, $[(RO)_2P({:}O)OB \cdot NR]_3$[86].

8. Polycondensates having boron, nitrogen, and carbon in the main chain

Certain polymers derived from diamines and boron trichloride, *e.g.*, (VII), have already been discussed in Section 2. Reactions of the phenylenediamines with boron trichloride and related com-

$$\left[\begin{array}{c} | \\ (C_6H_4)_{0.5} \\ | \\ N \\ ClB \quad\quad BCl \\ | \quad\quad\quad | \\ -N \quad\quad N-C_6H_4- \\ B \\ Cl \end{array}\right]_n \qquad \text{(XXXV)}$$

pounds have also been investigated[51,87–90]. Each of the isomeric diamines was said to give a 1:1-adduct with boron trichloride or phenyldichloroborane[87]; *p*-phenylenediamine, however, was also reported to give a 1:2 complex, formulated[51] as $[Cl_2B \cdot NH \cdot C_6H_4 \cdot NH_3]^+[BCl_4]^-$, which, on heating[51,90], lost hydrogen chloride and gave a light-brown, infusible and organic-solvent-insoluble resin, formulated as a polycondensate (XXXV). On the other hand[87], the 1:1 boron trichloride complexes, whilst also losing hydrogen chloride on heating, gave products of empirical formulae $C_6H_5N_2B$ or $C_6H_5N_2HB$. The *ortho* product, $(C_6H_5N_2HB)_3$, had m.p. 406°, was described as a borazole, (XXXVI; X = NH), was slightly soluble in benzene and was unaffected by boiling water, whereas the *meta* and *para* products were stable *in vacuo* at 500°, and were hygroscopic, and insoluble in hydrocarbons or ethers. The *o*-phenylenediamine-boron trichloride reaction, to give (XXXVI; X = NH), was confirmed[89]; 2,6-lutidine was recommended as a catalyst and

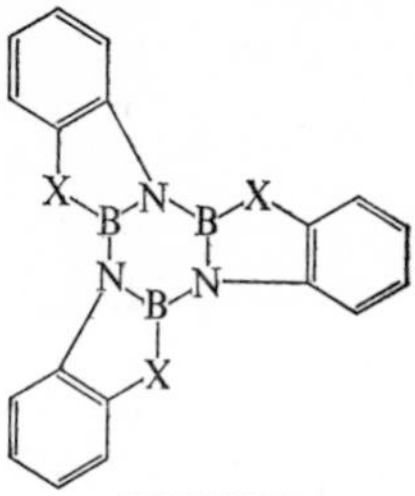

(XXXVI)

instead of *o*-phenylenediamine, *o*-aminophenol, or *o*-anisidine, or *o*-aminophenetole could also be used to give (XXXVI; X = O) and furthermore the benzene rings could bear nuclear substituents. The reaction of *p*-phenylenediamine with *p*-bis(dichloroboro)-benzene, *p*-$C_6H_4(BCl_2)_2$, has been suggested as a route to polymers of type $[C_6H_4 \cdot NH \cdot B(Cl)C_6H_4]_n$[90]. *m*-Aminophenyldichloroborane, *m*-phenylenediamine, and formaldehyde, in presence of hydrogen chloride, afforded products of uncertain composition, which were recommended for use as ion-exchange resins for separating sugar mixtures[91].

B-Trichloro-*N*-triphenylborazole eliminated hydrogen chloride when heated, and this, together with infrared spectroscopic data (1,4-disubstituted-benzene pattern), was taken as evidence for polycondensation by Friedel-Crafts cross-linking[51,90], particularly since Friedel-Crafts haloboration of benzene ($C_6H_6 \rightarrow Ph \cdot BX_2 + HX$) was established[92].

A number of poly(boroamides), *i.e.*, compounds which contain the ring system (XXXVII)[88,94a–c], have been prepared[93]. The impetus for this work probably came from the knowledge of the relative hydrolytic stability of *B*-alkyl- and *B*-aryl-derivatives of (XXXVII). Compounds of type (XXXVIII) were obtained[93] from diboronic acids, $(HO)_2B—X—B(OH)_2$ [X = *p*-C_6H_4 or $(CH_2)_4$] and the appropriate bis(*o*-phenylenediamine). Compounds (XXXVIII)

References, p. 52–56

were dark, insoluble materials, infusible when $X = p\text{-}C_6H_4$, and m.p. 350–370° when $X = (CH_2)_4$. Trimethylenediamine and diaminoneopentane also gave cyclic boroamides with boronic acids, but these were readily hydrolysed.

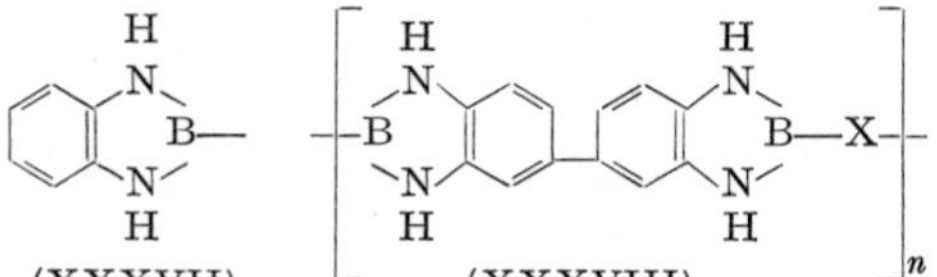

(XXXVII) (XXXVIII)

Water-soluble resins, potentially useful as sizes, textile coatings, or adhesives, were obtained from boric acid (or its derivatives) and polyamines of formula $NH_2(CH_2{\cdot}CH_2{\cdot}NH)_nH$, or certain amino-alcohols[95], for example, from boric acid and either triethylenetetramine, or 2-amino-2-methyl-1,3-propanediol. The hydrolytic stability may well arise from transannular cyclisation, as in the ethanolamine borates (see Chapter 3, p. 63, formula XI). Materials, having similar properties and potential uses, have been stated to be produced from boric acid and urea or substituted polyureas[96], particularly diureas[97]. For example, the structure (XXXIX) was proposed for the reaction product from hexaminethylenediurea and benzeneboronic acid.

Further reference to poly(boroamides) and poly(boroureas) is made in Section 9.

Polymeric materials have also been produced[23] by the reaction of dialkylaminoboranes with butadiene under pressure, but the major products were simple ring compounds, such as $R_2N{\cdot}B(CH_2CH_2)_2B{\cdot}NR_2$.

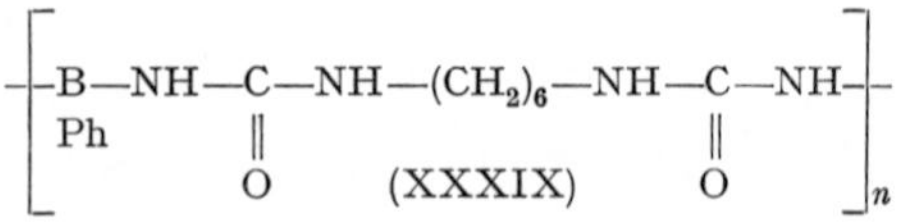

$$\left[-\underset{\text{Ph}}{\text{B}}-NH-\underset{\text{O}}{\overset{\|}{C}}-NH-(CH_2)_6-NH-\underset{\text{O}}{\overset{\|}{C}}-NH-\right]_n$$

(XXXIX)

9. Polymers derived from isocyanates

The reaction of boronic acids, $R{\cdot}B(OH)_2$ (especially R = Ph or $CH_2{:}CH$), with organic di-iso- or di-isothio-cyanates at 35–200° was said to provide a method for preparing poly(boroureas), with carbon dioxide as the other product[98a]. For example, benzeneboronic acid and hexamethylenedi-isocyanate were heated in benzene at 90° for 2 hours, during which time the benzene was distilled off. Further heating at 148° for 16 hours gave the polymer, which softened with decomposition at ~ 300° and was soluble in phenol. In other reactions, tertiary amines or glycols were catalysts and addition, after a stated time, of dodecyl alcohol was said to provide a controlled polymer termination reaction. Repetition of some of these reactions[98b], showed that these claims were specious and that

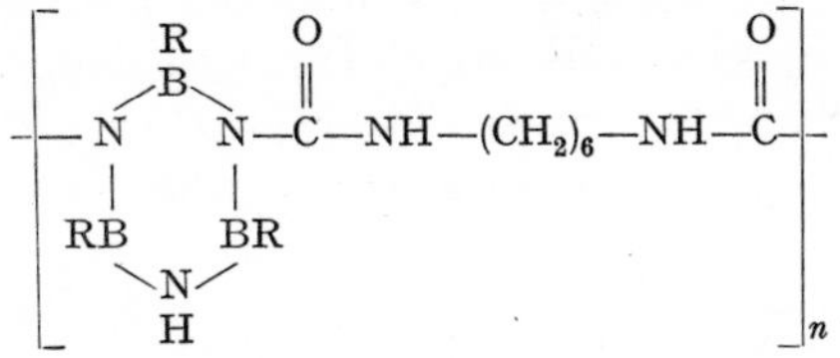

```
   ┌    R      O                    O ┐
   │   /B\     ‖                    ‖ │
  ─┼─N     N—C—NH—(CH2)6—NH—C─┼─
   │  |     |                         │
   │ RB     BR                        │        (XL)
   │   \N/                            │
   └    H                             ┘n

   ┌    R      O                    O ┐
   │   /B\     ‖                    ‖ │
  ─┼─N     N—C—NH—(CH2)6—NH—C─┼─
   │  |     |                         │
   │ RB     BR                        │        (XLI)
   │   \N/                            │
   │    |                             │
   └ O=C—NH—(CH2)3—                   ┘n
```

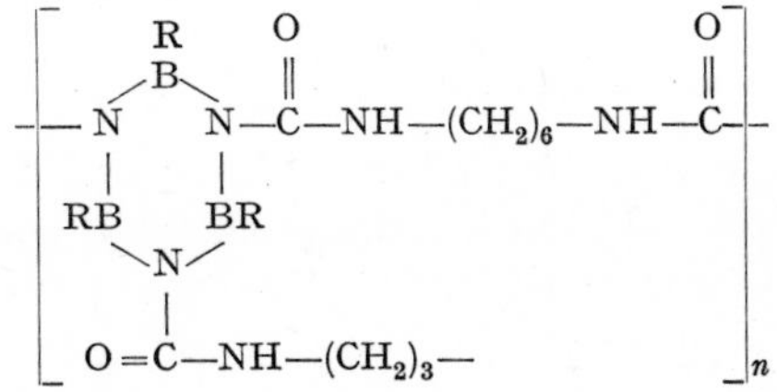

the di-isocyanate merely caused the dehydration of the benzeneboronic acid to form the anhydride, $(PhB\cdot O)_3$, and the water that formed then reacted with further di-isocyanate to give the appropriate boron-free polyurea. However, there is a still further con-

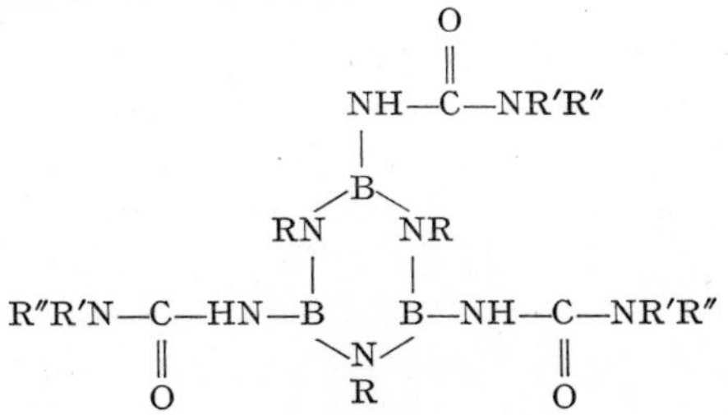

```
                         O
                         ‖
                   NH—C—NR'R"
                    |
                   /B\
                 RN   NR
                  |    |
R"R'N—C—HN—B    B—NH—C—NR'R"
      ‖          \N/        ‖
      O           R         O
               (XLII)
```

References, p. 52–56

flicting report, which is in line with the original observation[97], in that heating boric acid and phenyl isocyanate to 100° in presence of triethylamine was said to give tris(phenylamino)borane, $B(NHPh)_3$, and carbon dioxide[99]. Polymers, having structural units (XL) and (XLI), were obtained from *B*-trialkylborazoles and hexamethylenedi-isocyanate, using 1:1 or 1:1.5 molar stoicheiometry, respectively[100a]. Analogous materials have been obtained from di-isocyanates and bisaminoboranes, $R\cdot B(NHR')_2$[100b].

Instead of organic isocyanates,* the use of boron isocyanates[67] has been explored. At the time of writing, no polymers have been produced, but boroureas of type (XLII) have been obtained from *B*-tri(isocyanato)borazoles and amines[101].

Reactions of boron isocyanates with amines (to give boroureas) and alcohols (to give borourethanes) are not of general application, as in many instances, displacement of the isocyanate group(s) by amino- or alkoxy- group(s) occurs.

10. Evidence for π-bonding in 3-co-ordinate boron-nitrogen systems

The problem of π-bonding must be considered both for open-chain compounds, $>B—N<$, and also for cyclic ones (borazoles), since with the latter the related questions of delocalisation of π-bonds and aromaticity arise.

The boron-nitrogen bond energy appears to be about 105 kcal, both in open-chain and in cyclic compounds, and such a high value is consistent with π-bonding contributing to the bond strengths. Calculations[5], based on measurement of the heat of hydrolysis of tris(dimethylamino)borane, $B(NMe_2)_3$[4a], and of *B*-trichloroborazole, $(ClB\cdot NH)_3$[102], gave values of 104 and 106.5 kcal for the B—N bond energy in the two compounds, respectively. Thermochemical evidence for π-bonding is further provided[4b] by the demonstration that $Me_2N\cdot BCl_2$ [and to a lesser extent $(Me_2N)_2B\cdot Cl$] is more stable than would be the case if the B—Cl bonds had the same mean energy as in BCl_3 and the B—N bond as in $B(NMe_2)_3$. These results are consistent with the interpretation that both N and Cl can

* It has recently been shown[64b] that phenyl isocyanate and $BCl_{3-n}Ph_n$ (n = 1, 2 or 3) readily afford amido-boranes of type $X\cdot B[NPh(C:O\cdot Y)]_2$; using di-isocyanates this leads to addition polymers.

form π-bonds with B and that the effect is greater for BN than BCl.

It is difficult to obtain meaningful figures for the lengths of pure single and double B—N bonds. The single bond distance, based on a calculation using trigonal covalent radii of boron and nitrogen and allowing for the electronegativity difference between the two atoms, was estimated at 1·45 Å[47a]. This value is of much the same order as the measured B—N distance in hexagonal boron nitride (1.446 Å)[56] and in various borazoles [$(HB \cdot NH)_3$, 1.42 ± 0.02 Å[103]; $(HB \cdot NMe)_3$, 1.42 ± 0.02 Å[104]; and $(ClB \cdot NH)_3$, 1.41 ± 0.02 Å[104,105]]. The approximately planar hexagonal form of the ring in borazole and some of its substitution derivatives has been demonstrated both by electron[103,106] and X-ray[105] diffraction.

The bibliography up to 1959 on infrared spectra of three-co-ordinate open-chain boron-nitrogen compounds is compiled in Ref. 70. Particularly significant is the full co-ordinate analysis, based also on Raman spectra carried out on two borazens, which led to values for the B—N stretching force-constants[19a,108]. These values appeared to be appropriate[107] for a double bond (7.0 Mdynes/Å) in a mono-aminoborane ($Me_2B \cdot NMe_2$)[19a] and 4/3 of a bond in a trisamino-borane [$B(NMe_2)_3$][108]. It has been suggested[107] that 3.0 Mdynes/Å is the value of the stretching force-constant for a B—N single bond, which implies that 7.0 Mdynes/Å represents a value of 1.8 for the B—N bond order in dimethylaminodimethylborane. However, such results do not provide a conclusive answer to the problem of π-bonding in these systems, since inevitably the calculations depend on a significant number of simplifying assumptions.

A study of the infrared spectra of a large number of borazens provides four independent lines of evidence for the view that the B—N bonds possess considerable double bond character[70]. Thus, (i) the B—N asymmetric stretching vibration is at high frequency [~1495 cm^{-1} in $B(NHR)_3$; ~1510 cm^{-1} in $B(NHAr)_3$; ~1430 cm^{-1} in $B(NR_2)_3$; and ~1350 cm^{-1} in $B(NRAr)_3$] and is of high intensity; (ii) in the primary alkylamino-derivatives, *e.g.*, $B(NHEt)_3$, there is negligible hydrogen-bonding and the N—H vibrations are of similar frequencies and intensities as in secondary amides, $>$CO·NHR, (and not as in secondary amines); (iii) detailed comparisons of B—N bond strengths in various borazens, as deter-

References, p. 52–56

mined by variations in B—N stretching frequencies [*e.g.*, $B(NHAr)_3 > B(NHR)_3 > B(NR_2)_3 > B(NRAr)_3$; and $(R'O)_2B\cdot NR_2 > R'O\cdot B(NR_2)_2 > B(NR_2)_3$], are consistent with valence bond arguments, based on assumption of B—N and B—O π-bonding, and BN > BO, [*e.g.*, the BN bond order in $B(NHR)_3$ is greater than in $B(NR_2)_3$, because of the possibility in the former compound of contributary canonical structures of the type $\overset{+}{H}RN{=}\overline{B}(NHR)_2$]; and (iv) in arylaminoboranes, *e.g.*, $B(NHPh)_3$, the normal monosubstituted aromatic CC stretching (A_1) vibration at ~ 1600 cm^{-1} is accompanied by a well-developed (B_1) vibration at ~ 20 cm^{-1} lower, this indicating extended conjugation of the aromatic ring with an unsaturated side-chain.

The infrared spectra of borazole and of a number of its *B*- and *N*-tri- and hexa- substituted derivatives have been interpreted by analogy with those of benzene and appropriate derivatives[69,109]. The values for B—N ring stretching vibrations[71] at 1450 cm^{-1} differ but little from exocyclic B—N stretching modes[70] in borazens. Of diagnostic value, particularly, is the medium-to-strong doublet near 720 cm^{-1}, which appears to be characteristic of borazoles having substituents on the boron atoms which can conjugate with the ring[68,71]; this absorption was assigned to one of the out-of-plane ring vibrations and is similar in frequency to corresponding absorptions in 1,3,5- trisubstituted benzenes and in melamine[71].

The ultraviolet spectra of borazole[110] and of a number of its simple derivatives[101,111] have been determined. Some of the observed spectra were related to those of benzene and its derivatives[110]. Molecular orbital methods were used to compare computed excitation energies with those obtained from spectra[112].

A consequence of there being appreciable π-bonding in the borazens, is that there should be restriction to rotation about the B—N bond. The potential energy barriers (17 ± 5 kcals $mole^{-1}$) to rotation about the B—N bond in two borazens—*N*-phenylmethylaminodimethylborane, $Me_2B\cdot N(Me)Ph$[113], and dimethylaminophenylchloroborane, $Ph(Cl)B\cdot NMe_2$[114], were calculated from the ^1H nuclear magnetic resonance spectra, taken at various temperatures. Methyl absorption in $Ph(Cl)B\cdot NMe_2$ occurs around $\tau = 7.2$ at 23°, and consists of a doublet (Fig. 4a), in accord with the two sets of ^1H

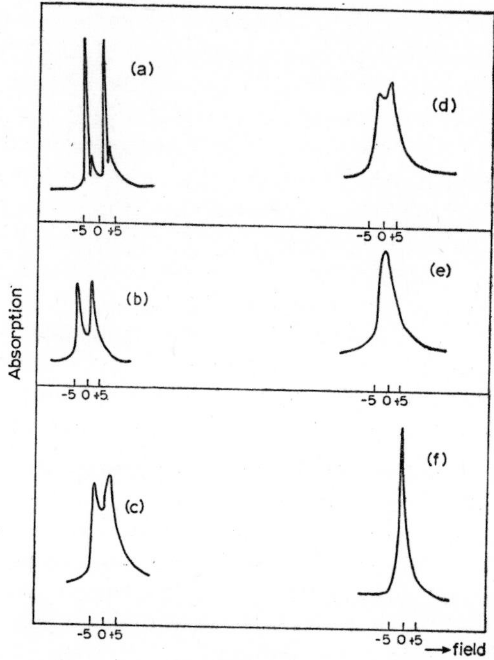

Fig. 4.

nuclei being in two chemically different and equally abundant environments (*cis* or *trans* to the phenyl group)[114]. At progressively higher temperatures (Figs. 4b–4d), band broadening and decrease of maxima separation are evident, the separation becoming zero at 118° ("coalescence") (Fig. 4e), and above this temperature, the single band becomes increasingly narrow (Fig. 4f). The association of this kind of spectral behaviour with variable isomeric interconversion is well-established. The high energy barrier to rotation about the B—N bond could be interpreted in electronic (π-bonding) and/or steric terms. Compelling evidence for the former comes from a comparison of barriers in Ph(Cl)B·NMe_2 and Ph·B$(NMe_2)_2$[114]; in the former compound it is 18±2 kcal.mole^{-1}, but in the latter $<$ 10 kcal.mole^{-1}. In the latter compound, steric hindrance to rotation is greater, but as for π-bonding, the two nitrogen atom

References, p. 52–56

lone pairs are competing for the single vacant orbital on boron. Circumstantial evidence for the existence of *cis*- and *trans*-isomerides of borazens of type RR′B·NR″R‴ had earlier been proposed[115], and was based largely on small variations in melting and boiling points.

The ^{1}H and ^{11}B nuclear magnetic resonance spectra of borazole[116] and some of its derivatives[117,118] have been interpreted by assuming significant B—N π-bonding. From ^{11}B nuclear magnetic resonance studies on powdered hexagonal boron nitride and *B*-trichloroborazole, the ^{11}B nuclear electrical quadrupole interactions were measured, and these were used in the Townes and Dailey approach to estimate the probable bonding electron configuration[117]; it was estimated that in hexagonal boron nitride the B—N bonding comprised 55% single and 45% double bond configurations.

The significant π-bonding in dimethylaminodimethylborane, $Me_2B\cdot NMe_2$, should result in a high dipole moment ($Me_2\overset{-}{B}{=}\overset{+}{N}Me_2$). In fact, the dipole moment is low, 1.40 ± 0.03 D[18] and this has been accounted for in terms of unsymmetrical electron sharing in the sense B $\longrightarrow$ N, owing to the electronegativity difference between boron and nitrogen[19b]. In dimethylaminodiphenylborane, $Ph_2B\cdot NMe_2$, the small dipole moment was in the sense N $\longrightarrow$ B, whilst in diphenylaminodiphenylborane, $Ph_2B\cdot NPh_2$, it was in the opposite sense. Dipole moment measurements on borazoles support the view that the hexagonal nucleus is approximately planar[119].

The most conclusive evidence in favour of aromaticity in borazoles comes from measurement of the molecular diamagnetic anisotropy of a number of compounds and relation with results on appropriate benzenoid derivatives[120,121]. The experimental and calculated values were compared, and this led to the conclusion that the extent of contribution of the donor-acceptor double bond structure to the normal state of borazole is ~ 24% and that the π-electron bond order of B—N bonds is ~ 0.45[121].

The chemical behaviour of borazens and borazoles also suggests that π-bonding between boron and nitrogen is significant[3,47]. Particularly relevant is, in general, their scarcely-developed acceptor properties (although they are usually susceptible to attack by nucleophilic reagents; see, *e.g.*, Section 11). Thus, as a rule, in borazens boron achieves co-ordination saturation intramolecularly

($\rangle\overline{B}=\overset{+}{N}\langle$), and only in those cases (see Section 2) where steric conditions are favourable does it do so intermolecularly, by dimer, (VI), trimer (VIII), or polymer (IX)–(XI) formation.

11. Hydrolytic susceptibility; hydrolysis and some other nucleophilic substitution reactions of 3-co-ordinate boron-nitrogen compounds

Acyclic boron-nitrogen compounds are generally easily hydrolysed, even by atmospheric moisture[3].

$$\rangle B-N\langle + H_2O \longrightarrow \rangle B-OH + HN\langle$$

There are two general exceptions. Firstly, some four-co-ordinate complexes, such as $C_5H_5N \cdot BCl_3$[122] are unaffected by cold water (however, others, such as $RCN \cdot BCl_3$[123] are easily hydrolysed). Secondly, certain borazens, of such a nature that they have the boron atom surrounded by highly-branched or bulky substituents[77], for example, tris(*N*-alkylarylamino)boranes, $B(NRAr)_3$[77,124], are hydrolytically-stable. Tris(*N*-methylphenylamino)borane, $B(NMePh)_3$, is not even attacked by boiling aqueous alkali, whilst tris(2,4,6-tribromophenylamino)borane, $B(NHC_6H_2Br_3)_3$, is only slowly hydrolysed by boiling water. In the case of the stable four-co-ordinate complexes, the factor making for stability appears to be the strong donor-acceptor bond. In considering the hydrolysis of borazens, it is relevant to discuss the mechanism of substitution at a three-co-ordinate boron atom in general terms.

Replacement of a group X (by Y) at a three-co-ordinate boron atom is, in general, likely to involve an S_N2 mechanism, with a transition state, or intermediate, (XLIII), in which the boron atom is using sp^3-hybrid orbitals[77]. Steric factors may be manifested either (i) kinetically, in hindering collision between the nucleophile and the substrate, or (ii) thermodynamically, in influencing the stability of (XLIII) and particularly its direction of decomposition, *i.e.*, into products (steric assistance) or reactants (steric hindrance). Resistance of highly hindered substrates, such as $B(NRAr)_3$ towards hydrolysis provides evidence of (i) (steric hindrance in substrate). Evidence for (ii) is the observation that the relative displacement tendencies of groups X and Y are, in general, in the order OH > OR > NH_2 > NHR > NR_2 (R ≠ highly branched alkyl group)[10,77].* On the other hand, further evidence for (i) (steric hindrance in reagent) is the observation that *t*-butylamine does not react even with dialkylaminoboranes (*i.e.*, NR_2 > $NHBu^t$)[10a].** The relative positions of the variously-substituted amino groups in the displacement series receive further support from the infrared spectra of appropriate borazens[70], which show that the B—N bond order in $B(NHR)_3$ is greater than in $B(NR_2)_3$. The mechanism also requires that polar factors influence the reaction. The replacement of mercapto groups attached to boron by amino groups (NH_2 > NHR > NR_2 > SR) indicates polar control in the reagent (*i.e.*, an amine is a stronger donor, in general, than a mercaptan). The high reactivity of *o*-$C_6H_4O_2\cdot B\cdot NCO$, compared with $(HN\cdot BNCO)_3$,

$$\geq B\ddot{X} + H\ddot{Y} \underset{\text{fast}}{\overset{\text{slow}}{\rightleftharpoons}} H^+ \left[\ddot{Y}\!>\!B\!<\!\ddot{X} \right]^- \underset{\text{slow}}{\overset{\text{fast}}{\rightleftharpoons}} \geq B\ddot{Y} + H\ddot{X}$$

(XLIII)

towards substitution by NR_2, by reaction with an amine (see Section 9)[101] demonstrates polar control in the substrate (*i.e.*, the acceptor strength of a three-co-ordinate boron atom is at a minimum in a borazole). Finally, the mechanism requires, providing that steric and polar factors in products and reactants are of similar order, the demonstration of a volatility factor and this is illustrated by the conversion of tris(diethylamino)borane into the higher homologue, $B(NBu^n_2)_3$, if the reaction is carried out by continuous distillation[125].

The significance of steric effects in B—N chemistry will have been evident in much of the material discussed in this chapter.*** Another example, in borazen chemistry, is the failure to prepare trisaminoboranes where the amino groups are highly hindered [*e.g.*, —NPh_2, —$N(C_6H_{11})_2$, —N(Me)(α-Nap), —$NPhBu^t$][124] although a wide variety of other trisaminoboranes is known[72].

Cyclic boron-nitrogen compounds are almost invariably less

* It has recently been shown that the NR_2 group may also be displaced by —NH_2, —NHCOR, —$NHNH_2$, and —NHOH[94d].

** Likewise, piperidine and *N*-methylaniline do displace isopropylamine from $B(NHPr^i)_3$[128].

*** Another recent example[94e] is the lack of reactivity of $(Pr^i_2N)_2B\cdot Cl$ with di-isopropylamine, although the chlorine atom may be replaced by —$NHBu^t$.

readily hydrolysed than analogous acyclic materials. The stability of some four-co-ordinate cyclic materials [see (VI)] has already been referred to (Section 2). Among three-co-ordinate systems which possess considerable resistance towards hydrolysis, are the cyclic borazens, such as (XXXVII), some borazoles, and the borazocines, (XIII). With compounds (XXXVII), this may be due to the aromaticity possessed by the boron-containing ring; this receives support from the measured ultraviolet spectra, which resemble the isoconjugate indole derivatives[94c]. With borazoles, there are two possible points of attack by water. With reference to (III), these are firstly the exocyclic B—X bonds, and secondly the cyclic B—N bonds. The former provide weak points mainly when the groups X are such that the atoms adjacent to boron have lone pairs of electrons (*e.g.*, O, N, or Hal). When this is not so, the ring is reasonably stable, *e.g.*, *B*-trimethyl-*N*-triphenylborazole, $(MeB \cdot NPh)_3$, is unaffected by boiling in water during one hour's reflux[126]. It is interesting, however, that the structural isomer *B*-triphenyl-*N*-trimethylborazole, $(PhB \cdot NMe)_3$, is 90% hydrolysed under the same conditions. It is likely that the explanation is the same as the one that accounts for the stability of $B(NPhMe)_3$ compared with $B(NR_2)_3$—and this may be a steric question. *B*-Triphenyl- and *B*-tri(2-chlorovinyl)-borazoles are also stable under similar conditions, but evolve ammonia when boiled with aqueous alkali[127]. The stability of the hydroxide (XXVI; Y=H; X=OH)[33b,48], already referred to, is also of a compound which has *N*-aryl substituents, and these, moreover, are highly-hindered. The relative hydrolytic stability of borazocines (XIII)[33a,48], even of the *B*-tetrachloro-derivatives, is again probably due to a steric factor (see Section 3).

12. Summary and Conclusion

It will have been seen that whereas many reports of polymers containing boron and nitrogen have appeared in the literature, only a fraction of this work was carried out with the deliberate intent of studying polymers. For example, several polymeric species have been encountered in the course of studies on the diborane-ammonia and related reactions (see Figs. 2 and 3), but their formation, structure, average degree of polymerisation, thermal and

References, p. 52–56

hydrolytic stability, and chemical reactivity were of secondary interest; much of the discussion in this chapter relating to such materials has therefore been speculative. Indeed, with the exception of the allotropes of boron nitride, it is only with the polycondensates of aminoborazoles[68,72] and aminoboroxoles[77], among the presumed-high-molecular-weight materials, that physical evidence as to structure is available. Preliminary conclusions as to the likelihood of boron-nitrogen polymers being, in general, thermally-stable would appear to be favourable, since at any rate one group—the polycondensates of aminoborazoles—are stable up to at least 600° in dry air[68,72].*

As yet, most of the presumed high-polymers which have been described in the literature, except those having substantial proportions of carbon in the main chain, have been hard, infusible, intractable, and usually organic solvent-insoluble resins; this has largely contributed to the absence of significant physico-chemical studies. Such properties are undoubtedly associated with there being extensive crosslinking in the polymers and future progress will certainly be significantly affected by any successful developments in synthesis of bi-, instead of tri-, functional boron monomers.

* At 450° the following order of increasing thermal stability has been established: $(PhB\cdot NMe)_3 < (PhB\cdot NPh)_3 < (MeB\cdot NPh)_3 < (PhB\cdot NH)_3 < (MeB\cdot NMe)_3$[129]; in general, B–C homolysis was believed to be the primary step.

REFERENCES

1 E. Wiberg, *Naturwiss.*, 35 (1948) 182, 222.
2 M. J. S. Dewar, V. P. Kubba and R. Pettit, *J. Chem. Soc.*, (1958) 3073.
3 M. F. Lappert, *Chem. Rev.*, 56 (1956) 959; W. Gerrard and M. F. Lappert, *ibid.*, 58 (1958) 1081; B. M. Mikhailov, *Uspekhi Khim.*, 28 (1959) 1450.
4a H. A. Skinner and N. B. Smith, *J. Chem. Soc.*, (1953) 4025.
4b H. A. Skinner and N. B. Smith, *J. Chem. Soc.*, (1954) 2324.
5 T. L. Cottrell, *The Strengths of Chemical Bonds*, 2nd. Ed., Butterworths Scientific Publications, London (1958) p. 240.
6 E. Wiberg and K. Schuster, *Z. anorg. Chem.*, 213 (1933) 77.
7 E. Wiberg and K. Schuster, *Z. anorg. Chem.*, 213 (1933) 89.
8 J. F. Brown, *J. Am. Chem. Soc.*, 74 (1952) 1219.
9 C. A. Brown and R. C. Osthoff, *J. Am. Chem. Soc.*, 74 (1952) 2340.
10a M. F. Lappert and M. K. Majumdar, unpublished observations.
10b M. F. Lappert and M. K. Majumdar, *Proc. Chem. Soc.*, (1961) 425.
11 O. C. Musgrave, *J. Chem. Soc.*, (1956) 4305.
12 R. C. Osthoff and C. A. Brown, *J. Am. Chem. Soc.*, 74 (1952) 2378.

[13] E. WIBERG, *F.I.A.T. Review of German Science: Inorganic Chemistry*, Vol. I, p. 125; J. GOUBEAU, *op. cit.*, p. 215.
[14] A. B. BURG and J. BANUS, *J. Am. Chem. Soc.*, 76 (1954) 3903.
[15] E. WIBERG, A. BOLZ and P. BUCHHEIT, *Z. anorg. Chem.*, 256 (1948) 285.
[16] E. WIBERG, K. HERTWIG and A. BOLZ, *Z. anorg. Chem.* 256 (1948) 177.
[17] E. WIBERG and P. BUCHHEIT, unpublished work, cited by J. GOUBEAU in *F.I.A.T. Reviews of German Science: Inorganic Chemistry*, Vol. I, p. 218.
[18] H. J. BECHER, *Z. anorg. Chem.*, 270 (1952) 273.
[19a] H. J. BECHER and J. GOUBEAU, *Z. anorg. Chem.*, 268 (1952) 133.
[19b] G. E. COATES and J. G. LIVINGSTONE, *J. Chem. Soc.*, (1961) 1000.
[20a] E. WIBERG and K. HERTWIG, *Z. anorg. Chem.*, 255 (1947) 141.
[20b] B. M. MIKHAILOV and N. S. FEDOTOV, *Izvest. Akad. Nauk S.S.S.R., Otdel. Khim. Nauk*, (1959), 1482.
[20c] A. B. BURG and J. L. BOONE, *J. Am. Chem. Soc.*, 78 (1956) 1521.
[21a] A. SHEPP and S. H. BAUER, *J. Am. Chem. Soc.*, 76 (1954) 265.
[21b] G. W. CAMPBELL and L. JOHNSON, *J. Am. Chem. Soc.*, 81 (1959) 3800.
[21c] L. M. TREFONAS and W. N. LIPSCOMB, *J. Am. Chem. Soc.*, 81 (1959) 4435.
[22] O. C. MUSGRAVE *et al.*, unpublished observations (personal communication from J. M. C. THOMPSON).
[23] J. DEWING, unpublished observations (personal communication).
[24] T. C. BISSOT and R. W. PARRY, *J. Am. Chem. Soc.*, 77 (1955) 3481.
[25a] A. STOCK, E. WIBERG, H. MARTINI and A. NICKLAS, *Ber.*, 65 (1932) 1711.
[25b] G. H. DAHL and R. SCHAEFFER, *J. Amer. Chem. Soc.*, 83 (1961) 3032.
[26] E. WIBERG and A. BOLZ, *Z. anorg. Chem.*, 257 (1948) 131.
[27] A. B. BURG and C. L. RANDOLPH, *J. Am. Chem. Soc.*, 73 (1951) 953.
[28] A. B. BURG and E. S. KULJIAN, *J. Am. Chem. Soc.*, 72 (1950) 3103.
[29] H. J. EMELÉUS and K. WADE, *J. Chem. Soc.*, (1960) 2614.
[30] A. B. BURG, *Record Chem. Progr. (Kresge-Hooker Sci. Lib.)*, 15 (1954) 159.
[31] H. I. SCHLESINGER, D. M. RITTER and A. B. BURG, *J. Am. Chem. Soc.*, 60 (1938) 2297.
[32] A. STOCK and E. POHLAND, *Ber.*, 59 (1926) 2215.
[33] P. C. MOEWS and A. W. LAUBENGAYER, 136*th Meeting American Chemical Society*, New Jersey, Sept. 1959, p. 53N; A. W. LAUBENGAYER, P. C. MOEWS and R. F. PORTER, *J. Am. Chem. Soc.*, 83 (1961) 1337.
[33a] H. S. TURNER and R. J. WARNE, *Proc. Chem. Soc.*, (1962) 69.
[33b] R. K. BARTLETT, H. S. TURNER, R. J. WARNE, M. A. YOUNG and W. S. McDONALD, *Proc. Chem. Soc.*, (1962) 153.
[34] E. WIBERG and A. BOLZ, *Ber.*, 73 (1940) 209.
[35] S. G. SHORE and R. W. PARRY, *J. Am. Chem. Soc.*, 80 (1958) 12.
[36] G. W. SCHAEFFER, M. D. ADAMS and F. J. KOENIG, *J. Am. Chem. Soc.*, 78 (1956) 725.
[37] G. W. SCHAEFFER and L. J. BASILLE, *J. Am. Chem. Soc.*, 77 (1957) 331.
[38] S. G. SHORE, P. R. GIRARDOT and R. W. PARRY, *J. Am. Chem. Soc.*, 80 (1958) 20.
[39] R. W. PARRY, D. R. SCHULTZ and P. R. GIRARDOT, *J. Am. Chem. Soc.*, 80 (1958) 1.
[40] M. J. STEINDLER and H. I. SCHLESINGER, *J. Am. Chem. Soc.*, 75 (1953) 756.
[41] H. J. EMELÉUS and F. G. A. STONE, *J. Chem. Soc.*, (1951) 840.
[42] A. JOANNIS, *Compt. rend.*, 139 (1904) 364.
[43] A. STOCK and W. HOLLE, *Ber.*, 41 (1908) 2095.
[44] A. JOANNIS, *Compt. rend.*, 135 (1902) 1106.

[45] A. PFLUGMACHER and W. DIENER, *Angew. Chem.*, 69 (1957) 777.
[46] A. B. BURG, *130th Meeting American Chemical Society*, Atlantic City, Sept. 1956, p. 34R.; *134th Meeting American Chemical Society*, Chicago, Sept. 1958, p. 26N.
[47a] J. C. SHELDON and B. C. SMITH, *Quart. Rev.* 14 (1960) 200.
[47b] B. M. MIKHAILOV, *Uspekhi Khim.*, 29 (1960) 972.
[48] H. S. TURNER, unpublished observations (personal communication).
[49] E. WIBERG and G. HORELD, *Z. Naturforsch.*, 6b (1951) 338.
[50] T. C. BISSOT, D. H. CAMPBELL and R. W. PARRY, *J. Am. Chem. Soc.*, 80 (1958) 1868.
[51] W. GERRARD, paper presented at the Plastics and Polymer Group of the Society of Chemical Industry, *Symposium on High Temperature Resistance and Thermal Degradation of Polymers*, London, Sept., 1960; S.C.I. Monograph No. 13, London, 1961, p. 328.
[51a] W. GERRARD, E. F. MOONEY and H. R. HUDSON, *J. Chem. Soc.*, (1962) 113.
[52] W. J. McDOWELL and C. W. KEENAN, *J. Am. Chem. Soc.*, 78 (1956) 2069.
[53] D. T. HAWORTH and L. F. HOHNSTEDT, *134th Meeting American Chemical Society*, Chicago, Sept. 1958, p. 26N.; *J. Am. Chem. Soc.*, 81 (1959) 842.
[54] E. WIBERG and K. HERTWIG, *Z. anorg. Chem.*, 257 (1948) 138.
[55] H. J. BECHER, *Z. anorg. Chem.*, 289 (1957) 262.
[56] R. S. PEASE, *Nature*, 165 (1950) 722; *Acta Cryst.*, 5 (1952) 356; *J. Am. Chem. Soc.*, 74 (1952) 4219.
[57] F. G. A. STONE, in *Advances in Inorganic and Radiochemistry*, Vol. II, Eds. H. J. EMELÉUS and A. G. SHARPE, Academic Press, New York, 1960, p. 291.
[58] R. H. WENTORF, *J. Chem. Phys.*, 26 (1957) 956.
[59] A. HEIDEMANN, *Urania*, 21 (1958) 38.
[60] R. H. WENTORF, *J. Chem. Phys.*, 34 (1961) 809.
[61] M. CHAIGNEAU, *Compt. rend.*, 239 (1954) 1220.
[62] J. GUY and M. CHAIGNEAU, *Bull. soc. chim. France*, (1956) 257.
[63] E. C. EVERS, W. O. FREITAG, J. N. KEITH, W. A. KRINER, A. G. MACDIARMID, and S. SUJISHI, *J. Am. Chem. Soc.*, 81 (1959) 4493.
[64a] E. C. EVERS, W. O. FREITAG, W. A. KRINER and A. G. MACDIARMID, *J. Am. Chem. Soc.*, 81 (1959) 5106.
[64b] M. F. LAPPERT and B. PROKAI, unpublished observations.
[65] G. L. BRENNAN, G. H. DAHL and R. SCHAEFFER, *J. Am. Chem. Soc.*, 82 (1960) 6248.
[66] J. GOUBEAU and H. GRÄBNER, *Chem. Ber.*, 93 (1960) 1379.
[67] M. F. LAPPERT and H. PYSZORA, *Proc. Chem. Soc.*, (1960) 350.
[67a] R. I. WAGNER and J. L. BRADFORD, *Inorg. Chem.*, 1 (1962) 93.
[67b] R. I. WAGNER and J. L. BRADFORD, *Inorg. Chem.*, 1 (1962) 99.
[68] M. F. LAPPERT, *Proc. Chem. Soc.*, (1959) 59.
[69] B. L. CRAWFORD and J. T. EDSALL, *J. Chem Phys.*, 7 (1939) 223; W. C. PRICE, R. D. B. FRASER, T. S. ROBINSON and H. L. LONGUET-HIGGINS, *Discussions Faraday Soc.*, 9 (1950) 131; H. J. BECHER and S. FRICK, *Z. anorg. Chem.*, 295 (1958) 83.
[70] D. W. AUBREY, M. F. LAPPERT and H. PYSZORA, *J. Chem. Soc.*, (1960) 5239.
[71] D. W. AUBREY, M. F. LAPPERT and H. PYSZORA, *J. Chem. Soc.*, (1961) 1931.
[72] D. W. AUBREY and M. F. LAPPERT, *J. Chem. Soc.*, (1959) 2927.
[73] H. I. SCHLESINGER, D. M. RITTER and A. B. BURG, *J. Am. Chem. Soc.*, 60 (1938) 1296.
[74] J. H. SMALLEY and S. F. STAFIEJ, *J. Am. Chem. Soc.*, 81 (1959) 582.

[75] G. E. Ryschkewitsch, J. J. Harris and H. H. Sisler, *J. Am. Chem Soc.*, 80 (1958) 4515.
[76] G. W. Schaeffer, R. Schaeffer and H. I. Schlesinger, *J. Am. Chem. Soc.*, 73 (1951) 1612.
[77] D. W. Aubrey and M. F. Lappert, *Proc. Chem. Soc.*, (1960) 148.
[78] B. M. Mikhailov and P. M. Aronovich, *Izvest. Akad. Nauk S.S.S.R., Otdel. Khim. Nauk*, (1957) 1123.
[79] B. M. Mikhailov and T. K. Kozminskaya, *Doklady Akad. Nauk S.S.S.R.*, 121 (1958) 656.
[80a] B. M. Mikhailov and T. V. Kostroma, *Zhur. Obshcheĭ Khim.*, 29 (1959) 1477.
[80b] J. J. Harris, *J. Org. Chem.*, 26 (1961) 2155.
[81] D. H. Campbell, T. C. Bissot and R. W. Parry, *J. Am. Chem. Soc.*, 80 (1958) 1549.
[82] R. N. Keller, *138th Meeting American Chemical Society*, New York, Sept. 1960, p. 23N.
[83] L. L. Quill, P. R. Ogle, L. G. Kallander and W. T. Lippincott, *129th Meeting American Chemical Society*, Dallas, April 1956, p. 40N.
[84] M. F. Lappert, *J. Chem. Soc.*, (1958), 3256.
[85a] M. F. Lappert and B. P. Tilley, unpublished observations.
[85b] W. Gerrard, M. F. Lappert and B. A. Mountfield, *J. Chem. Soc.*, (1959) 1529.
[86] K. Niedenzu and J. W. Dawson, *Angew. Chem.*, 72 (1960) 920.
[87] L. J. Schupp and C. A. Brown, *128th Meeting American Chemical Society*, Minneapolis, Sept. 1955, p. 48R; C. A. Brown, P.B. *Report No. 135*, (1956) 739.
[88] L. F. Hohnstedt and A. M. Pellicciotto, *137th Meeting American Chemical Society*, Cleveland, April 1960, p. 7 O.
[89] B. Rudner and J. J. Harris, *138th Meeting American Chemical Society*, New York, Sept. 1960, p. 61P.
[90] W. Gerrard, *J. Oil & Colour Chemists' Assoc.*, 42 (1959) 625.
[91] J. Solms and H. Deuel, *Chimia*, 11 (1957) 311.
[92] E. L. Muetterties, *J. Am. Chem. Soc.*, 81 (1959) 2597; Z. J. Bujwid, W. Gerrard and M. F. Lappert, *Chem & Ind. (London)*, (1959) 1091; K. Niedenzu and J. W. Dawson, *Angew. Chem.*, (1959) 651.
[93] W. R. Bamford and S. Fordham, paper presented at the Plastics and Polymer Group of the Society of Chemical Industry, *Symposium on High Temperature Resistance and Thermal Degradation of Polymers*, London, Sept. 1960; S.C.I. Monograph No. 13, London, 1961, p. 320.
[94a] D. Ulmschneider and J. Goubeau, *Ber.*, 90 (1957) 2733.
[94b] R. L. Letsinger and S. B. Hamilton, *J. Am. Chem. Soc.*, 80 (1958) 5411.
[94c] M. J. S. Dewar, V. P. Kubba and R. Pettit, *J. Chem. Soc.*, (1958) 3076.
[94d] H. Nöth, *Angew. Chem.*, 72 (1960) 40; *Z. Naturforsch.*, 16b (1961) 470, 471.
[94e] D. W. Aubrey, M. F. Lappert and M. K. Majumdar, *J. Chem. Soc.* (1962), in the press.
[95] J. B. Rust, *U.S.P.*, 2,366,129 (1944).
[96] W. L. Morgan, *U.S.P.*, 2,501,783 (1950).
[97] R. W. Upson, *U.S.P.*, 2,599,144 (1952).
[98a] R. W. Upson, *U.S.P.*, 2,517,944 (1950).
[98b] W. L. Ruigh, C. E. Erickson, F. C. Gunderloy and M. Sedlak, *WADC Technical Report 55–26*, Part II (May, 1955); W. L. Ruigh, W. R. Dunnevant, F. C. Gunderloy, A. D. Olin and M. Sedlak, *133rd Meeting American Chemical Society*, San Francisco, April 1958, p. 32L.

99 R. S. Aries, *U.S.P.*, 2,931,831 (1960).

100a V. V. Korshak, V. A. Zamyatina, N. I. Bekasova and Ma Zhui-Zhan, *Vysokomol. Soedineniya*, 2 (1960) 1287; 3 (1961) 525.

100b V. V. Korshak, N. I. Bekasova, V. A. Zamyatina and G. I. Aristarkhova, *Vysokomol. Soedineniya*, 3 (1961) 521.

101 M. F. Lappert and H. Pyszora, unpublished observations.

102 E. R. van Artsdalen and A. S. Dworkin, *J. Am. Chem. Soc.*, 74 (1952) 3401.

103 S. H. Bauer, *J. Am. Chem. Soc.*, 60 (1938) 524.

104 K. P. Coffin and S. H. Bauer, *J. Phys. Chem.*, 59 (1955) 193.

105 D. L. Coursen and J. L. Hoard, *J. Am. Chem. Soc.*, 74 (1952) 1742; K. Lonsdale, *Nature*, 184 (1959) 1060.

106 A. Stock and R. Wierl, *Z. anorg. Chem.*, 203 (1931) 228.

107 J. Goubeau, *Angew. Chem.*, 69 (1957) 77.

108 H. J. Becher, *Z. anorg. Chem.*, 287 (1956) 285.

109 H. Watanabe, M. Narisada, T. Nakagawa and M. Kubo *Spectrochim. Acta*, 16 (1960) 78.

110 J. R. Platt, H. B. Klevens and G. W. Schaeffer, *J. Chem. Phys.*, 15 (1947) 598; L. E. Jacobs, J. R. Platt and G. W. Schaeffer, *J. Chem. Phys.*, 16 (1948) 116.

111 C. W. Rector, G. W. Schaeffer and J. R. Platt, *J. Chem. Phys.*, 17 (1949) 460; H. J. Becher and S. Frick, *Z. phys. Chem. (Frankfurt)*, 12 (1957) 241.

112 C. C. J. Roothaan and R. S. Mulliken, *J. Chem. Phys.*, 16 (1948) 118; D. W. Davies, *Trans. Faraday Soc.*, 56 (1960) 1713.

113 G. E. Ryschkewitsch, W. S. Brey and A. Saji, *J. Am. Chem. Soc.*, 83 (1961) 1010.

114 P. A. Barfield, M. F. Lappert and J. Lee, *Proc. Chem. Soc.*, (1961) 421; and unpublished observations.

115 K. Niedenzu and J. W. Dawson, *J. Am. Chem. Soc.*, 82 (1960) 4223.

116 K. Ito, H. Watanabe and M. Kubo, *J. Chem. Phys.*, 32 (1960) 947.

117 A. H. Silver and P. J. Bray, *J. Chem. Phys.*, 32 (1960) 288.

118 K. Ito, H. Watanabe and M. Kubo, *J. Chem. Phys.*, 34 (1961) 1043; *Bull. Chem. Soc. Japan*, 33 (1960) 1588.

119 K. L. Ramaswamy, *Proc. Indian Acad. Sci.*, A2 (1935) 364; H. Watanabe and M. Kubo, *J. Am. Chem. Soc.*, 82 (1960) 2428.

120 K. Lonsdale and E. W. Toor, *Acta Cryst.*, 12 (1959) 1048.

121 H. Watanabe, K. Ito and M. Kubo, *J. Am. Chem. Soc.*, 82 (1960) 3294.

122 W. Gerrard and M. F. Lappert, *J. Chem. Soc.*, (1951) 1020; *Chem. Ind.*, (1952) 53; M. F. Lappert, *J. Chem. Soc.*, (1953) 667.

123 W. Gerrard, M. F. Lappert and J. W. Wallis, *J. Chem. Soc.*, (1960) 2178.

124 A. Dornow and H. H. Gehrt, *Z. anorg. Chem.*, 294 (1958) 81.

125 W. Gerrard, M. F. Lappert and C. A. Pearce, *J. Chem. Soc.*, (1957) 381.

126 S. J. Groszos and S. F. Stafiej, *J. Am. Chem. Soc.*, 80 (1958) 1357.

127 W. L. Ruigh, XVIth International Congress of Pure and Applied Chemistry, Paris, 1957; *Papers presented to the Section on Mineral Chemistry*, Butterworths Scientific Publications, London, 1958, p. 545.

128 W. D. English, A. L. McCloskey and H. Steinberg, *J. Am. Chem. Soc.*, 83 (1961) 2122.

129 H. C. Newsom, W. D. English, A. L. McCloskey and W. G. Woods, *J. Am. Chem. Soc.*, 83 (1961) 4134.

Chapter 3

Other Boron-Containing Polymers

by

J. M. C. THOMPSON

1. Introduction

Elementary boron forms a three-dimensional polymer, one form of which has m.p. 2300° and is nearly as hard as diamond.

Boron forms a large number of high-molecular-weight compounds with many other elements, involving particularly bonds of boron with hydrogen, carbon, oxygen, nitrogen, and phosphorus. The high bond energies of some of these bonds [*e.g.*, B—O, 119.3; B—N, 104.3; B—C, 89.0; and B—B, 80.0 kcal/mole (*cf.*, C—C 80.0)] indicate the strength of the bonds formed. This has led to much effort in preparing polymers containing such bonds, in the hope that they would possess unusually good high-temperature stability. Unfortunately, the bonds which boron forms with other elements are usually fairly susceptible to attack by many chemical reagents, in particular by the ever-present reagents, oxygen and water. This has proved a major obstacle to the synthesis of stable boron-containing polymers of technical interest.

The simplest hetero-chain polymers of boron are the hydrides. These compounds have been reviewed elsewhere[1,2]. The common boron hydrides are:

B_2H_6 Diborane
B_4H_{10} Tetraborane
B_5H_9 Stable pentaborane (pentaborane-9)
B_5H_{11} Unstable pentaborane (pentaborane-11)
B_6H_{10} Hexaborane
$B_{10}H_{14}$ Decaborane

References, p. 83–86

All these compounds contain B—B bonds, B—H bonds of normal electron pair type, and, in addition, hydrogen-bridge links between boron atoms.

It was reported[3] that while diborane reacted with olefins to give trialkylboranes, it reacted with paraffins to form polymeric products containing boron, carbon, and hydrogen.

The reaction of diborane with alkene oxides at —80° has been studied[4]. Relatively low polymers, of 6 to 8 units, of the type $H\cdot(CHRCH_2O)_nBH_2$ were obtained:

$$(CH_2CH_2)O + B_2H_6 \longrightarrow (EtO)_2BH + \underset{\text{(wax-like polymer)}}{H(CH_2CH_2O)_8BH_2}$$

$$(CHMeCH_2)O + B_2H_6 \longrightarrow (MeCHO)_2BH + \underset{\text{(liquid polymer)}}{H(CHMeCH_2O)_6BH_2}$$

Boron carbide, B_4C (m.p. 2450⁰), has a structure similar to diamond and is almost as hard. It is very stable chemically.

Boric anhydride is a polymer containing irregular tetrahedra of BO_4 units[5].

Boron-containing glasses are polymeric materials of great technical importance.

2. Materials containing B–B bonds and their derivatives

Diboron tetrachloride, B_2Cl_4, is formed when gaseous boron trichloride is passed through a glow discharge between mercury electrodes. It is a substance with considerable potential for making polymers; *e.g.*, it reacts with ethylene and with acetylene:

$$B_2Cl_4 + CH_2 = CH_2 \longrightarrow Cl_2BCH_2CH_2BCl_2$$

$$B_2Cl_4 + CH \equiv CH \longrightarrow Cl_2BCH = CHBCl_2$$

Similar materials can be made from dichloroborane[7], $HBCl_2$, another intermediate of potential interest for making polymers. It can be prepared by passing hydrogen and boron trichloride over magnesium at 400–450° and, at ordinary temperature, it reacts readily with olefins and alkynes such as acetylene[7].

$$HC{\equiv}CH + 2HBCl_2 \longrightarrow Cl_2BCH_2CH_2BCl_2$$

Diboronic acids, which are useful intermediates for making polymers (see Section 4), may readily be made by hydrolysis of bisdichloroboranes.

The action of water vapour on diboron tetrachloride gave subboric acid, $B_2(OH)_4$, in quantitative yield[6]. When heated for 4 hours at 220°, this acid lost water to give a white form of boron monoxide, which was substantially unchanged at temperatures up to about 500°. At 650° and under vacuum, it changed to another form of boron monoxide which is brown and which is much less soluble in water and methanol. If the white form is incompletely dehydrated, as when it is heated to about 400° in a vacuum, it undergoes a rapid and spontaneous change to the brown form with liberation of heat sufficient to cause incandescence.

The white form is considered to have the structure (I) and the brown form the structure (II).

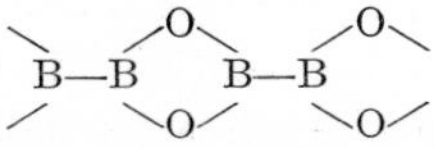

(I)

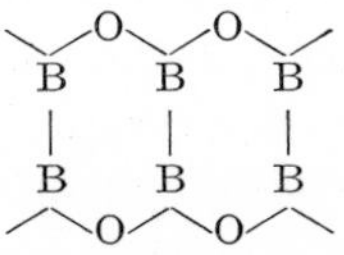

(II)

Possible contributions to the latter by quinonoid structures such as (III) may account for the observed colour.

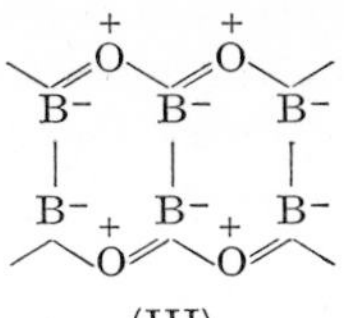

(III)

3. Boric esters of di- and poly-hydroxy compounds

Boric acid and its anhydride react with glycols with elimination of water to give polymers ranging from viscous liquids to vitreous solids. This type of polymer was referred to as early

References, p. 83–86

as 1866[8]. Products known commercially as "Aquaresins" were formed from boric acid and ethylene glycol or glycerol at a temperature of 140–160°[9]. These materials are used as adhesives, as plasticisers for "cellophane," as glues with gum arabic, as textile spinning aids, as detergents, and in the refining of vegetable fats and oils. There are many references to polymeric boric esters[10–16]. The literature on the condensation of polyhydric alcohols with boric acid or with boron halides has recently been reviewed[17], but with particular reference to the condensation of boric acid with diols; all the materials reported were readily hydrolysed by water.

Boric esters of glycols and polyhydroxybenzenes have been suggested as lubricants[18]. There are ion-exchange resins containing boric acid groups[19], and the use of a borate polyester plastic in slow neutron scintillation counters has been described[20].

The use of boric acid to modify other polymers has been reviewed[12,13]. Boric acid has been used to modify both phenol-aldehyde-alkyd resins[21] and purely alkyd resins[22]. Thermoplastic water-soluble resins, useful as textile size, were made by heating substituted ureas with boric acid at 150–200°[23]. Boric acid-modifications of polyhydroxy polymers, such as partially esterified cellulose, or poly(vinyl alcohol) and its partial esters and acetals have been described[24–26]. Even small amounts of boric acid greatly modify the properties of polyhydroxylated materials in a manner similar to the cross-linking effects of vulcanising agents in rubber. The ester linkage in such highly polymeric materials is still very sensitive to hydrolysis, so that these modified polymers often recover their original properties by the action of water.

Boronic acids, $R \cdot B(OH)_2$, have also been used to modify polyhydroxy compounds. For example, cellulose and poly(vinyl alcohol) and its derivatives have been esterified with phenyl-, ethyl- and β-chlorovinyl-boronic acids to give tough film- and fibre-forming materials[27,28].

Some of the reactions of polyhydroxy compounds with boric acid or boron trichloride have been examined in greater detail. In the reaction of ethylene glycol with boric acid or boron trichloride, the limit of polymerisation realised under one set of experimental conditions used[29] was the triethylene bisborate (IV).

By the reaction of glycerol with boron acetate a product was obtained[30] which seemed to have the structure (V), which at 155° and 12 mm lost water and gave a polymer of high molecular weight, presumed to be a polyether, which was easily hydrolysed.

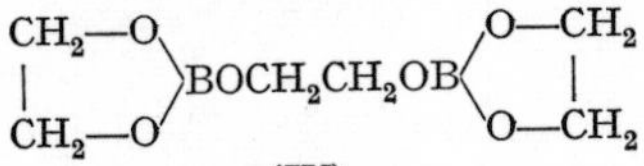

(IV) 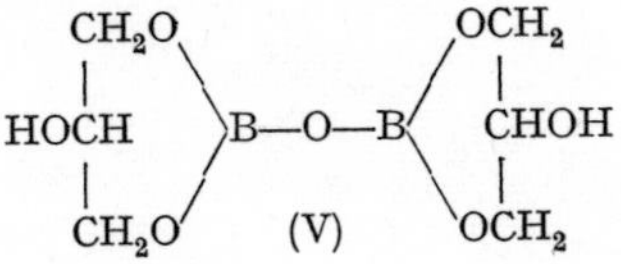 (V)

Higher glycols gave linear polymeric esters of high molecular weight[31]. With 1,1,1-tri(hydroxymethyl)propane, boric acid afforded a polymeric ester[32].

The reactions of dihydric and polyhydric phenols with boron trichloride have been investigated[33,34]. The limit of polymerisation effected with catechol was the tris-*o*-phenylene diborate, (VI), which was obtained together with boron trichloride, by prolonged

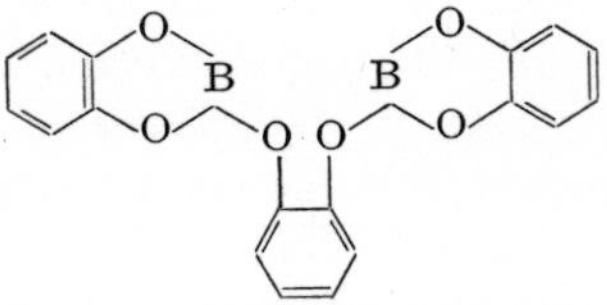

(VI)

heating of the chloroboronate (VII), or by reacting the chloroboronate with more catechol.

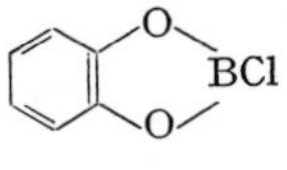

(VII)

Resorcinol gave an acyclic chloroboronate, which at 300° and 0.3 mm gave boron trichloride and a glass. A product was also obtained from three moles of resorcinol and two moles of boron trichloride which did not distil at 310° and 0.3 mm.

Polymeric material only was obtained from boron trichloride

References, p. 83–86

and quinol. Pyrogallol and boron trichloride gave a short chain polymer, (VIII), probably involving *o*-phenylene rings.

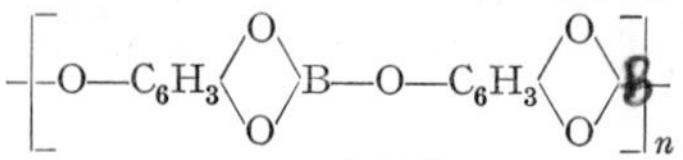

$$\left[-O-C_6H_3{<}^{O}_{O}{>}B-O-C_6H_3{<}^{O}_{O}{>}B-\right]_n$$

(VIII)

At 300° and 0.01 mm (VIII) lost 6.5% of its weight and became a deep red, very hard and tough material. All these products derived from polyhydric phenols were easily hydrolysed.

It has been shown[35] that phenyldichloroborane cleaves alkyl-aryl ethers.

$$ArOR + PhBCl_2 \longrightarrow PhB(Cl)OAr + RCl$$

This led to the investigation of the production of a polymer from *p*-methoxyphenyldichloroborane (IX)[36]. At 290–300° the dichloride gave the expected amount of methyl chloride, some hydrogen chloride, and a hard resin-like solid, which contained chlorine. The latter was easily hydrolysed, *p*-hydroxyphenylboronic acid being the main product isolated. It was considered that as well as the production of the polymer, formulated as in (X), some cross-linking occurred by a Friedel and Crafts type of reaction involving the Lewis acid function of three-co-ordinate boron:

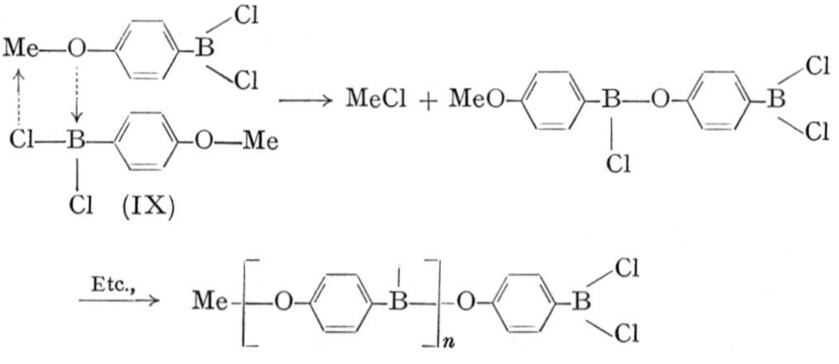

$$\begin{array}{l} Me-O-C_6H_4-BCl_2 \\ \uparrow \quad \downarrow \\ Cl-B(Cl)-C_6H_4-O-Me \quad (IX) \end{array} \longrightarrow MeCl + MeO-C_6H_4-B(Cl)-O-C_6H_4-BCl_2$$

$$\xrightarrow{Etc.,} Me\left[-O-C_6H_4-\overset{|}{B}-\right]_n-O-C_6H_4-BCl_2$$

(X)

In ordinary circumstances the B—O—C linkage is readily hydrolysed and this is a considerable disadvantage if it is to be used in polymers. A possible solution to this difficulty lies in the choice of an ester group containing a nitrogen atom suitably placed to co-ordinate with the boron atom, and so reduce its acceptor properties. The resistance to hydrolysis of triethanolamine borate[37] and di-ethanolamine phenylboronate[38] can be explained in this way [see (XI) and (XII)].

CH_2 CH_2 O OCH_2CH_2 B ← N O CH_2 CH_2

(XI)

CH_2 O CH_2 C_6H_5—B ← NH O CH_2 CH_2

(XII)

4. Boronic esters

A fairly detailed study has been made[39] of the formation of boron-containing polymers derived from boronic acids. Although the short-chain aliphatic boronic acids are usually readily oxidised in air, the aromatic acids are quite stable. It was found that both *p*-phenylenediboronic acid and several polymethylenediboronic acids are also stable to atmospheric oxidation and it was considered that these polyfunctional acids might prove interesting polymer components.

The acids prepared are listed in Table 1; melting points of the diethanolamine esters are given, as the free diboronic acids cannot be characterised because they form polymeric anhydrides on heating. The anhydride of *p*-phenylenediboronic acid does not melt or volatilise at temperatures up to 450°[40].

The first three of these acids were selected for detailed examination of their esters.

With diols, monoboronic acids form cyclic esters, wherever possible, in preference to linear polyesters, and most boronic esters are not much more stable to hydrolysis than are the esters of boric acid. Thus the cyclic esters of phenylboronic acid with ethylene glycol and pinacol and its fibre-forming ester with diphenylol-

References, p. 83–86

propane were all readily hydrolysed on exposure to moist air. On the other hand, the esters of phenylboronic acid with diethanolamine, (XII), or neopentyl glycol, (XIV), had much higher hydrolytic stability. In the first case, the stability was attributed to back co-ordination of the nitrogen to the boron atom, as in (XII). In this

TABLE 1

Acid		*Formula*	*Diethanolamine Ester m.p. (°)*
Phenylboronic		$C_6H_5B(OH)_2$	210°
p-Phenylenediboronic		$(HO)_2B-C_6H_4-B(OH)_2$ 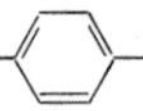	298–300°
Tetramethylenediboronic	$n = 4$	in $(HO)_2B(CH_2)_nB(OH)_2$	245–247°
Pentamethylenediboronic	$n = 5$		218–220°
Hexamethylenediboronic	$n = 6$		254–256°
Decamethylenediboronic	$n = 10$		211–213°

molecule, the nitrogen atom is spatially well placed for intramolecular co-ordination to the boron. The bis-2-pyridylglycol ester, (XIII), might be expected to show some degree of intermolecular co-ordination, but it showed little enhanced hydrolytic stability. The ester (XII) had m.p. 210° and could be crystallised from water; (XIII), m.p. 177–179°, was readily hydrolysed in boiling water; (XIV), m.p. 65–66°, could be crystallised from aqueous methanol.

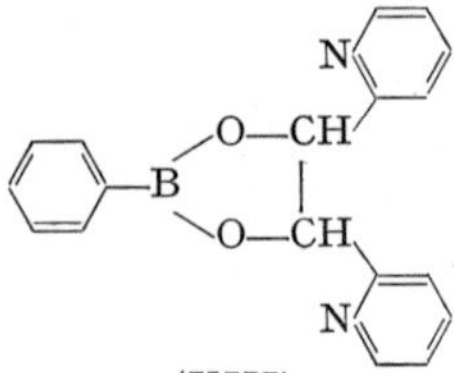

(XIII)

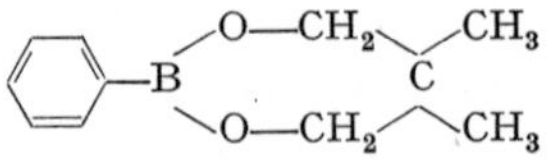

(XIV)

The intramolecular co-ordination formulation (XII) is supported by the infrared absorption spectra of a number of substituted derivatives, (XV), in which the variation in the N—H stretching frequency can be attributed to the presence of an N ⟶ B co-ordinate link through which electronic effects can be transmitted (Table 2)[38].

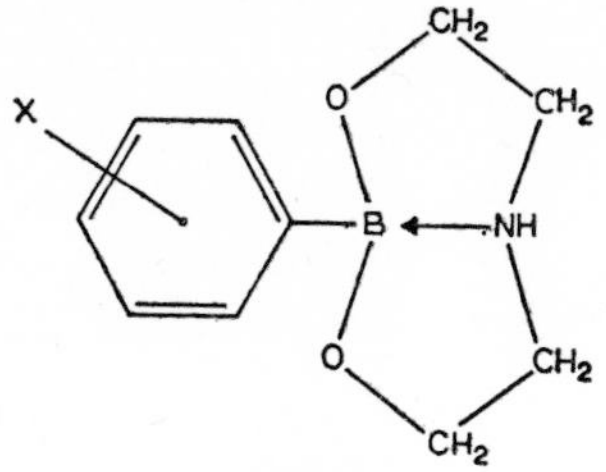

(XV)

TABLE 2

X	*M.p. (°)*	*ν N—H (cm⁻¹)*
p-MeO	223 –223.5	3135
p-Me	232 –233	3110
H	209.5–210	3100
p-Br	272.5–273	3090
m-NO_2	222.5–223	3090

Tables 3 and 4 list data on the esters of tetramethylenediboronic and *p*-phenylenediboronic acids and it is again evident that the diethanolamine esters and esters containing the neopentyl group have enhanced hydrolytic stability.

The bicyclic structure was used in two ways in forming polymers. In one method, polyesters of diboronic acids were formed with tetrakishydroxyalkylated polymethylenediamines to give compounds of the type shown in (XVI), which were white powders and had the properties described in Table 5.

These esters (XVI) were made by one of three methods: (i) from the acid and the tetrol in benzene solution, with azeotropic removal of water; (ii) from the acid and the tetrol, in an alcoholic solution, which was then evaporated to dryness; and (iii) by ester exchange between the tetrabutyl ester of the acid and the tetrol. The most

References, p. 83–86

TABLE 3

ESTERS OF TETRAMETHYLENEDIBORONIC ACID: $R\langle O,O\rangle B(CH_2)_4B\langle O,O\rangle R$

R	*Properties*
$—CH_2CH_2—$	B.p. 77–79°/0.1 mm; hydrolyses slowly in moist air.
$—CH(CH_3)CH(CH_3)—$	B.p. 99–101°/0.5 mm; hydrolyses slowly in moist air.
$—CH(CH_3)CH_2—$	B.p. 92–94°/0.4 mm; hydrolyses slowly in moist air.
$—C(CH_3)_2C(CH_3)_2—$	B.p. 81–82°/0.03 mm; hydrolyses slowly in moist air. M.p. 42–44°.
$—C(C_6H_5)_2C(C_6H_5)_2—$	M.p. 212–214°; stable in moist air.
$—CH_2CH_2CH_2CH(CH_3)—$	B.p. 96–98°/0.01 mm; hydrolyses slowly in moist air.
$—CH_2C(CH_3)_2CH_2—$	B.p. 110°/0.2 mm; stable in moist air. M.p. 57–59°.
$—CH_2C(C_6H_5)_2CH_2—$	B.p. 167–168°/0.5 mm; stable in moist air. M.p. 47–49°.
$—CH_2C(CH_3)_2CH[CH(CH_3)_2]—$	B.p. 140–142°/0.2 mm; hydrolyses slowly in moist air.
$—CH_2C(CH_2Cl)_2CH_2—$	B.p. 198°/0.3 mm; stable in most air.
$(—CH_2)_2C\langle(CH_2—O)_2\rangle CH_2—$	M.p. 120–122°; stable in moist air, but hydrolyses in boiling water.
$—CH_2CH_2NHCH_2CH_2—$	M.p. 245–247°; stable in moist air and soluble in water.

promising of these polyesters was that from *p*-phenylenediboronic acid and "Quadrol", *i.e.*, (XVI), in which $n=2$ and $R=CH_3$. On heating at 300° for 5 hours it turned only slightly brown, and it was recovered unchanged after boiling for 4 hours in water.

In a second method for making chelated polymers, the bis-trialkanolamine esters of diboronic acids were used (as diols) for reaction with other difunctional intermediates. In this way the bis-trialkanolamine esters (XVII) were prepared, and their melting points are listed in Table 6.

TABLE 4

ESTERS OF *p*-PHENYLENEDIBORONIC ACID: $R\langle O,O \rangle BC_6H_4B \langle O,O \rangle R$

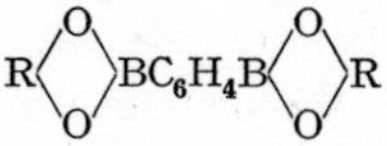

R	*Properties*
$—CH_2CH_2—$	M.p. 231–233°; hydrolyses slowly in water, but stable to moist air.
$—CH(CH_3)CH_2—$	M.p. 94–96.5°; hydrolyses slowly in water, but stable to moist air.
$—CH_2CH_2CH(CH_3)—$	M.p. 180–181°; hydrolyses slowly in water, but stable to moist air.
$—CH(CH_3)CH(CH_3)—$	M.p. 176–178°; hydrolyses slowly in water, but stable to moist air.
$—C(CH_3)_2C(CH_3)_2—$	M.p. 243–245°; hydrolyses slowly in water, but stable to moist air.
$—CH_2C(CH_3)_2CH[CH(CH_3)_2]—$	M.p. 116–119°; hydrolyses slowly in water, but stable to moist air.
$—o\text{-}C_6H_4—$	M.p. 312–316°; hydrolyses slowly in boiling water.
$—CH_2CH_2NHCH_2CH_2—$	M.p. 298–300°; stable to hydrolysis.
$—CH_2CH_2NCH_3CH_2CH_2—$	M.p. 304–306°; stable to hydrolysis.
$—CH_2C(CH_3)_2CH_2—$	M.p. 233°; stable to hydrolysis.
$—CH_2C(CH_2Cl)_2CH_2—$	M.p. 269–271°; stable to hydrolysis.

TABLE 5

Compounds (XVI)	*Properties*
$n=6$; R=H; $X=(CH_2)_4$	M.p. 230–250°; soluble in water and forms fibres which soften in moist air.
$n=6$; R=H; $X=p\text{-}C_6H_4$	Decomposes at 380°; insoluble in water.
$n=2$; $R=CH_3$; $X=(CH_2)_4$	M.p. 300–320°; soluble in water and does not form fibres.
$n=2$; $R=CH_3$; $X=p\text{-}C_6H_4$	Decomposes at 320–330°; insoluble in water, but soluble in dibutyl phthalate.

References, p. 83–86

Melt polymerisation of the three diols (XVII) with dimethyl terephthalate gave only low-melting, dark-brown polyesters. This is a general experience in making *N*-containing polyesters by melt polymerisation, and has been attributed to a base-catalysed degradation of the ester. Condensation with di-isocyanates gave polymers which melted at about 200°.

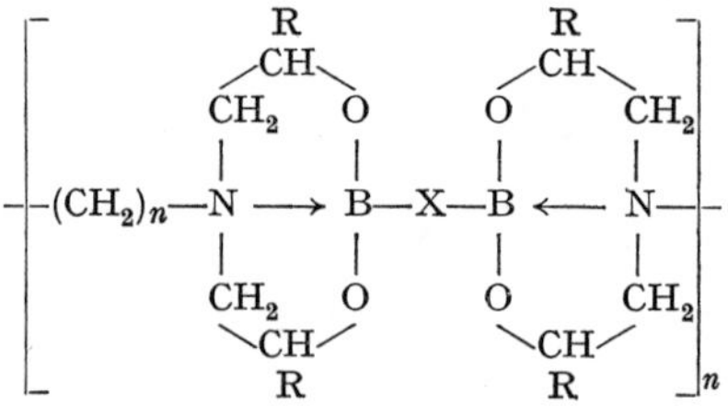

$$\left[\begin{array}{ccccccc} & \multicolumn{2}{c}{R} & & \multicolumn{2}{c}{R} & \\ & \multicolumn{2}{c}{\diagup CH \diagdown} & & \multicolumn{2}{c}{\diagup CH \diagdown} & \\ & CH_2 & O & & O & CH_2 & \\ & | & | & & | & | & \\ -(CH_2)_n- & N & \longrightarrow B & -X- & B \longleftarrow & N & - \\ & | & | & & | & | & \\ & CH_2 & O & & O & CH_2 & \\ & \multicolumn{2}{c}{\diagdown CH \diagup} & & \multicolumn{2}{c}{\diagdown CH \diagup} & \\ & \multicolumn{2}{c}{R} & & \multicolumn{2}{c}{R} & \end{array}\right]_n$$

(XVI)

Of the simple esters of diboronic acids, those containing the neopentyl group had also abnormal stability towards hydrolysis. Use was made of this, in forming polymers, by condensing the diboronic

TABLE 6

Compounds (XVII)	*M.p. (°)*
$X=(CH_2)_4$; $R=H$	210–212
$X=p\text{-}C_6H_4$; $R=H$	236–238
$X=(CH_2)_4$; $R=CH_3$	203–205

acids with two of the most readily available tetrols containing the neopentyl group, namely pentaerythritol and tetramethylol-cyclo-pentanone. The products obtained were compounds (XVIII) and their properties are listed in Table 7.

The polyester from pentaerythritol and *p*-phenylenediboronic acid was the most interesting, on account of its high thermal and hydrolytic stability. It turned slightly brown on heating above 400°. Attempts to obtain this polymer in a form suitable for use as a thermally-stable coating or as a moulding powder were unsuccessful, the end-product always being an intractable powder.

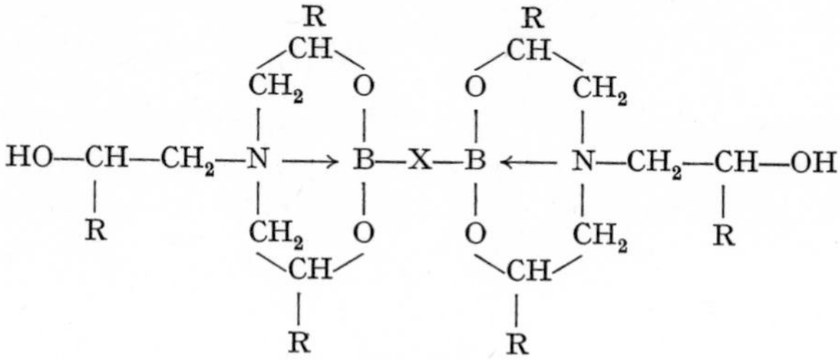

```
                       R                   R
                     /CH\                /CH\
                   CH2    O             O    CH2
                    |     |             |     |
HO—CH—CH2—N ——→ B—X—B ←—— N—CH2—CH—OH
   |                |     |             |     |           |
   R               CH2    O             O    CH2          R
                     \CH/                \CH/
                       |                   |
                       R                   R
```

(XVII)

The diester from trimethylolpropane and *p*-phenylenediboronic acid provided another interesting diol (XIX).

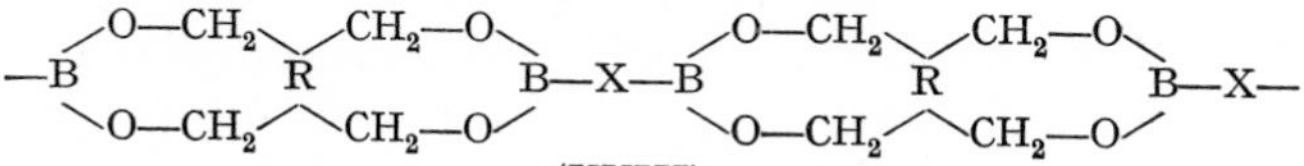

```
   /O—CH2\   /CH2—O\          /O—CH2\   /CH2—O\
—B         R         B—X—B         R         B—X—
   \O—CH2/   \CH2—O/          \O—CH2/   \CH2—O/
```

(XVIII)

TABLE 7

Compounds (XVIII)	*Properties*
X = $(CH_2)_4$; R = C	Fibre-forming soluble polymer, which softens at 70°.
X = *p*-C_6H_4; R = C	Infusible and insoluble.
X = $(CH_2)_4$; } R 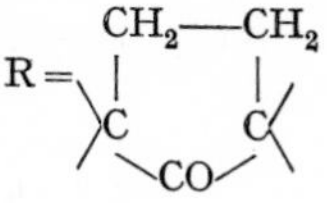 = CH_2—CH_2 bridging two C, joined by CO	M.p. 210–230°; fibre-forming, but hydrolysed by water.
X = *p*-C_6H_4; }	Decomposes above 400°; insoluble.

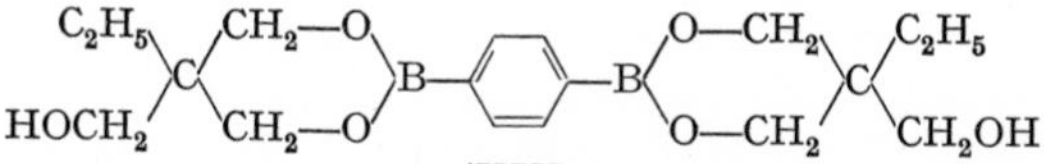

```
C2H5   CH2—O                    O—CH2   C2H5
     \C/      \B—⟨C6H4⟩—B/      \C/
HOCH2/ \CH2—O/                  \O—CH2/ \CH2OH
```

(XIX)

It was found, however, that condensation of (XIX) with diesters or with di-isocyanates gave materials which did not possess appreciably greater thermal stability than similar polymers not containing

References, p. 83–86

boron. They had good film-forming properties, but there was little to distinguish them from their purely organic counterparts.

5. Boroxoles

These compounds have also been called boroxines. They are trimers containing a 6-membered B—O—B ring (XX) (for early work, see Ref. 40a). Alkyl and aryl substituted boroxoles are obtained

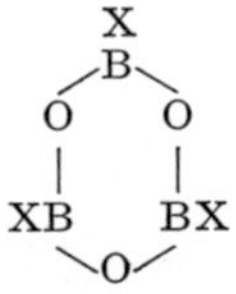

```
       X
      ╱B╲
     O   O
     |   |
    XB   BX
      ╲O╱
```

(XX)

readily by the dehydration of the corresponding boronic acids. Trimethyl-, tris(dimethylamino)-, trimethoxy-, trifluoro-, trichloro-, and tribromo-boroxole were obtained by heating boric oxide with trimethylborane, tris(dimethylamino)boron, trimethyl borate, and boron trihalides, respectively[41–43]. They may also be made by the decomposition of RO·(X)B·Cl (X = Cl, R, or OR), in presence of traces of Lewis acids, such as aluminium chloride[43a]. Boroxoles in general are easily hydrolysed by water; they are oxidised with varying ease, depending upon the nature of the substituent X.

Trimethoxyboroxole is useful for extinguishing burning metals, such as magnesium, titanium, and zirconium, which are extremely difficult to extinguish by other methods[44].

When *n*-butylmagnesium bromide was reacted with trimethyl borate and the Grignard complex decomposed by hydrogen chloride at 100°, the reaction product was said to be a mixture of tri-*n*-butylboroxole and a polymeric butylboron oxide, $(BuBO)_n$, which may have a linear structure, and which had a molecular weight of 2200[45].

6. *p*-Vinylphenylboronic acid and related substances

p-Vinylphenylboronic acid has been made by the action of *p*-vinylphenylmagnesium bromide or chloride on trimethyl or tributyl borate[46–48]. It has also been made[49] from the *p*-ethylphenyl Grignard reagent:

$$\text{Et-}C_6H_4\text{-MgBr} \longrightarrow \text{Et-}C_6H_4\text{-B(OH)}_2 \longrightarrow (\text{Et-}C_6H_4\text{-BO})_3$$

$$(\text{Et-}C_6H_4\text{-BO})_3 \xrightarrow{\text{CH}_2\text{—CO}>\text{NBr} / \text{CH}_2\text{—CO}} (\text{CH}_3\text{CHBr-}C_6H_4\text{-BO})_3 \xrightarrow{\text{Quinoline}} (\text{CH}_2\text{=CH-}C_6H_4\text{-BO})_3$$

$$(\text{CH}_2\text{=CH-}C_6H_4\text{-BO})_3 \xrightarrow{H_2O} p\text{-CH}_2\text{=CH}\cdot C_6H_4B(OH)_2$$

"Popcorn"-type of co-polymers have been made from the ethyl tartrate ester of *p*-vinylphenylboronic acid with styrene and diallyl maleate[47]. The acid itself has been polymerised by free radical initiation in aqueous solution[48], *e.g.*, by using potassium persulphate. The white, air-stable polymer did not melt below 300°; in the range 300–350°, it softened somewhat and became brown. Polymers of *p*-vinylphenylboroxole[50] and of various esters of *p*-vinylphenylboronic acid[51] have been described.

Various other monomers of similar type, suitable for polymerisation or co-polymerisation have been described; *e.g.*, β-chlorovinylboronic acid and its derivatives[52], allylboronic acid[53], potassium tetrastyrylborate[54], vinylboranes[55], vinylboronic acid[56], and methyl-substituted vinyl-boronic acids. Little has been reported regarding the polymerisation of this class of monomer.

Polymers have also been made from unsaturated esters of boric acid[57].

7. Si–O–B-containing polymers

Polymeric borosiloxanes have been prepared by a number of investigators[58–64]. These compounds were prepared using borate esters, or boron acetate, and are probably highly cross-linked. The reaction products from boric acid and alkylchlorosilanes have also been studied[65].

References, p. 83–86

The preparation of a linear borosiloxane polymer was claimed from the condensation of phenylboronic acid with diphenylsilanediol[66]. Other silanols and boronic acids were claimed to be suitable, particularly those boronic acids having unsaturation in the α-β position relative to the boron atom. These polymers were soluble in organic solvents and from the solutions fibres and films were formed. They were considered to have a linear structure [see (XXI), in Fig. 5]. Similar linear polymers were claimed to arise from the reaction of boronic esters with chlorosilanes[67]. The co-hydrolysis

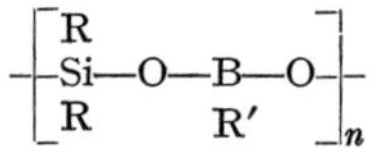

$$\left[\begin{array}{c}\mathrm{R}\\ -\mathrm{Si}-\mathrm{O}-\mathrm{B}-\mathrm{O}-\\ \mathrm{R}\quad\quad\ \ \mathrm{R'}\end{array}\right]_n$$

(XXI)

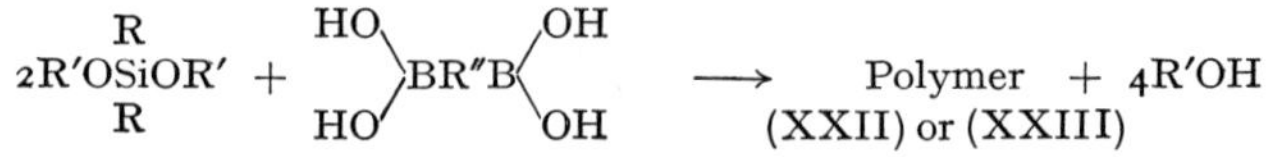

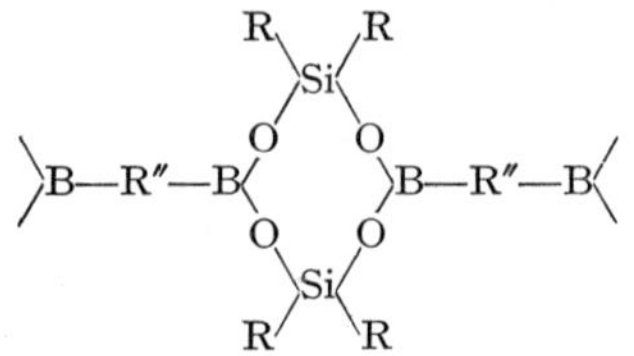

$$2\,\mathrm{R'O}\overset{\mathrm{R}}{\underset{\mathrm{R}}{\mathrm{Si}}}\mathrm{OR'} + (\mathrm{HO})_2\mathrm{BR''B}(\mathrm{OH})_2 \longrightarrow \text{Polymer (XXII) or (XXIII)} + 4\,\mathrm{R'OH}$$

```
            R   R
             \ /
              Si
             /  \
            O    O
 >B—R″—B<          >B—R″—B<
            O    O
             \  /
              Si
             /  \
            R    R
```

(XXII)

```
                              |
    R           R            R″     R
    |           |            |      |
 —Si—O—B—O—Si—O—B—O—Si—
    |     |     |                   |
    R     R″    R                   R
          |
    R     |     R                   R
    |     |     |                   |
 —Si—O—B—O—Si—O—B—O—Si—
    |           |            |      |
    R           R            R″     R
                             |
```

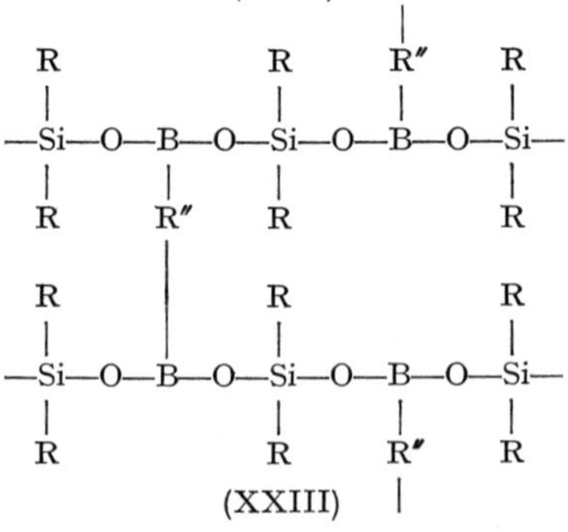

(XXIII)

Fig. 5. Linear products (XXI) from silanediols and boronic acids and cross-linked products (XXII) and (XXIII) from diboronic acids.

product of phenyldifluoroborane and dichlorodiphenylsilane, after heating for 16 hours at 230°, gave a heat resistant resin[68].

None of these products appeared to be particularly stable to hydrolysis. Analogous derivatives of diboronic acids were prepared[39], to find whether the cross-linked structures which should arise [see (XXI) and (XXIII) in Fig. 5] had increased hydrolytic stability. In order to minimise the self-condensation which is liable to occur when using silanols, these reactions were carried out between dialkoxysilanes and the free diboronic acid. The results obtained using various combinations of diboronic acids and alkoxysilanes are shown in Table 8.

TABLE 8

Components	*Polymer*
1. $(HO)_2B(CH_2)_4B(OH)_2$ (1 Mole) $Me_2Si(OEt)_2$ (2 Moles)	Very viscous liquid.
2. *p*-$(HO)_2BC_6H_4B(OH)_2$ (1 Mole) $Me_2Si(OEt)_2$ (2 Moles)	Solid, softening point ~ 40°.
3. $(HO)_2B(CH_2)_4B(OH)_2$ (1 Mole) $Ph_2Si(OMe)_2$ (2 Moles)	Tough, very viscous, slightly sticky solid; gives clear melt at 90°.
4. *p*-$(HO)_2BC_6H_4B(OH)_2$ (1 Mole) $Ph_2Si(OMe)_2$ (2 Moles)	Brittle solid; softening point ~ 120°.
5. $(HO)_2B(CH_2)_4B(OH)_2$ (1 Mole) *p*-$(HO)_2BC_6H_4B(OH)_2$ (2 Moles) $Ph_2Si(OMe)_2$ (6 Moles)	A reasonably tough, not too brittle solid; softens at ~ 100°.
6. $(HO)_2B(CH_2)_4B(OH)_2$ (1 Mole) *p*-$(HO)_2BC_6H_4B(OH)_2$ (2 Moles) $MePhSi(OEt)_2$ (6 Moles)	A very viscous liquid.

All these polymers had low softening points and were soluble in the common organic solvents. They were all, to a greater or lesser extent, attacked by atmospheric moisture, the attack being most noticeable with materials derived from the components tetra-

References, p. 83–86

methylenediboronic acid and dimethyldiethoxysilane. The polymers derived from *p*-phenylenediboronic acid tended to be hard and brittle, whereas those from tetramethylenediboronic acid were softer. The best composition was derived from a mixture of *p*-phenylene- and tetramethylene-diboronic acids in the ratio 2:1, reacted with dimethoxydiphenylsilane (composition No. 5 in Table 8).

The irradiation of a polymer derived from boric oxide and dichlorodimethylsilane has been reported to improve its hydrolytic stability[69]. On the other hand, attempts to improve the hydrolytic stability of borosiloxane polymers by the incorporation of pyridyl co-ordinating groups into the molecule were not successful[70].

Derivatives of boron have been used also to modify the properties of silicone polymers in important ways. Thus, "bouncing putty", a rubber-like material having plastic cold flow, was made by treating a silicone fluid with boric oxide[71,72]. Related to this, is a composition derived from boric acid and tetramethyldisiloxane-1,3-diol, which was mobile at 25°, resembling starch paste, whereas at 50° it became solid with properties similar to those of "bouncing putty". On cooling the mobile liquid was reformed[73].

Condensation of boric acid with 1,7-dichloro-octamethyltetrasiloxane afforded a water-repellent product, which was stated to be superior to organosilicon halides in producing water-repellency of vitreous surfaces[74]. Triethyl borate has been used to convert partially condensed silicone fluids to solid polymers[75] and the condensation of silanols to polysiloxanes has been effected with small amounts of boric oxide[76]. Tris(trimethylsilyl) borate has been used to condense dimethylsilicones and also as a plasticiser for the same polymers[77]. Boron hydrides have been used to polymerise methylsilicone oils to silicone-rubber stock or to cross-link silicone-rubbers[78,79].

It has been pointed out that whereas Si—O—B-containing polysiloxanes which have 3 to 100 silicon atoms per boron atom are "bouncing putties" which are sensitive to hydrolysis, at lower concentrations of boron (150 to 300 Si:B) the compositions are curable to elastomers which have remarkable properties of self-adhesion and which are hydrolytically stable[80].

Polysiloxane polyboranes such as $(Bu \cdot B \cdot CH_2SiMe_2OSiMe_2CH_2)_n$ have been prepared[81]. An application for such materials is as an oxygen scavenger for silicone fluids.

8. B–O–P-containing polymers

Dialkyl hydrogen phosphites form 1:1 complexes with boron trichloride, which eliminate alkyl chloride, probably by a carbonium ion mechanism[82].

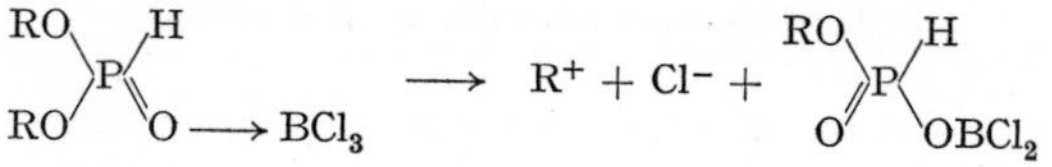

$$(RO)_2P(H)\!=\!O \longrightarrow BCl_3 \longrightarrow R^+ + Cl^- + (RO)(O)P(H)OBCl_2$$

The temperature at which the main evolution of alkyl chloride occurred varied with the alkyl group. Hydrogen chloride was also evolved, but more slowly, and even at 300° the glassy residue contained easily-hydrolysed chlorine. It was considered that hydrogen is lost as hydrogen chloride when the electron density on a phosphorus atom has been sufficiently reduced by attachment to two boronoxy groups, as in (XXIV).

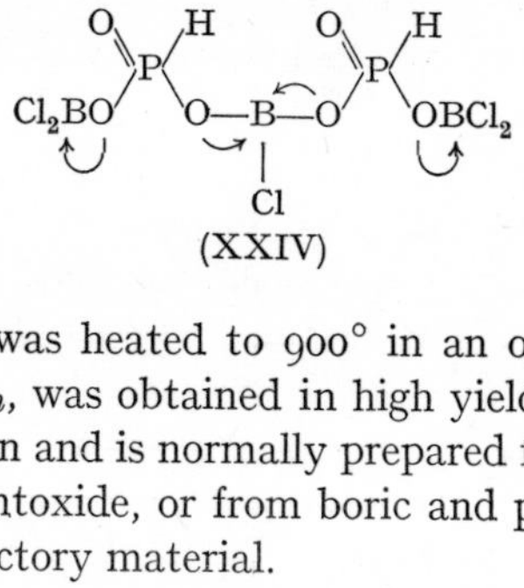

$$Cl_2BO-P(=O)(H)-O-B(Cl)-O-P(=O)(H)-OBCl_2$$

(XXIV)

When the residue was heated to 900° in an open crucible boron phosphate, $(PBO_4)_n$, was obtained in high yield. Boron phosphate has long been known and is normally prepared from boron trioxide and phosphorus pentoxide, or from boric and phosphoric acids[82a]; it is used as a refractory material.

Phenyldichloroborane reacted with diethyl hydrogen phosphite with elimination of ethyl chloride and formation of an infusible solid, which was soluble in methylene chloride, but reprecipitated by pentane, and from analysis and infrared spectrum appeared to be $(PhBO_3PH)_n$ with the P—H bond intact. Hydrolysis of the material with hot water gave phenylboronic acid.

References, p. 83–86

The reaction of trialkyl phosphates with boron trichloride gave 1:1-complexes, $(RO)_3P{=}OBCl_3$, which on heating eliminated alkyl chloride, olefin and hydrogen chloride, to give eventually boron phosphate[83]. The material obtained at 1000° was hydrolytically stable. As an extension of this work it was hoped that by attaching certain hydrocarbon groups to boron and to phosphorus [$RBCl_2$ and $R'PO(OR'')_2$], polymers which have useful properties might be obtained.

9. Polymers containing B–P bonds

The primary reaction product from phosphine and diborane is $B_2H_6,2PH_3$, which probably has a structure analogous to that of the diammoniate of diborane[86]. When phosphine and diborane were heated for 19 days at 65°, an insoluble, inert compound, (XXV), and hydrogen were the sole products.

$$2PH_3 + B_2H_6 \longrightarrow B_2H_6,\ 2PH_3 \longrightarrow H_2 + \underset{\text{(XXV)}}{(PBH_{3.75})_n}$$

Methylphosphine and dimethylphosphine reacted with diborane to give adducts, from which hydrogen was lost by heating and polymers were thus formed[87,88].

$$2MePH_2 + B_2H_6 \longrightarrow \underset{\text{m.p.} -49°,\ \text{b.p. } 150°}{2MePH_2.BH_3} \xrightarrow[\text{for 20 hours}]{\text{heated at 100°}}$$

$(MePHBH_2)_n$, a viscous oil, not hydrolysed by 4 N HCl

$$2Me_2PH + B_2H_6 \longrightarrow \underset{\text{m.p.} -22.6°,\ \text{b.p. } 174°}{2Me_2PHBH_3} \xrightarrow[\text{for 40 hours}]{\text{heated at 150°}}$$

$$\underset{\text{m.p. 86° (89\% yield)}}{(Me_2PBH_2)_3} + \underset{\text{m.p. 161° (9\% yield)}}{(Me_2PBH_2)_4}$$

The trimeric and tetrameric phosphinoboranes, $(Me_2PBH_2)_{3 \text{ or } 4}$, are crystallisable from benzene or methanol, and are very unreactive towards air, acids, bases, or water. They are hydrolysed by heating for 10 days with hydrochloric acid at 300°, and are very resistant to thermal decomposition. The trimer is the more stable form; it begins to decompose slowly at 360°[89]. Both the trimer and the tetramer on hydrolysis gave one mole of boric acid, one mole of dimethylphosphinic acid, and four moles of hydrogen for each unit of monomer. The trimer may be regarded as a resonance hybrid of (XXVI) and (XXVII).

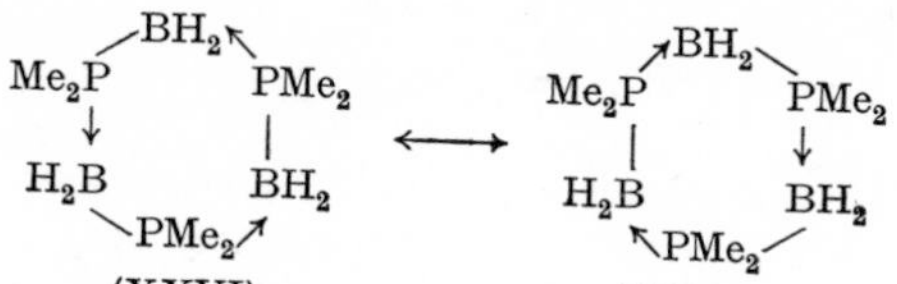

$$\begin{array}{ccc} & BH_2 & \\ Me_2P & & PMe_2 \\ \downarrow & & | \\ H_2B & & BH_2 \\ & PMe_2 & \end{array} \quad \longleftrightarrow \quad \begin{array}{ccc} & BH_2 & \\ Me_2P & & PMe_2 \\ | & & \downarrow \\ H_2B & & BH_2 \\ & PMe_2 & \end{array}$$

(XXVI) (XXVIII)

The unusual stability of this system is considered to be due to additional bonding, involving the *d*-orbitals of the phosphorus atom and the B—H bonds.

The fully methylated compounds, corresponding to those above, could not be obtained by heating dimethylphosphinodimethylborane (this disproportionated above 40°), but the trimer (m.p. 333°) was prepared by treatment of dimethylphosphine, with dimethylbromoborane, in the presence of triethylamine.

$$3Me_2PH + 3Me_2BBr + 3Et_3N \longrightarrow (Me_2PBMe_2)_3 + 3Et_3N.HBr$$

This trimer was also very resistant to hydrolysis and thermal decomposition. Hydrolysis at 300° gave dimethylphosphinic acid and methane.

Phosphine and dimethylbromoborane, in the presence of triethylamine, behaved similarly.

$$PH_3 + Me_2BBr + Et_3N \longrightarrow \overset{+}{P}H_2{=}\overset{-}{B}Me_2 + Et_3N.HBr$$

The initial product was monomeric, but quickly polymerised in solution, giving $(PH_2BMe_2)_n$. In contrast to the cyclic polymers, which are obtained when there are methyl groups on the phosphorus, the polymer $(PH_2BMe_2)_n$ is considered to have a linear structure.

References, p. 83–86

The preparation of fused polycyclic phosphinoboranes, *e.g.*, (XXVIII), has also been reported[90,91].

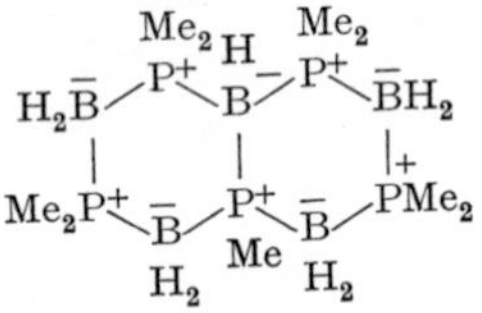

$$\begin{array}{c} \quad Me_2 \; H \quad Me_2 \\ H_2\bar{B}\diagup P^+\diagdown \bar{B}\diagup P^+\diagdown \bar{B}H_2 \\ | \qquad\quad | \qquad\quad |+ \\ Me_2P^+\diagdown \bar{B}\diagup P^+\diagdown \bar{B}\diagup PMe_2 \\ H_2 \quad Me \quad H_2 \end{array}$$

(XXVIII)

Monoalkyl- and monoaryl-phosphines readily gave 1:1 adducts with diborane[84], and from these hydrogen was eliminated at 100°.

The degree and nature of polymerisation of phosphinoboranes has been correlated to some extent with the substituent groups on both phosphorus and boron atoms. When both the groups attached to phosphorus are hydrocarbon radicals, cyclic six- or eight-membered phosphinoboranes are the main products, whereas with one or two hydrogen atoms on phosphorus, linear polymers result. Substitution of methyl groups for hydrogen on the boron atom gives monomeric phosphinoboranes, which polymerise slowly.

In addition to the synthetic methods already mentioned, the reduction of phosphorus compounds such as phosphinehaloboranes, phosphonium halides, halophosphines and phosphoryl halides, with lithium aluminium hydride, borohydrides, or diborane, gave intermediate phosphine-boranes which were then dehydrogenated[92–95].

$$R_2HP \cdot BX_3 + LiAlH_4 \longrightarrow R_2PBH_2 + H_2 + LiAlX_4$$

$$R_2H_2PX + LiBH_4 \longrightarrow R_2PBH_2 + H_2 + LiX$$

$$R_2PX + NaBH_4 \longrightarrow R_2PBH_2 + H_2 + NaX$$

$$R_2PX + B_2H_6 \longrightarrow R_2PBH_2 + BX_3 + H_2$$

$$R_2POX + NaBH_4 \longrightarrow R_2PBH_2 + H_2 + NaX$$

B-halogenated phosphinoboranes have been made from the corresponding BH compounds as follows:

$$(Me_2PBH_2)_3 + 6MeX \xrightarrow{AlX_3} (Me_2PBX_2)_3 + 6\ CH_4$$

$$(Me_2PBH_2)_3 + 6HF \longrightarrow (Me_2PBF_2)_3 + 6H_2$$

Phosphinoboranes have been prepared containing a variety of substituents[96]; and these include hydrogen, methyl, ethyl, isopropyl, trimethylene, cyclotetramethylene, phenyl, *p*-tolyl, trifluoromethyl, and fluorine on phosphorus, and hydrogen, fluorine, chlorine, bromine, iodine, methyl, and *n*-butyl on boron.

The effects of various substituents on the melting point, boiling point, and viscosity of phosphinoboranes have been investigated. Similarly, the effect of various substituents on chemical properties was established by standardised tests for oxidative and hydrolytic stability and by visual observation for thermal stability. The test for oxidative stability was the determination of the spontaneous ignition temperature of the compound on a heated copper block in air. Of the compounds tested, dicyclohexylphosphinoborane trimer had the highest spontaneous ignition temperature, namely 484°[97]. Hydrolytic stability was measured by the extent of hydrolysis effected by heating the compound for 24 hours at 202° with 1.0 ml of water in a 5.5-ml sealed Pyrex tube. Cyclic phosphinoboranes, having only hydrogen on boron, are far more resistant to hydrolysis than linear polymers or *B*-halogen substituted compounds. No correlation has been found between the end-group and the hydrolytic stability of dimethylphosphinoborane linear polymers

A fluorinated product, $[(CF_3)_2PBH_2]_3$, m.p. 31°, b.p. 176°, was obtained by the reaction of bis(trifluoromethyl)phosphine and diborane in the presence of dimethyl ether as a catalyst. It was also formed from the reaction at room temperature of $(CF_3)_2PF$, with diborane[98,99]. This trimer decomposed appreciably at 200° and was hydrolysed slowly in acid solution at 150°; it was hydrolysed in alkaline solution at room temperature, in a similar manner to many other fluorocarbon compounds, giving fluoroform, HCF_3, as main product. Thus it is considerably less stable than $(Me_2PBH_2)_3$.

Another variant of the P—B system involves the use of a boron hydride of the condensed type, such as the stable pentaborane B_5H_9. In this way, resins may be formed in which the phosphinoborane unit is bonded into a B_xH_y boride-like aggregate. Transparent, glassy materials, withstanding 500°, have been made by this method[98,100]. In these materials, stable electron donor units are trapped within an electron-deficient boron hydride network.

References, p. 83–86

The proportion of electrons available to boron is thus increased and the boron has less metallic-type bonding and a lower degree of bond lability. The electron donor unit is also stabilised by partial isolation in the boron hydride aggregate.

The reaction between pentaborane-9 and dimethylaminodimethylphosphine, Me_2NPMe_2, gave very stable transparent, brittle, glassy materials, each approximating to the average formula $[B_9H_8(Me_2P)_2Me_2N]_n$. These were regarded as chains of phosphinoborane rings, linked through boron by condensed boron hydride aggregates and cross-linked by the amino-groups.

In order to improve the mechanical properties of such materials, it was felt that, while retaining the strong B—B bonding and the stable P—B trimer rings, larger proportions of plasticising bases should be incorporated into the structure. It was found that tertiary phosphines could be used and, with a view to forcing the boron hydride units further apart in the resin, the compound $Me_2NPC_4H_8$ was reacted with pentaborane-9[100]. The resin thus produced, was transparent up to 400°, but turned brown and lost small amounts of light hydrocarbons at higher temperatures. It appeared to be slightly tougher than the MeP resins, but not appreciably stronger. Thermally-stable resins of this type adhere well to metals and to glass at elevated temperatures, but they are very weak mechanically at ordinary temperatures. Further studies on phosphinoboranes containing the C_4H_8P group have been reported recently[101].

The diphosphine, P_2Me_4, is stable up to about 300°. With diborane, it gave the adducts $P_2Me_4 \cdot BH_3$ and $P_2Me_4 \cdot 2BH_3$[98,102]. At 200°, the latter gave a 90% combined yield of the trimeric and tetrameric dimethylphosphinoborane. Pyrolysis of the mono-adduct gave a product, corresponding to about 50% yield of Me_2PBH_2 units, in the form of a chain polymer with a basic end group. This system was formed at 174°, but at 330° it broke down almost entirely to trimeric dimethylphosphinoborane.

A resin made from tetramethyldiphosphine and pentaborane-9 and having the approximate formula $[B_{10}H_9(Me_2P)_4]_n$ was thermoplastic around 300°, above which temperature it lost some hydrogen (and also methane above 400°), with conversion to a cindery brown product at 440°[103].

When the aminodiphosphine $Me_2P \cdot NH \cdot PMe_2$ was reacted with excess pentaborane-9 in a molar ratio of 9:7, and then heated to 356°, a white non-volatile solid of formula $[B_{15}H_9N_4(Me_2P)_y]_n$ was obtained. It was plastic at high temperatures but very fragile and brittle at room temperature.

Trimethylenediphosphine and polymeric alkylphosphines of the formula $PH_2CH(CH_3)CH_2[PHCH(CH_3)CH_2]_nPH_2$ formed adducts with diborane, which lost hydrogen on heating to yield highly cross-linked brittle foams having considerable thermal stability.

Pyrolysis of dimethylphosphineborane in the presence of a base gave[97,104] high molecular weight materials:

$$n\,Me_2PHBH_3 + R_3N \longrightarrow \underset{\text{(XXIX)}}{R_3N[Me_2PBH_2]_nNR_3} + nH_2$$

The addition of a basic chain end-blocking group to the reaction mixture should cause formation of a co-ordinate link between the basic group and the boron atom of dimethylphosphinoborane monomer, so that formation of cyclic trimer and tetramer is suppressed; structures (XXIX) are considered to be linear.

Experiments were carried out to test the effect of temperature, heating time, and the nature of the chain end-blocking group on the yield of linear polymer. It was found that above 200°, the yield of linear polymer fell and that of the cyclic trimer and tetramer rose. Thermal stability studies confirmed the greater thermodynamic stability of the cyclic forms. The yield of linear polymer was also greatly affected by the choice of base. Triethylamine, tri-*n*-butylamine and *N,N,N'N'*-tetraethylethylenediamine favoured the formation of linear polymer, but the use of triethylenediamine gave negligible yields of polymer. In general, the yield of polymer was better when tertiary amines were used as chain end-blocking groups rather than phosphines.

Using triethylamine as chain-stopper, a linear polymer was prepared on a large scale from dimethylphosphinoborane; the yield was 53.3%. The polymer had m.p. 170–172°, and its molecular weight was ~ 6000, corresponding to a degree of polymerisation of 80. Other linear *P,P*-disubstituted phosphinoborane polymers were prepared using triethylamine as chain-stopper. Methylethyl-

References, p. 83–86

phosphinoborane was obtained in 43% yield, as a translucent, colourless plastic material, m.p. 118–126°, having molecular weight of ~ 1850 which corresponds to a degree of polymerisation of 20. Diethylphosphinoborane was prepared in 16.7 % yield, as a brittle, translucent, white solid, m.p. 263–267°, which was too insoluble in benzene for the determination of molecular weight. Methyl-*n*-propylphosphinoborane linear polymer of molecular weight ~ 1050 (degree of polymerisation 10–11) was obtained in 55.4% yield as an extremely viscous, colourless liquid. In other cases, the amount of linear polymer formed was small. The decreased yields of polymers formed when various organic radicals were substituted for methyl radicals on phosphorus suggests that steric requirements for polymer formation are fairly rigorous.

Treatment of the dimethylphosphinoborane linear polymer (degree of polymerisation 80) at 180° with a deficiency of hydrogen chloride, (in order to remove some of the basic end-groups and thus allow the new free chains to combine with other polymer chain-ends) gave a product slightly more flexible than the starting material. Molecular weight determination showed the degree of polymerisation to have increased from 80 to 167.

10. Compounds with B–As bonds

Various arsinoboranes have been prepared by methods analogous to those used for the corresponding phosphorus compounds[105, 106].

Arsine and diborane reacted at room temperature to give hydrogen and an insoluble polymer of formula $(BAsH_4)_n$. At 80°, more hydrogen was lost and the polymer became cross-linked. Methylarsinoborane also lost hydrogen at room temperature and gave a non-volatile polymer, $(MeAsBH_3)_n$. Dimethylarsinoborane lost hydrogen on heating at 100° for 48 hours, giving a solid which could be separated by sublimation into $(Me_2AsBH_2)_3$ (80%), $(Me_2AsBH_2)_4$ (6%), and $(Me_2AsBH_2)_n$. The tetramer and polymer gave some trimer on heating to 180° (the phosphorus analogues required 350°). The trimer was unchanged after heating for one week at 150°, but was 90% decomposed after 8 days at 200°, and thus is less stable than its phosphorus analogue.

11. Compounds with B–S bonds

Sulphur compounds, analogous to the very stable phosphinoboranes, have not been made. Methanethiol and diborane at —78° gave a very unstable adduct, which lost hydrogen to give a polymeric product which was easily hydrolysed.

$$MeSH + B_2H_6 \longrightarrow \text{adduct} \longrightarrow H_2 + (Me\overset{+}{S}{=}\overline{B}H_2)_n$$

The fully methylated product obtained from methanethiol and tetramethyldiborane was not polymeric and decomposed on keeping.

Borsulpholes, the sulphur analogues of the boroxoles, are known[107]. Treatment of metathioboric acid, (XXXI), with trimethylborate, or boron tribromide and dimethylamine, gave trimethoxyborsulphole, (XXXII), or tris(dimethylamino)borsulphole, (XXXIII), respectively.

(XXXIII) $\xleftarrow[Me_2NH]{BBr_3}$ (XXXI) $\xrightarrow{B(OMe)_3}$ (XXXII)

REFERENCES

[1] W. N. LIPSCOMB, *J. Chem. Phys.*, 22 (1954) 985.
[2] F. G. A. STONE, *Quart. Rev.*, 9 (1955) 174.
[3] D. T. HURD, *J. Am. Chem. Soc.*, 70 (1948) 2053.
[4] F. G. A. STONE and H. J. EMELÉUS, *J. Chem. Soc.*, (1950) 2755.
[5] H. RICHTER, G. BREITLING and F. HERRE, *Z. Naturforsch.*, 9b (1954) 390.
[6] T. WARTIK and E. F. APPLE, *J. Am. Chem. Soc.*, 77 (1955) 6400.
[7] L. LYNDS and D. R. STERN, *J. Am. Chem. Soc.*, 81 (1959) 5006.
[8] H. SCHIFF and K. BECHI, *Z. Chem.*, 9 (1866) 147.
[9] H BENNETT, *U.S.P.* 1,953,741.
[10] I.G. Farben, A.G., *French Patent* 743,942.
[11] E. P. IRANY, *Colloid Chem.*, 6 (1946) 1089.
[12] C. ELLIS, *The Chemistry of Synthetic Resins*, Vol. II, Reinhold, New York, 1935, p. 893.
[13] J. J. MATTIELLO, *Protective and Decorative Coatings*, Vol. V, John Wiley & Sons, New York, 1946, p. 77.

14 L. E. Stout and D. F. Chamberlain, *W.A.D.C. Tech. Rept.*, 52–192 (June, 1952).
15 V. Gasselin, *Ann. chim. et phys.*, 7 (1894) 3, 5.
16 L. H. Thomas, *J. Chem. Soc.*, (1946) 823.
17 A. W. Laubengayer, B. C. Smith, R. G. Hayter and W. J. Watt, *134th Meeting American Chemical Society*, Chicago, Sept. 1958, p. 16T.
18 J. R. Thomas and O. L. Harle, *U.S.P.* 2,795,548.
19 J. Solms and H. Deuel, *Chimia*, 11 (1957) 311.
20 K. H. Sun, P. R. Malmberg and F. A. Pecjak, *Nucleonics*, 14, No. 7 (1956) 46.
21 See Reference 79.
22 I.G. Farben, A.G., (A. Carpmael), *British Patent* 358,491.
23 W. L. Morgan, *U.S.P.* 2,501,783.
24 F. J. Binda, *U.S.P.* 2,544,850.
25 M. Hyman and C. D. West, *U.S.P.* 2,445,579.
26 C. S. Marvel and C. E. Dennoon, *J. Am. Chem. Soc.*, 60 (1938) 1048.
27 W. A. Lazier and P. L. Salzberg, *U.S.P.* 2,402,591.
28 P. L. Salzberg and F. K. Signaigo, *U.S.P.* 2,457,603.
29 J. A. Blau, W. Gerrard and M. F. Lappert, *J. Chem. Soc.*, (1957) 4116.
30 W. Gerrard and E. F. Mooney, *Chem. & Ind. London*, (1958) 227.
31 R. E. Rippere and V. K. La Mer, *J. Phys. Chem.*, 47 (1943) 204.
32 H. C. Brown and E. A. Fletcher, *J. Am. Chem. Soc.*, 73 (1951) 2808.
33 W. Gerrard, M. F. Lappert and B. A. Mountfield, *J. Chem. Soc.*, (1959) 1529.
34 J. A. Blau, W. Gerrard, M. F. Lappert, B. A. Mountfield and H. Pyszora, *J. Chem. Soc.*, (1960) 380.
35 S. H. Dandegaonker, W. Gerrard and M. F. Lappert, *J. Chem. Soc.*, (1957) 2893.
36 S. H. Dandegaonker, W. Gerrard and M. F. Lappert, *J. Chem. Soc.*, (1959) 2076.
37 R. L. Letsinger and I. Skoog, *J. Am. Chem. Soc.*, 77 (1955) 2491.
38 O. C. Musgrave and T. O. Park, *Chem. & Ind., London*, (1955) 1552.
39 W. R. Bamford and S. Fordham, *Symposium on High Temperature Resistance and Thermal Degradation of Polymers*, organised by the Plastics and Polymer Group of the Society of Chemical Industry, London, 1960; see S.C.I. Monograph No. 13, London, 1961, p. 320.
40 O. C. Musgrave, *Chem. & Ind., London*, (1957) 1152.
40a M. F. Lappert, *Chem. Rev.*, 56 (1956) 959.
41 J. Goubeau and H. Keller, *Z. anorg. Chem.*, 267 (1951) 1.
42 P. A. McCusker, E. C. Ashby and H. S. Makowski, *J. Am. Chem. Soc.*, 79 (1957) 5179.
43 C. F. Hennion, P. A. McCusker, E. C. Ashby and A. J. Rutkowski, *J. Am. Chem. Soc.*, 79 (1957) 5194.
43a W. Gerrard and M. F. Lappert, *J. Chem. Soc.*, (1955) 3084; P. B. Brindley, W. Gerrard and M. F. Lappert, *ibid.*, (1956) 1540; M. F. Lappert, *ibid.*, (1956) 1768; (1958) 2790.
44 W. H. Schechter, *U.S.P.* 2,787,329.
45 F. Balacco, *Ann. Chim.*, 40 (1950) 707.
46 J. Cazes, *Compt. rend.*, 247 (1958) 2019.
47 R. L. Letsinger and S. B. Hamilton, *J. Am. Chem. Soc.*, 81 (1959) 3009.
48 W. J. Lennarz and H. R. Snyder, *J. Am. Chem. Soc.*, 82 (1960) 2169.

49 A. K. Hoffman and W. M. Thomas, *J. Am. Chem. Soc.*, 81 (1959) 580.
50 A. K. Hoffmann and W. M. Thomas, *U.S.P.* 2,934,526.
51 A. K. Hoffmann and W. M. Thomas, *U.S.P.* 2,931,788.
52 H. R. Arnold, *U.S.P.* 2,402,590.
53 W. L. Ruigh, C. E. Erickson, F. C. Gunderloy and M. Sedlak, *W.A.D.C. Tech. Rept.* 55–26, Pt. II.
54 V. A. Sazanova and N. Y. Kronrod, *Zhur. Obshcheĭ Khim.*, 26 (1956) 1876.
55 T. D. Parsons, M. B. Silverman and D. M. Ritter, *J. Am. Chem. Soc.*, 79 (1957) 5091.
56 H. Normant and J. Braun, *Compt. rend.*, 248 (1959) 828.
57 Shell Research Ltd., *French Patent* 1,198,633.
58 E. Wiberg and U. Kruerke, *Z. Naturforsch.*, 8b (1953) 608.
59 F. A. Henglein, R. Lang and K. Scheinost, *Makromol. Chem.*, 15 (1955) 177.
60 F. A. Henglein, R. Lang and K. Scheinost, *Makromol. Chem.*, 18–19 (1956) 102.
61 C. F. Gibbs, H. Tucker, G. Shkapenko and J. C. Park, *W.A.D.C. Tech. Rept.*, 55–453, Pt. II.
62 K. A. Andrianov, *9th Congress on the Chemistry and Physics of High Polymers*, Moscow, January 1957.
63 K. A. Andrianov and L. M. Volkova, *Izvest. Akad. Nauk. S.S.S.R., Otdel. Khim. Nauk.*, (1957) 303.
64 R. V. Kudryavtsev, D. N. Kursanov and K. A. Andrianov, *Zhur. Obshcheĭ Khim.*, 29 (1959) 1497.
65 M. G. Voronkov and V. N. Zgonnik, *Zhur. Obshcheĭ Khim.*, 27 (1957) 1476.
66 R. W. Upson, *U.S.P.* 2,517,945.
67 K. Hizawa and E. Nojimoto, *Japanese Patent* 4791 (1953).
68 E. Nijimoto, *Japanese Patent* 1441 (1952).
69 R. L. Vale, *J. Chem. Soc.*, (1960) 2252.
70 R. P. Anderson and M. M. Sprung, *Second Dayton Conference on High Temperature Polymer and Fluid Research, 1959*, Paper No. 15.
71 R. R. McGregor and E. L. Warrick, *U.S.P.* 2,431,878.
72 J. G. E. Wright, *U.S.P.* 2,541,851.
73 *British Patent* 705,639.
74 W. I. Patnode, *U.S.P.* 2,434,953.
75 E. G. Rochow, *U.S.P.* 2,371,068.
76 R. R. McGregor and E. L. Warrick, *U.S.P.* 2,375,998; also *British Patent* 563,995.
77 R. H. Krieble, *U.S.P.* 2,440,101.
78 M. M. Safford and D. T. Hurd, *U.S. P.* 2,558,559 and 2,558,561.
79 M. M. Safford, *U.S.P.* 2,558,560.
80 M. Wick, *Kunstoffe*, 50 (1960) 433.
81 D. Seyferth, *U.S.P.* 2,902,505.
82 R. Bedell, M. J. Frazer and W. Gerrard, *J. Chem. Soc.*, (1960) 4037.
82a G. Meyer, *Ber.*, 22 (1889) 2919; *Gmelins Handbuch der anorganische Chemie, Bor*, Ergänzungsband, 1954, p. 135.
83 W. Gerrard and P. F. Griffey, *J. Chem. Soc.*, (1960) 3170.
84 S. Yolles, *136th Meeting American Chemical Society*, New Jersey, Sept. 1959, p. 9N.
85 A. Leffler, F. Groch and E. Teach, *136th Meeting American Chemical Society*, New Jersey, Sept. 1959, p. 10N.

86 E. L. GAMBLE and P. GILMONT, *J. Am. Chem. Soc.*, 62 (1940) 717.
87 A. B. BURG and R. I. WAGNER, *J. Am. Chem. Soc.*, 75 (1953) 3872.
88 A. B. BURG and R. I. WAGNER, *U.S.P.* 2,916,518, 2,921,095 and 2,921,096.
89 R. E. FLORIN, L. A. WALL, F. L. MOHLER and E. QUINN, *J. Am. Chem. Soc.*, 76 (1954) 3344.
90 R. I. WAGNER, *First Dayton Conference on High Temperature Polymer and Fluid Research, 1957. W.A.D.C. Tech. Rept.* 57–657, p. 25.
91 R. I. WAGNER and F. F. CASERIO, *135th Meeting American Chemical Society*, Boston, April 1959, p. 49 O.
92 R. D. STEWART and D. R. STERN, *U.S.P.* 2,879,301.
93 C. P. HABER and C. O. WILSON, *U.S.P.* 2,892,873.
94 A. B. BURG and P. J. SLOTA, *J. Am. Chem. Soc.*, 82 (1960) 2145.
95 A. B. BURG and P. J. SLOTA, *U.S.P.* 2,877,272.
96 A. B. BURG and R. I. WAGNER, *U.S.P.* 2,920,107.
97 R. I. WAGNER, *Second Dayton Conference on High Temperature Polymer and Fluid Research, 1959*, Paper No. 25.
98 A. B. BURG, *First Dayton Conference on High Temperature Polymer and Fluid Research, 1957. W.A.D.C. Tech. Rept.* 57–657, p. 19.
99 A. B. BURG AND C. BRENDEL, *J. Am. Chem. Soc.*, 80 (1958) 3198.
100 A. B. BURG, *134th Meeting American Chemical Society*, Chicago, Sept. 1958, p. 15T.
101 A. B. BURG and P. J. SLOTA, *J. Am. Chem. Soc.*, 82 (1960) 2148.
102 A. B. BURG, *J. Inorg. & Nuclear Chem.*, 11 (1959) 258.
103 A. B. BURG, *Second Dayton Conference on High Temperature Polymer and Fluid Research, 1959*. Paper No. 26.
104 R. I. WAGNER and F. F. CASERIO, *J. Inorg. & Nuclear Chem.*, 11 (1959) 259.
105 F. HEWITT and A. K. HOLLIDAY, *J. Chem. Soc.*, (1953) 530.
106 F. G. A. STONE and A. B. BURG, *J. Am. Chem. Soc.*, 76 (1954) 386.
107 E. WIBERG and W. STURM, *Z. Naturforsch.*, 8b (1953) 529, 530 and 689.

Chapter 4

Phosphorus-Nitrogen Polymers

by

N. L. PADDOCK

1. Introduction

The current interest[1] in phosphorus–nitrogen polymers arises from early observations that trimeric phosphonitrilic chloride $(PNCl_2)_3$ can be polymerised above about 250° to a rubber-like solid[2] which is stable to 350°. Most investigators have become disheartened on finding that the elastic properties disappear after a few days, the the hard product becoming covered with drops of hydrochloric acid solution as a result of slow hydrolysis. Not all phosphonitrilic derivatives are hydrolysed as readily as the polymeric chloride; some are more, some are less resistant to high temperatures. The range of compounds is now very wide, and it seems likely that some other properties, more directly dependent on their inorganic constitution, may be at least as important as thermal stability.

This chapter will be concerned with those compounds which contain the formally unsaturated grouping $—\breve{\mathrm{P}}=\mathrm{N}—$. Although high polymers are often found, the main emphasis will be on the smaller and cyclic molecules. It is very fortunate that some inorganic polymeric series, particularly the phosphonitrilics, are available as accurately characterised compounds in a molecular weight region which is not always accessible; organic polymers are rarely found in the range between the monomer and the very high polymer. The phosphonitrilic fluorides, on the other hand, are known as individuals[3] up to $(PNF_2)^{17}$, and such compounds consequently

References, p. 108–109

form good models for studying the relations between polymer structure and properties.

They have also a more general interest, in that the skeletal bonds are of a new type (not necessarily confined to phosphonitrilic derivatives), the theory of which has been discussed[4], and a large amount of physical and chemical information has accumulated which is relevant to the theoretical ideas. This chapter, therefore, has the two objects: (a) to give some account of the interplay of theory and experiment, and (b) to suggest some probable connections between electronic structure and polymer properties, both chemical and physical. Both aspects have some importance in other series of inorganic polymers.

2. Preparation

The phosphonitrilic chlorides are prepared by the ammonolysis of phosphorus pentachloride[5] according to the equation:

$$PCl_5 + NH_4Cl \longrightarrow \frac{1}{n}(PNCl_2)_n + 4HCl$$

the reaction being usually carried out[6] in an inert solvent such as *sym*-tetrachloroethane. There are two types of product, the cyclic polymers[2] of the above formula, and linear polymers $(PNCl_2)_n \cdot PCl_5$ in which a phosphonitrilic chain is end-stopped with the elements of phosphorus pentachloride[7]. Their proportions may be varied by adjusting reaction conditions. If an excess of the pentachloride is used, linear chlorides predominate; if the pentachloride is added slowly to a suspension of ammonium chloride in refluxing tetrachloroethane, the product is almost wholly cyclic[7,8]. There is here a close analogy with the silicone series, characterised by a skeletal unit $-\check{S}i-O-$, isoelectronic with the phosphonitrilic unit $-\check{P}=N-$. Acid hydrolysis of dimethyldichlorosilane yields mainly cyclic dimethylsiloxanes; if an excess of the halide is used, the product is linear[9].

Typical proportions of the individual phosphonitrilic chlorides are: $(PNCl_2)_3$, 35%; $(PNCl_2)_4$, 12%; $(PNCl_2)_5$, 12%; $(PNCl_2)_6$, 3%; $(PNCl_2)_7$ and above, 18%; linear polymers, 20%. It is interesting that although the trimeric chloride is the main constituent, the proportions of the higher polymers do not fall off at all rapidly with increase in ring size.

By the use of differently-substituted phosphorus compounds or of other ammonium halides, similar reactions can be used for the preparation of other phosphonitrilic derivatives, such as the bromides[10] $(PNBr_2)_{3,4}$, the chlorobromides[11] $P_3N_3Cl_5Br$, $P_3N_3Cl_4Br_2$, and $P_3N_3Cl_2Br_4$, the methyls[12] $(PNMe_2)_{3,4}$, the phenyls[13] $(PNPh_2)_{3,4}$, and the phenyl-chloro-derivatives[14] $(PNPh\cdot Cl)_4$. A mechanism for the reaction of phosphorus pentachloride with ammonium chloride has been proposed[8], which is based on the formation of ammonium hexachlorophosphate, followed by its breakdown to $NH{:}PCl_3$. This compound subsequently condenses either with itself or with more phosphorus pentachloride to give linear derivatives, which then cyclise at a suitable chain length. Different types of intermediate compound have been isolated from the reaction of diphenyltrichlorophosphorane with ammonium chloride or ammonia[15]; the reaction mechanism here may be quite different.

A different method has recently been developed[16], in which a halogenophosphine is treated with an alkali-metal azide, according to the equation $R_2PX + MN_3 \rightarrow R_2PN_3 + MX$. Thermal decomposition of the product gives a high-polymeric phosphonitrilic derivative. This method, which is based in principle upon that used for phosphine-imines[17], has been applied particularly to the preparation of polymeric bisperfluoromethylphosphonitrile[16a], which has not so far been prepared in any other way.

These reactions vary considerably in their ease and convenience, and far more derivatives have been prepared by substitution reactions of the chlorides, which are readily available. Some of these reactions are shown in Fig. 6.

Hydrolysis of the trimeric chloride to the acid[18] takes place very slowly, with a tautomeric change as shown; derivatives of alcohols[19] and amines[20] are comparatively easily prepared. The trimeric chloride undergoes a Grignard reaction with phenylmagnesium bromide[13a], but the yield of the hexaphenyl derivative is low. Potassium fluorosulphite, on the other hand, reacts readily to give

References, p. 108–109

a good yield of the trimeric fluoride[21]. Many other substituents can be introduced, for instance, the hydrazide[22], azide[23], and isothiocyanate[24] have been prepared, and the total number of derivatives is now very large.

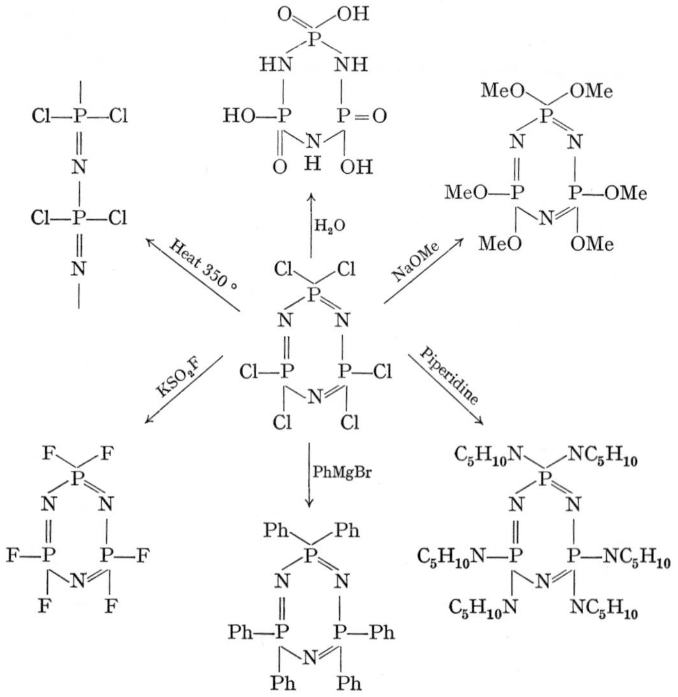

Fig. 6. Typical reactions of triphosphonitrilic chloride. [Reproduced, with permission, from N. L. PADDOCK, *Research*, 13 (1960) 94.]

Some examples of phosphonitrilic derivatives are shown in Fig. 7. The trimeric chloride (A) is the best-known phosphonitrilic derivative. The chlorobromide (B) was the first mono-derivative to be discovered[11]. Substitution often occurs pair-wise, as in (C), the *gem*-difluoride[25], but substitution on the same phosphorus atom is not invariable, even with two similar substituents. Amine substituents usually take the 1:3:5 positions, as in the trisdimethylamide (D)[26]. Of the tetrameric derivatives, besides the methyl compound (E)[12], there is one of a pair of tetraphenyl derivatives (F) prepared by the action of phenylmagnesium bromide on the chloride[13b]. The isomeric tetraphenyl derivative (G) should exist in four stereoisomeric forms, of which two have been isolated[14]. The remaining three compounds are the hexameric fluoride (H)[3], a trichlorotrifluoro-derivative which is potentially optically active (I)[25], and the unique condensed ring compound (J)[2].

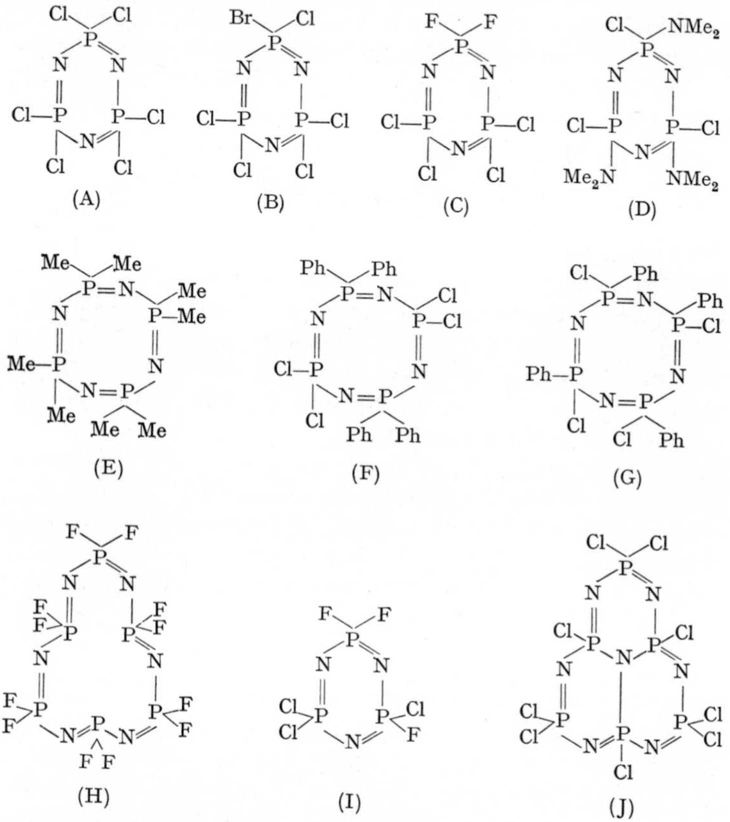

(A) (B) (C) (D)

(E) (F) (G)

(H) (I) (J)

Fig. 7. Typical phosphonitrilic derivatives. [Reproduced, with permission, from N. L. PADDOCK, *Endeavour*, 19 (1960) 134.]

References, p. 108–109

These compounds exhibit a wide range of behaviour without much alteration in skeletal stability. The methyl and fluoro-derivatives represent the extremes. The trimeric methyl compound has a high melting point (195–196°) and is very soluble in water to give a neutral solution[12]. It does not polymerise on heating. (It is interesting to compare its behaviour with that of the isoelectronic trimeric dimethylsiloxane, which polymerises readily, and whose water-repellent properties are usually attributed to the "sheath" of methyl groups which is common to the two compounds.) The fluoride is quite different; it melts at 27.1°, boils at 51.0°, and resembles the fluorocarbons. It is insoluble in water, and not very soluble in organic solvents, particularly those of high internal pressure[3]. Other properties of the fluorides will be discussed later.

3. Theoretical aspects

The existence of such a variety of derivatives is a consequence of the high stability of the phosphonitrilic nucleus, and the nature of the binding in the ring system has attracted some attention. Of the five electrons belonging to the phosphorus, four are taken up in tetrahedral bonds to two ring atoms and two exocyclic atoms; two of the electrons from each ring nitrogen form bonds to neighbouring phosphorus atoms. Of the remaining electrons, two are coupled in an unshared pair on the nitrogen, leaving one electron on each phosphorus and nitrogen unaccounted for.

Since the phosphonitrilic chlorides are diamagnetic, these electrons must be paired, the extreme cases being (a) entirely ionic, or (b) entirely covalent. If both electrons are paired on the nitrogen atom, the electronic state can be represented by $\overset{+}{P}\overline{N}$, in agreement with the relative electronegativities of phosphorus and nitrogen. Since this would result in the presence of two unshared pairs on the nitrogen, the ring angle here would be expected to be the regular tetrahedral angle of 109°28′ or smaller, whereas in fact it is close to 120° in the trimeric molecule[27]. If both electrons are paired in the sense $\overline{P}\overset{+}{N}$, the angle at the nitrogen atom is correct, but the stereochemistry of the phosphorus atom is wrong; a configuration resembling that in phosphorus pentachloride would be expected. If the two electrons are used to form a new covalent bond, however, the correct stereochemistry is obtained, a new type of bond being formed, as explained below.

To a first approximation, we may take the tetrahedral bonds from the phosphorus atom to be formed from sp^3 hybridised orbitals; to a similar approximation, the unshared pair and the bonding electrons of the nitrogen atom occupy sp^2 hybrid orbitals. The extra bond is therefore formed by overlap of a $3d$-orbital on the phosphorus and a $2p$-orbital (perpendicular to the P—N—P plane) on the nitrogen. The new bond must therefore be of π-symmetry, changing sign on reflection in the molecular plane.

For two orbitals to form a bond, not only must they be of appropriate symmetry, but their overlap must also be large and in the high-field region between the two atoms on which they are centred. The requirements for the effective use of d-orbitals in chemical binding have been examined[28] for both σ- and π-bonds, and the characteristic features of the d_π—p_π bonds in the phosphonitrilic series may be understood on the basis of that work and the special symmetry conditions of the ring system[4].

Within the second row of the Periodic Table, from sodium to chlorine, the $3d$-orbital of the neutral atom is too big and diffuse to partake effectively in either σ- or π-bonds. On the basis of the Slater radial wave-functions, the d-orbital in the sp^3d configuration of the phosphorus atom, for instance, has its maximum value about 4.5 Å from the nucleus, and would not be expected to interact at all strongly with s- and p-orbitals on central or ligand atoms.

It can do so, however, if the ligands are strongly electronegative, because they then induce a partial positive charge on the central atom, and the d-orbital contracts because it is moving in a higher (more positive) nuclear field[28,29]. Not only is a larger overlap obtained on contraction, but it occurs between the atoms, and a strong bond is formed. The normal valency of two, exhibited by sulphur in hydrogen sulphide, can be so increased to six in sulphur hexafluoride.

In this instance the d-orbitals are contributing to σ-bonds, and some new features arise if they are used in π-bonds. The formation

References, p. 108–109

of a π-bond by two p-orbitals and by a p- and a d-orbital is shown in Fig. 8; typically, such bonds occur in a ketone (A) and in a

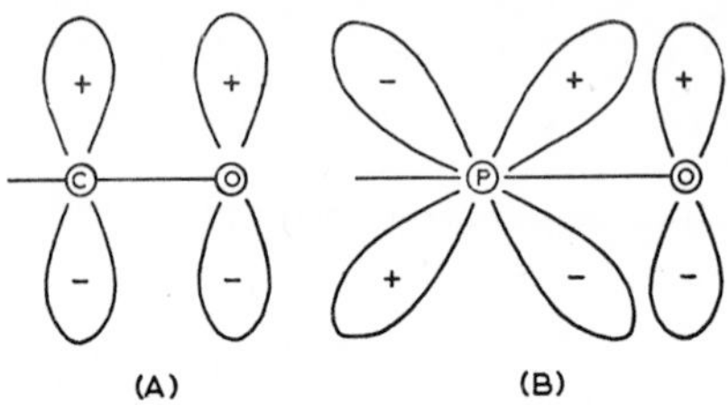

Fig. 8. The formation of a π-bond by (A) two p-orbitals and (B) by a p- and d-orbital. [Reproduced, with permission, from N. L. Paddock, *Endeavour*, 19 (1960) 134.]

phosphoryl compound such as phosphorus oxychloride (B). The principal difference to be noticed at present, is that in the case of the d_π—p_π bond the greatest overlap occurs in the region of the p-orbital. The electronegativity requirement is therefore somewhat relaxed, since the d-orbital need not be brought in so close as for the formation of strong d-bonds[28]. Also, since the π-bond electron density is unsymmetrical, formation of a pure covalent bond of this sort induces a dipole in the sense $\overset{+}{\mathrm{P}}\overset{-}{\mathrm{N}}$, which is conceptually different from ionic character, although the effects are similar. On this account, there is less difference than is commonly supposed between the two formulations $\rightarrow \mathrm{P}{=}\mathrm{O}$ and $\rightarrow \overset{+}{\mathrm{P}}—\overline{\mathrm{O}}$. Other consequences of the polar character of d_π—p_π bonds will be referred to later.

In the phosphonitrilic ring system, the phosphorus d-orbital interacts with p-orbitals on the nitrogen atoms on each side of it. Two of the five d-orbitals have the correct symmetry for combining in this way, the d_{xz} orbital, concentrated in a plane tangential to the ring and perpendicular to it, and the radial d_{yz} orbital, perpendicular to both these planes. The first of these orbitals is directed more towards the nitrogen atoms, is more strongly polarised, and therefore contributes more to the bonding[30]. Interaction can clearly take place all round the ring, with the formation of a delocalised system, but there are characteristic differences from carbocyclic aromatics.

These arise from the different symmetries of d- and p-orbitals, the first symmetric, the second antisymmetric with respect to inversion in the atomic centres; for similarly oriented *p*-orbitals, the sign of interaction is different on two sides of the *d*-orbital. The difference in inversion properties also inverts the π-electron levels, with characteristic effects on the energy.

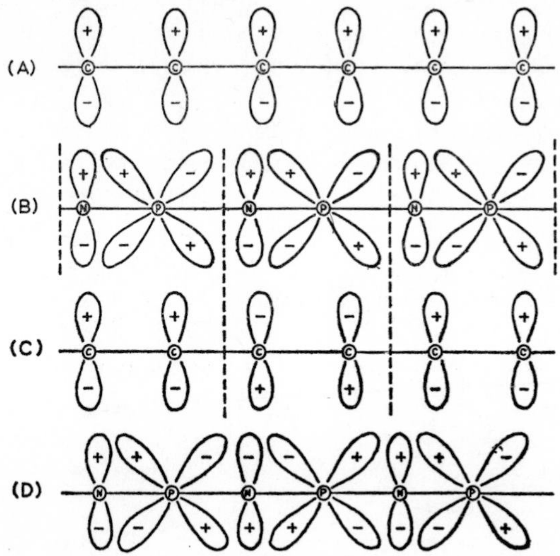

Fig. 9. Overlap schemes for the formation of delocalised π-bonds from *p*-orbitals (A and C), and from alternate *d*- and *p*-orbitals (B and D). The dotted lines correspond to interatomic nodes. [Reproduced, with permission, from N. L. PADDOCK, *Endeavour*, 19 (1960) 134.]

The way in which this happens may be seen from Fig. 9, which shows the formation of delocalised systems from *p*- and from mixed *d*-*p*-orbitals. If the orbital signs are all the same, the *p*-orbitals are matched and delocalisation is complete. Fig. 9(A) corresponds to the lowest level of a carbocyclic aromatic; because of the difference in inversion properties, however, nodes are introduced between each pair of *d*- and *p*-orbitals, 9(B), so that the π-electrons in this state are confined and have a high energy. On the other hand, if the orbitals are inverted in pairs, complete delocalisation of the*p*-*d*-orbitals occurs, 9(D), but the nodes between the pairs of *p*-orbitals,

References, p. 108–109

9(C), show that this arrangement belongs to a higher energy-state.

The comparative π-electron energy levels for benzene and a trimeric phosphonitrilic derivative are shown in Fig. 10.

The inversion of levels shown is general; for a carbocyclic system, the highest level is always degenerate, so that a filled shell is attained only for $4n + 2$ electrons and π-electron energies alternate. In the d_π—p_π system, on the other hand, any even number of electrons constitutes a filled shell, and π-electron energies increase steadily to a limit[4].

The theory, discussed qualitatively above, is of course only a first approximation, and some possible extensions to it will be discussed later. Nevertheless, it seems worth while to examine the

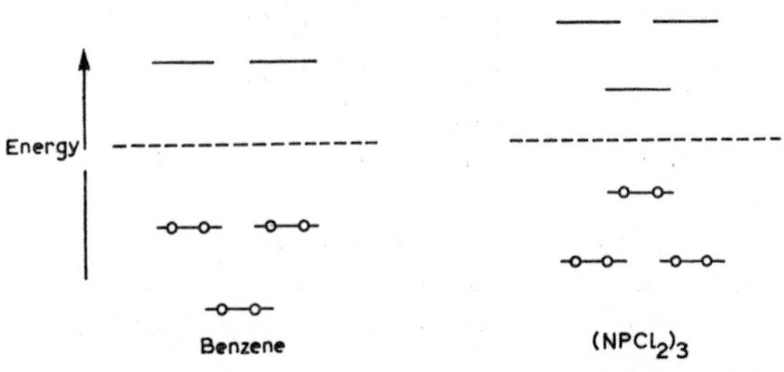

Fig. 10. Comparative π-electron energy levels for benzene and triphosphonitrilic chloride. [Reproduced, with permission, from D. P. Craig and N. L. Paddock, *Nature*, 181 (1958) 1052.]

properties of phosphonitrilic derivatives in the light of the two principal consequences of the theory, which are:

(1) for a given ring size, π-electron energies increase with the electronegativity of the ligand;

(2) for the same ligand, the π-electron energy per electron increases steadily to a limit.

4. Comparison with experiment

As will be seen below, the experimental evidence is in general agreement with these two deductions, but in some respects it seems necessary to extend the theory to accommodate new facts.

Starting with the trimeric molecules, the Raman and infrared spectra together show that the trimeric fluoride is flat, as expected of an aromatic molecule[31]. Further, the observed frequencies agree with the assignment of the molecule to the point-group D_{3h}, implying that the ring bonds are all equal in length. In the case of the trimeric chloride, we have more detailed information from X-rays[27]. The molecular geometry resembles that of the fluoride closely, but the close approach of two chlorine atoms in neighbouring molecules distorts the ring slightly, one atom being 0.05 Å out of the plane. The P—N bond length is short (1.60 Å) compared with that[32] in the phosphoramidate ion $[NH_3PO_3]^-$, where it is 1.78 Å. At the same time the infrared band corresponding most nearly to P—N stretching[33] is at an appreciably higher frequency (1220 cm^{-1}) than that expected for a P—N single bond (about 750 cm^{-1})[34].

In the case of the tetrameric chloride we again have X-ray structural data. The molecule is boat-shaped (Fig. 11 A) like cyclo-octatetraene, but differs in that the ring bonds are all equal in length[35]. The P—N bond length was found to be 1.67 Å but recent refinement of a preliminary nature has shortened this to 1.62 Å with some alteration of the shape. The tetrameric fluoride has an appreciably different structure (Fig. 11 B). Here the bond length is shortened to 1.51 Å, (as expected, since fluorine is more electro-negative than chlorine), and the angle at nitrogen is increased to 147°, the ring being quite flat[36]. The tetrameric methyl derivative has the same molecular symmetry as the chloride, the P—N bond length being 1.60 Å, equal to that in the trimeric chloride[37].

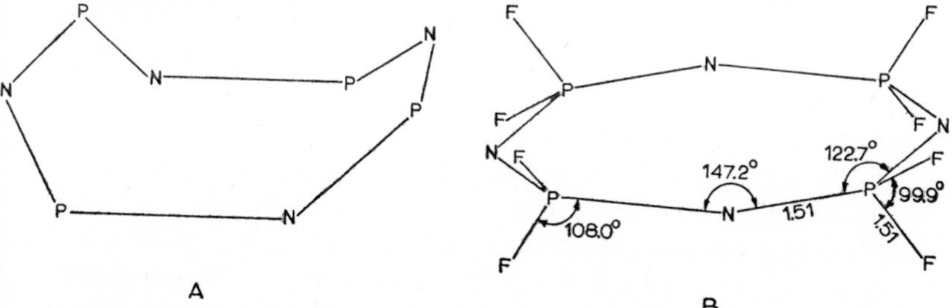

Fig. 11. The molecular structure of (A) tetraphosphonitrilic chloride (skeletal bonds only) and (B) tetraphosphonitrilic fluoride.

References, p. 108–109

The general effect of electronegativity can be seen in Fig. 12, in which the frequency of the degenerate E' ring vibration of some trimeric derivatives, approximately representative of P—N

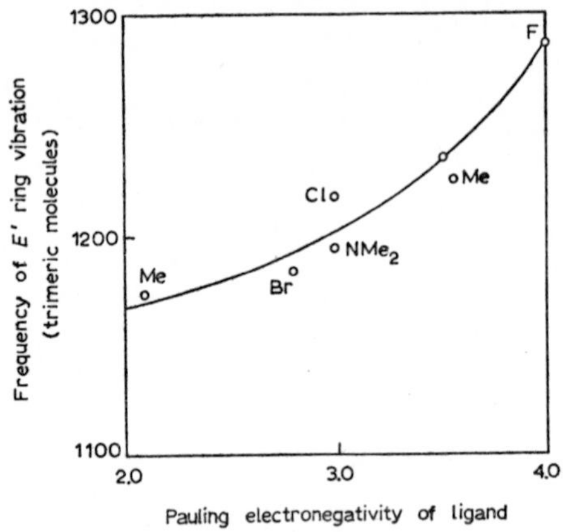

Fig. 12. The effect of ligand electronegativity on ring-vibration frequency. [Reproduced, with permission, from N. L. PADDOCK, *Endeavour*, 19 (1960) 134].

stretching, is plotted against the Pauling electronegativity of the ligand. Although it is an oversimplification to take frequencies of this nature as characteristic of an isolated group, the effect is a big one, and, in spite of the approximate nature of the argument, it seems certain that the P—N bond is weakest in the methyl derivative and strongest in the fluoride.

Further up the series, spectroscopic evidence shows that at least there is no decrease in bond strength with increase in ring size. In Fig. 13, the P—N "stretching frequency" (*i.e.*, the frequencies of corresponding degenerate modes[3], as above), is plotted against ring size for the series of cyclic fluorides up to $(PNF_2)_{14}$. The dotted curve shows the variation in frequency expected for a ring of simple mass-coupled oscillators, there being a constant angle at each atom, and the same P—N stretching constant being assumed for each polymer. Again, it would be wrong to attach too much importance to model calculations of this sort, but the near-coincidence of observed and calculated frequencies for the higher polymers can be taken as showing that at least the bonds do not weaken with increase in ring size.

More direct evidence comes from thermochemical investigations. The heats of formation of the trimeric and tetrameric chlorides have been determined[38], and show that the ring bonds are slightly stronger in the larger molecule. This result is based on the determination of heats of combustion, and emerges as a small difference between two large numbers. We can get a better value for the dif-

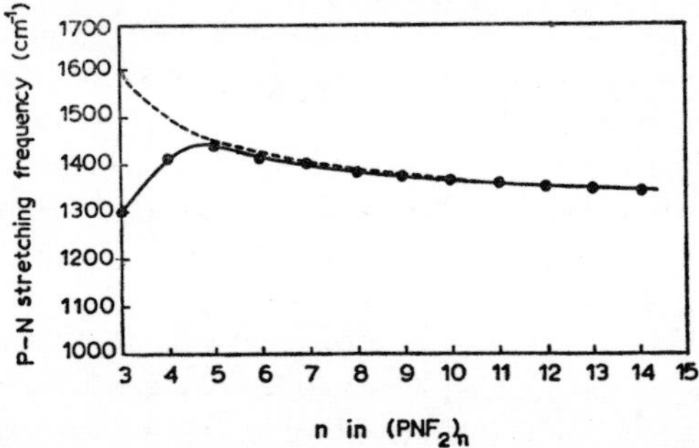

Fig. 13. The effect of ring size on the P—N stretching frequency in the phosphonitrilic fluorides.

ference from the heats of polymerisation in the vapour phase, which have now been determined[39] for all the adequately characterised cyclic chlorides. They show that the P—N bond energy term increases steadily to a limit with increase in ring size. The preliminary results are that E(P—N) increases from 72.2 kcal in the trimer to 72.8 kcal in the rubber-like high polymer. This is the behaviour expected if the π-bonding is predominantly due to the d_{xz} orbital; the transformation properties of the d_{yz} orbital are different, and, in so far as it is used, its effect on the energies is different[30]. If the two orbitals are involved to exactly equal extents[40], the π-electron energy per electron is independent of ring size, and polymerisation should be athermal.

It is interesting to compare these results with the thermochemistry of benzene[41] and the non-aromatic cyclo-octatetraene[42].

If we arbitrarily take an average bond energy term for the strictly unequal bonds in the latter molecule, we find, not the increase of approximately 0.2 kcal as between the trimeric and tetrameric phosphonitrilic chlorides, but a decrease of 2.75 kcal. In the case of the phosphonitrilics, the resonance energy is unobtainable, because nothing is known, thermochemically, about a true P=N double bond. For a P—N single bond, a value of 66.8 kcal has been found in the trisdiethylamide, $P(NEt_2)_3$[43], and a slightly lower value[39] in the isocyanate, $PO(NCO)_3$. If we take 72.5 kcal as the average P—N bond energy term in the phosphonitrilic chloride, it appears to be about 7 kcal stronger than a true single bond.

This figure may give us some sense of arithmetical proportion. The interaction of the π-electrons accounts for only 10% of the total skeletal binding energy, a fact which should be remembered in discussions on the type of binding in these compounds. In benzene, by contrast, the π-electron energy is about 30% of the skeletal binding energy. The difference may serve to emphasise that, even when contracted by strongly electronegative ligands, $3d$-orbitals are still diffuse, and are not expected to overlap as strongly as two $2p$-orbitals. Within this quantitative limitation, the two qualitative consequences of the theory (the dependence of π-electron energies on electronegativity and ring size) seem well borne out by experiment.

5. Resistance to high temperatures

It may be worth while here to say a little about the importance of a high bond energy in polymers intended for use at high temperatures. Some order-of-magnitude calculations can be made by considering a simple model, in which pyrolytic breakdown is regarded as a unimolecular process with a rate constant given by $k = Ae^{-E/RT}$. The frequency factor, A, is here taken to be 10^{13} sec^{-1}, and the appropriate bond energy term is taken as a minimum value of the activation energy, E. On this simple basis, a paraffinic hydrocarbon should have a half-life of 100 days at 630°. In general terms, this is about 300° higher than is observed, partly because thermal stability is limited more by reactions of the side-groups than by pyrolysis of the carbon framework. The phosphonitrilic chlorides, with a lower bond-energy, should, on the same basis, have a half-life of 100 days at 520°, and, while this behaviour is not observed, pyrolysis temperatures in the phosphonitrilic series are often closer to the limit than are those of the paraffinic hydrocarbons.

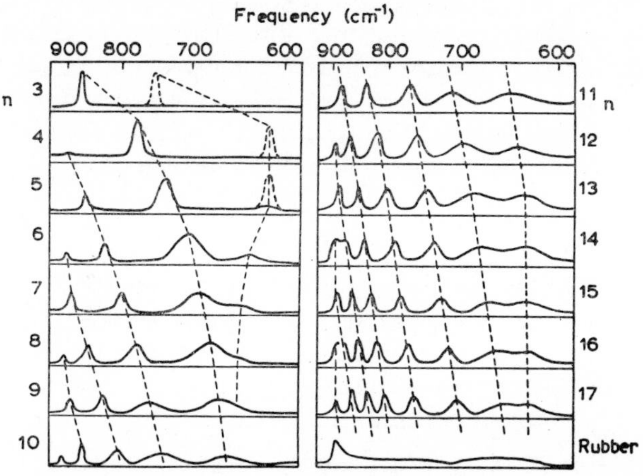

Fig. 14. The infrared spectra from 900 to 600 cm^{-1} of the phosphonitrilic fluorides $(PNF_2)_n$ from $n=3$ to $n=17$, and of the rubbery high polymer. Dotted peaks represent polarised Raman bands. [Reproduced, with permission, from A. C. Chapman, N. L. Paddock, D. H. Paine, H. T. Searle and D. R. Smith, *J. Chem. Soc.* (1960) 3608.]

It is clear that high bond energies are not the only important factor in attaining a high resistance to pyrolysis, and it is probable that electronic delocalisation is important here, just as it is in chemical effects; it is well known that carbocyclic aromatics are more resistant to heat than other organic compounds. If the bonds are strictly localised, the vibrational energy acquired by collision remains in the bond, which can acquire more energy in subsequent collisions, until eventually the bond breaks. This process has to compete with energy transfer, both to other molecules and along the chain. This last process always occurs to some extent, but it seems reasonable to expect that energy can redistribute itself most readily in delocalised systems.

References, p. 108–109

A reasonably high bond energy is therefore not the only thing to look for: it is equally important to obtain close coupling between polymeric units. A normal co-ordinate analysis of the trimeric chloride shows that interaction of P—Cl and P—N vibrations is very strong all round the ring. Qualitatively, this strong coupling may be seen in Fig. 14, which shows how the set of symmetrical PF_2 stretching vibrations spreads out with increasing molecular size. The diagram contains a great deal of information, but the immediate point is the large spread (600–900 cm^{-1}), implying strong coupling, and consistent with the high-temperature properties and with the degree of aromatic character already discussed.

6. Flexibility

We may now turn to another feature of the phosphonitrilic derivatives, in which there seems to be a discrepancy between theory and experiment; the phosphonitrilics are more flexible than might be expected. Even in the smaller molecules, there is some evidence

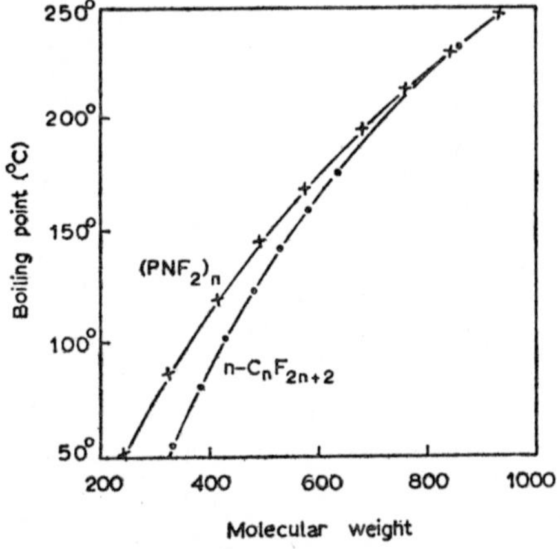

Fig. 15. The boiling points of the phosphonitrilic fluorides $(PNF_2)_n$ compared with those of the *n*-fluorocarbons. [Reproduced, with permission, from N. L. PADDOCK, *Endeavour*, 19 (1960) 134.]

that internal molecular movements take place easily. Two forms of the tetrameric chloride exist[7], with different molecular symmetry;

interconversion of the two forms nevertheless takes place easily, with only a small change in heat content. The tetrameric fluoride is flat in the crystal[36], but the weak infrared activity of the symmetrical out-of-phase PF_2 stretching vibration in some solvents (see Fig. 14) shows that a lower symmetry than D_{4h} sometimes occurs. Ideally, such quantities as bond torsion constants are required, but since these are unavailable, we have to fall back on secondary arguments. These are applied here mainly to the phosphonitrilic fluorides, because more is known about them than other derivatives.

Their boiling points are shown in Fig. 15 as a function of molecular weight, in comparison with the normal fluorocarbons. Compounds in both series are very volatile, and boiling points converge

TABLE 9

ENTROPIES OF VAPORISATION

Polymer	$(PNF_2)_3$	$(PNF_2)_4$	$(PNF_2)_5$	$(PNF_2)_6$	$(PNF_2)_7$
$\Delta S_{vap.}$ (e.u.)	23.5	24.55	26.4	—	26.2
Polymer	$(PNF_2)_8$	$(PNF_2)_9$	$(PNF_2)_{10}$	$(PNF_2)_{11}$	
$\Delta S_{vap.}$ (e.u.)	25.8	26.1	26.9	28.0	

at high molecular weights, internal pressures being comparably low for the two series. The contrast with the *n*-paraffin series may be seen by comparing the boiling points of the trimeric fluoride (M = 249, b.p. 51°) and of *n*-eicosane, $C_{20}H_{42}$ [M = 282, b.p. (extrap.) 350°].

It is possible to get some information on flexibility from vapour data. Entropies of vaporisation are given in Table 9. These values are all much higher than expected from Trouton's rule, and could indicate a high mobility in the vapour state. They must, however, include a large contribution from the entropy of rotation of the molecule as a whole, so that the evidence is ambiguous.

More direct information comes from viscosity determinations. The viscosities of the phosphonitrilic fluorides are all low, being

References, p. 108–109

of the order of a few centipoises at room temperature. We can obtain a measure of chain flexibility from the temperature-coefficient of viscosity, expressed as the activation energy for viscous flow[44].

A molecule in a liquid is normally surrounded closely by a cage of similar molecules, and can only move if this cage is expanded by an amount equal to the volume of the unit of flow. We may take the activation energy to be the work done to expand the liquid by this activation volume, ΔV, against the internal pressure, P_i, so that

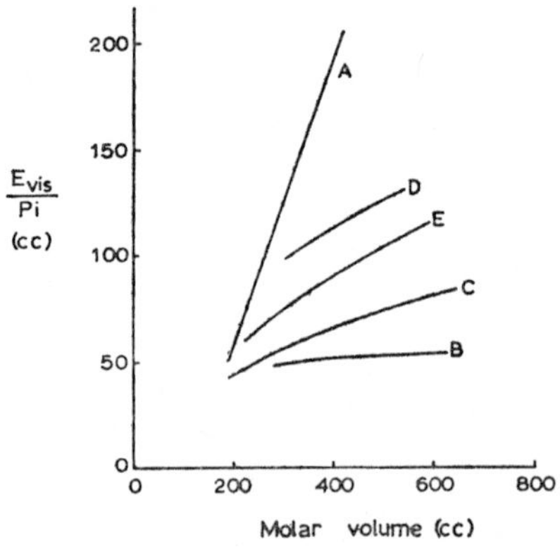

Fig. 16. The activation volume for viscous flow for some polymeric series. (A), Fluoroparaffins. (B), Linear dimethylsiloxanes. (C), *n*-Paraffins. (D), Cyclic dimethylsiloxanes. (E), Cyclic phosphonitrilic fluorides.

$E = P_i \Delta V$. The activation energy is obtained from the dependence of viscosity on temperature, as expressed by the equation $\eta = Be^{E/RT}$, and, to a good approximation, the internal pressure is equal to the energy of vaporisation per unit volume. The activation volume calculated from these two quantities, will depend on the molecular flexibility. The fluorocarbons are stiff, because the large fluorine atoms are tightly packed round the carbon skeleton; the activation volume is consequently a large fraction of the molar volume. In the silicones, on the other hand, the side-groups are widely spaced, and the molecular flexibility is reflected in a small value of the activation volume.

The variation of activation volume with molar volume is shown in Fig. 16 for a number of homologous series. For the fluorocarbons

(A), ΔV is small for small molar volumes, but increases almost proportionally with molecular size. For the linear dimethylsiloxanes (B), on the other hand, the activation volume soon becomes independent of molar volume, implying that molecular motion takes place by successive displacements of small segments, which is possible only if internal motion of the chain can take place freely. As might be expected, the *n*-paraffins (C) occupy an intermediate position, the freedom of rotational movement about the σ-bonds being hindered by the interaction of the hydrogen atoms on neighbouring carbon atoms. The cyclic siloxanes (D) are stiffer than the linear derivatives. This is not surprising, since if two ends of a chain are joined, segmental movements must become more closely co-ordinated. The curve for the cyclic phosphonitrilic fluorides (E) lies below that of the cyclic siloxanes, and it seems certain, therefore, that the phosphonitrilic fluoride chain is the most flexible of all those illustrated. The unit of flow for the monomeric fluoride is about two PNF_2 units, as compared with about ten C_2H_4 units in a very long hydrocarbon.

Such a marked flexibility is unexpected. Internal molecular motion should occur more freely than in the carbon aromatics, because the *d*-orbital is comparatively diffuse, and, since its direction is not strongly controlled by the underlying *s*- and *p*-orbitals, it can adjust itself to give effective overlap over a wide range of configurations. Nevertheless, on the simple theory, rather more restriction of movement would be expected than is observed.

7. Acceptor properties of phosphorus

The explanation of flexibility probably depends on a feature of phosphorus chemistry which has not hitherto appeared to be important to phosphonitrilics. This is the fact, already referred to, that d_π—p_π overlap induces a bond dipole with its positive end at the phosphorus[28, 29]. Formation of such a bond is therefore equivalent to increasing the electronegativity of the ligand, and if the system is delocalised, the effect is greater still. The delocalisation effect occurs even when most of the ring bonds are of the p_π—p_π type; it has been shown that the dipole moment of thiophen requires the

References, p. 108–109

sulphur atom in it to be effectively tetravalent, the effect of the ring system on the size of the *d*-orbitals being approximately that of one fluorine atom[45].

In the sulphur atom in thiophen, two *d*-orbitals are occupied, and it is natural that both should contribute to the binding. The phosphorus atom in phosphonitrilics carries only one, which is used in π-bonding in the sense described above. If this were the only effect, the angle at nitrogen should be 120°, or perhaps smaller, since the repulsive effect of unshared pairs is greater than that of bonding pairs[46]. In fact, in the tetrameric molecules, (where it is not restricted by the comparative rigidity of the configuration at the phosphorus atom), the angle at nitrogen is larger than 120°.

This suggests partial transfer of electrons from the unshared pair to the phosphorus atom. If, statistically, one whole electron is transferred, each atom carries one unshared electron, making possible the formation of a second, or supplementary, π-bond. There is further evidence that such bonding occurs. It should occur to the greatest extent in the fluorides, with the most electronegative ligands, and it is consistent that the tetrameric fluoride has the largest $P\hat{N}P$ angle so far determined (147°). (If electron transfer were complete, of course, this angle should be 180°, corresponding to $=\overset{+}{N}=$). Further, the base strength of the tetrameric chloride is less than that of the trimeric chloride, as expected if electron transfer from nitrogen is greater in the larger molecule. Finally, the ^{31}P N.M.R. shifts, determined for the series of cyclic phosphonitrilic chlorides[47], show that shielding at phosphorus is greater for the tetrameric than for the trimeric chloride, so that as electrons are removed from nitrogen they appear on phosphorus.

The importance of this type of bonding for our present purpose is that in so far as it occurs, the *p*-orbital involved must be perpendicular both to the P—N π-bond and to the *p*-orbital already used in σ-bonding. It must therefore lie in the local plane of the molecule, and must overlap with a *d*-orbital in the same plane. The two π-bonds together must have close to cylindrical symmetry, like the pair of π-bonds in acetylene, and only a small resistance to torsional motion would be expected. It follows that the strongest molecules should also be the most flexible.

It is also to be expected that the chemical effects, too, will be more complicated than in the carbocyclic series. The most readily-occurring substitution reactions appear to be nucleophilic in character, and so far two types of behaviour have been observed. Successive replacement of chlorine atoms in triphosphonitrilic chloride by amine groups occurs at different phosphorus atoms. Complete substitution is difficult to achieve, such products as the 1,3,5-tris-dimethylamido derivative, $P_3N_3Cl_3(NMe_2)_3$, being commonly obtained[26]. Fluorination by potassium fluorosulphite, on the other hand, is almost complete at one phosphorus atom before a second is attacked. Some of the chlorofluorides isolated[25] are shown in Fig. 17, the relative yields suggesting that substitution of fluorine for chlorine facilitates further substitution, particularly at the same phosphorus atom. These opposed effects can be understood in part in the electronic terms discussed above, but it is unlikely that the situation is as simple as in substitution at a tetrahedral carbon atom. The fact that the trimeric chloride reacts as readily as it does suggests, however, that nucleophilic reactions occur by "flank-attack", as with silicon[48], rather than by "rear-attack", as at a carbon atom. The stereochemical consequences of such a mechanism have yet to be explored.

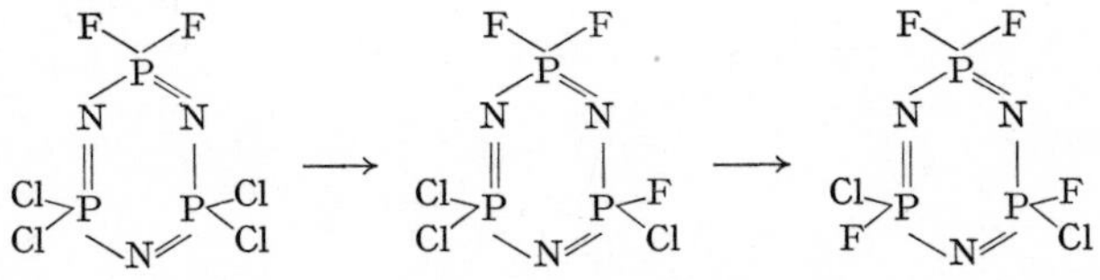

F F P N N Cl Cl P P Cl Cl N → F F P N N Cl Cl P P F Cl N → F F P N N Cl F P P F Cl N

Fig. 17. Some products of the fluorination of triphosphonitrilic chloride. In a typical experimemt, the relative quantities of the three compouds shown were in the ratios 4:1:14.

8. Conclusion

It is now possible to see some of the connections we can expect between electronic structure and properties. Good polymer properties require adequate bond strength, but this is not sufficient in itself. Resistance to high temperatures is helped by some degree of electronic delocalisation in the skeletal structure, and, as we have

References, p. 108–109

seen, this is closely connected in the phosphonitrilic series with a high skeletal flexibility. This, in turn, ensures that good mechanical properties at room temperature are maintained at low temperatures. The phosphonitrilic fluoride high polymer remained flexible to extremely low temperatures.

On the other hand, these properties are attained by use of the partially-filled *d*-orbital of phosphorus, and, if available for this purpose, they are also available for chemical reaction. Chemical stability is therefore linked in a subtle way with polymer properties. At present, it seems that the broad structural features of the phosphonitrilics are fairly well understood, and the foundation has been laid for a detailed study of their dynamical behaviour. We can expect further elucidation of the connection between physical and chemical properties from a detailed study of kinetics and mechanisms, particularly of substitution reactions.

REFERENCES

[1] A recent review by N. L. PADDOCK and H. T. SEARLE, in *Advances in Inorganic Chemistry and Radiochemistry*, H. J. EMELÉUS and A. G. SHARPE (Eds.), Vol. 1, Academic Press, New York, 1959, p. 347. Earlier work is described by L. F. AUDRIETH, R. STEINMAN and A. D. F. TOY, *Chem. Rev.*, 32 (1943) 109.
[2] H. N. STOKES, *Am. Chem. J.*, 19 (1897) 782.
[3] A. C. CHAPMAN, N. L. PADDOCK, D. H. PAINE, H. T. SEARLE and D. R. SMITH, *J. Chem. Soc.*, (1960) 3608.
[4] D. P. CRAIG, *J. Chem. Soc.*, (1959) 997. D. P. CRAIG and N. L. PADDOCK, *Nature*, 181 (1958) 1052.
[5] J. VON LIEBIG, *Ann.*, 11 (1834) 139.
[6] R. SCHENCK and G. RÖMER, *Chem. Ber.*, 57B (1924) 1343.
[7] L. G. LUND, N. L. PADDOCK, J. E. PROCTOR and H. T. SEARLE, *J. Chem. Soc.*, (1960) 2542.
[8] J. E. PROCTOR, *Thesis*, London, 1958.
[9] E. G. ROCHOW, *An Introduction to the Chemistry of the Silicones*, 2nd ed., Wiley & Sons, New York, 1951. pp. 80ff.
[10] H. BODE, *Z. anorg. Chem.*, 252 (1943) 113.
[11] R. G. RICE, L. W. DAASCH, J. R. HOLDEN and E. J. KOHN, *J. Inorg. & Nuclear Chem.*, 5 (1958) 190.
[12] H. T. SEARLE, *Proc. Chem. Soc.*, (1959) 7.
[13a] H. BODE and H. BACH, *Chem. Ber.*, 75B (1942) 215.
[13b] H. BODE and R. THAMER, *Chem. Ber.*, 76B (1943) 121.
[13c] C. P. HABER, D. L. HERRING and E. A. LAWTON, *J. Am. Chem. Soc.*, 80 (1958) 2116.
[14] R. A. SHAW and C. STRATTON, *Chem. & Ind. London*, (1959) 52.

[15a] I. I. Bezman and J. H. Smalley, *Chem. & Ind. London*, (1960) 839.
[15b] V.V. Korshak, I. A. Gribova, T. V. Artamonova and A. N. Bushmarina, *Vysokomol. Soedeninya*, 2 (3) (1960) 377.
[16a] G. Tesi, C. P. Haber and C. M. Douglas, *Proc. Chem. Soc.*, (1960) 219.
[16b] D. L. Herring, *Chem. & Ind. London*, (1960) 717.
[17] H. Staudinger and W. Braunholtz, *Helv. Chim. Acta*, 4 (1921) 897; H. Staudinger and E. Hauser, *Helv. Chim. Acta*, 4 (1921) 861.
[18] H. N. Stokes, *Am. Chem. J.*, 18 (1896) 629.
[19] B. Dishon, *J. Am. Chem. Soc.*, 71 (1949) 2251.
[20] H. Bode, K. Bütow and G. Lienau, *Chem. Ber.*, 81 (1948) 547.
[21] F. Seel and J. Langer, *Angew. Chem.*, 68 (1956) 461; *Z. anorg. Chem.*, 295(1958) 316.
[22] R. J. A. Otto and L. F. Audrieth, *J. Am. Chem. Soc.*, 80 (1958) 3575.
[23] C. Grundmann and R. Rätz, *Z. Naturforsch.*, 10b (1955) 116.
[24] R. J. A. Otto and L. F. Audrieth, *J. Am. Chem. Soc.*, 80 (1958) 5894.
[25] A. C. Chapman, D. H. Paine, H. T. Searle, D. R. Smith and R. F. M. White, *J. Chem. Soc.*, (1961)1768..
[26] M. Becke-Goehring, K. John and E. Fluck, *Z. anorg. Chem.*, 302 (1959) 103.
[27] A. Wilson and D. F. Carroll, *J. Chem. Soc.*, (1960) 2548; F. Pompa and A. Ripamonti, *Ricerca sci.*, 29 (1959) 1516.
[28] D. P. Craig, A. Maccoll, R. S. Nyholm, L. E. Orgel and L. E. Sutton, *J. Chem. Soc.*, (1954) 332; H. H. Jaffé, *J. Phys. Chem.*, 58 (1954) 185.
[29] D. P. Craig and E. A. Magnusson, *J. Chem. Soc.*, (1956) 4895.
[30] D. P. Craig, *Chem. Soc. Spec. Publ.*, No. 12 (1958) 343.
[31] H. J. Becher and F. Seel, *Z. anorg. Chem.*, 305 (1960) 148.
[32] E. Hobbs, D. E. C. Corbridge and B. Raistrick, *Acta Cryst.*, 6 (1953) 621
[33] L. W. Daasch, *J. Am. Chem. Soc.*, 76 (1954) 3403.
[34] B. Holmstedt and L. Larsson, *Acta Chem. Scand.*, 5 (1951) 1179.
[35] J. A. A. Ketelaar and T. A. de Vries, *Rec. trav. chim.*, 58 (1939) 1081.
[36] H. McD. McGeachin and F. R. Tromans, *Chem. & Ind. London*, (1960) 1131.
[37] M. W. Dougill, to be published.
[38] S. B. Hartley, N. L. Paddock and H. T. Searle, *J. Chem. Soc.*, (1961) 430.
[39] J. K. Jacques, to be published.
[40] M. J. S. Dewar, E. A. C. Lucken and M. A. Whitehead, *J. Chem. Soc.*, (1960) 2423.
[41] E. J. Prosen, R. Gilmont and F. D. Rossini, *J. Research Natl. Bur. Standards*, 34 (1945) 65.
[42] H. D. Springall, T. R. White and (in part) R. C. Cass, *Trans. Faraday Soc.*, 50 (1954) 815.
[43] R. A. Fowell and C. T. Mortimer, *J. Chem. Soc.*, (1959) 2913.
[44] G. Gee, *Proc. Chem. Soc.*, (1957) 111.
[45] D. P. Craig and E. A. Magnusson, to be published.
[46] R. J. Gillespie and R. S. Nyholm, *Quart. Revs. London*, 11 (1957) 339.
[47] R. F. M. White, quoted in Ref. 7.
[48] L. H. Sommer, O. F. Bennett, P. G. Campbell and D. R. Weyenberg, *J. Am. Chem. Soc.*, 79 (1957) 3295.

Chapter 5

Polymeric Sulphur and Phosphorus Compounds

by

MARGOT BECKE-GOEHRING

1. Introduction

Inorganic polymers, such as glasses of the silicate or the phosphate type, have been known since the days of the alchemists. Of more recent development is the chemistry of the silicones, which has revealed that polymeric silicon compounds can be synthesised which contain not only Si—O bonds but also ≡C—Si—O groups. Silicon shares many properties with other elements of the second Period, particularly with phosphorus and sulphur, and it is natural to wonder whether these elements are also capable of forming polymeric substances.

One of the reasons for the special behaviour of the second Period elements is the fact that *d*-orbitals are available. These, of course, possess a higher energy than the occupied *s*- and *p*-orbitals. In silicon, phosphorus, and sulphur compounds, the *d*-orbitals occasionally give rise to co-ordination number six, as in $[SiF_6]^{2-}$, $[PF_6]^-$, and SF_6. The use of high energy *d*-orbitals in the σ-bond base structure is stabilized by the high electronegativity of the ligands. Co-ordination number four occurs more frequently. The availability of *d*-orbitals then leads to the setting up of π-bonds (see, for example, Ref. 1). If the ligands are oxygen or nitrogen, the compounds may be polymeric. The following examples may be mentioned: $[SiO_3^{2-}]_n$ (in metasilicates), $[PO_3^-]_n$ (in metaphosphates), and $[SO_3]_n$ (polymeric sulphur trioxide).

The elements sulphur and phosphorus and their compounds will now be considered in somewhat closer detail.

2. Sulphur compounds

(i) Sulphur imides and nitrides

Elementary sulphur itself is a polymeric substance (see, for example, Ref. 2), which occurs in several modifications with different degrees of polymerisation. In the normal stable forms of elementary sulphur, *i.e.*, in the rhombic (S_{α}) and the monoclinic (S_{β}) modifications, as well as in the melt up to 160° (S_{λ}), it is known that molecules consisting of eight-membered rings (I) are present. Crystalline modifications of sulphur have a layer structure. Each layer is made up of units containing eight atoms per molecule. At higher temperatures, molecules of S_{λ} are probably in equilibrium with S_8 chains (S_{π}) (II)[3]. At other temperatures these chains can join to form longer chains which have free-radical character (III)[4]. The X-ray diffraction pattern of "amorphous" sulphur leads to the suggestion that this modification is largely orthorhombic sulphur coated by high-polymeric material[5]. Besides these modifications, there is also a form known as S_{ϱ} which consists of six-membered rings (IV)[6].

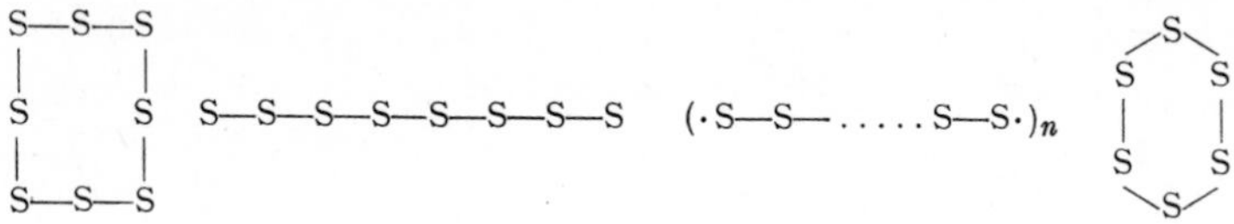

```
S—S—S                                                          S
|   |                                                        /   \
S   S   S—S—S—S—S—S—S—S   (·S—S—. . . . . S—S·)n             S     S
|   |                                                        |     |
S—S—S                                                        S     S
                                                             \   /
                                                               S
 (I)             (II)                  (III)                  (IV)
```

It has been found that sulphur atoms, whether in eight-membered rings or in chains, may be replaced by nitrogen atoms or by NH groups. Four eight-membered ring systems, which exist in crown form[7], are known, *i.e.*, S_8, S_7NH, $S_6(NH)_2$, and $S_4(NH)_4$. Fig. 18

References, p. 136–138

shows the structure of $S_6(NH)_2$, and S_7NH is similar[8]; Fig. 19 shows the structure of $S_4(NH)_4$[9].

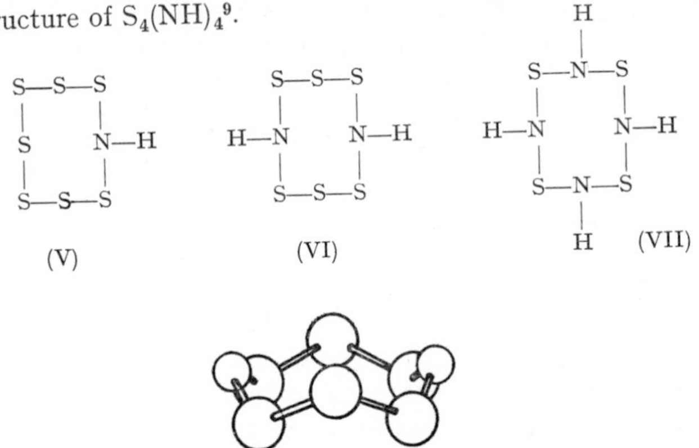

Fig. 18. The structure of $S_6(NH)_2$. S—N 1.66 Å; S—S 2.04 Å; S—S—S 109.5°; S—N—S 120°. [Reproduced, with permission, from J. WEISS, *Z. anorg. Chem.*, 305 (1960) 190.]

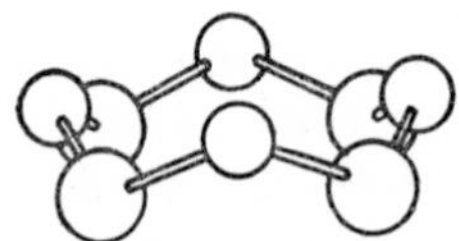

Fig. 19. The structure of $S_4(NH)_4$ S—N 1.67 Å; S—N—S 122°; N—S—N 108.4°. [Reproduced, with permission, from R. L. Sass and J. Donohue, *Acta Cryst.*, 11 (1958) 497.]

Tetrasulphur tetranitride has been known for a long time. It can be obtained by reacting sulphur chlorides with ammonia[10]. Fig. 20 shows its structure[11]. It is an eight-membered system, but not of the crown type as in the foregoing examples, but rather of the cage type, and must be considered as a hybrid of numerous canonical forms[10].

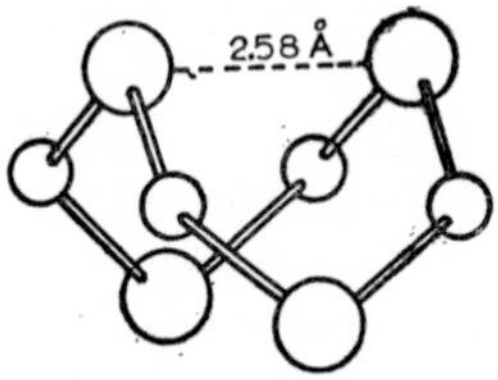

Fig. 20. The structure of S_4N_4. S—N 1.60 Å; S—N—S 115°; N—S—N 102°.

The S_4N_4 molecular cage can easily be opened. Thus, when the vapour is heated to about 300° in a vacuum[12], S_2N_2 is produced, which when warmed to 35° decomposes explosively into the elements. S_2N_2 can also dimerise to S_4N_4 and polymerise to $[SN]_n$. It is of interest that this polymer is a semi-conductor, indicating some delocalisation of π-electrons in the chain, and various canonical forms can be suggested (VIII).

$$(\text{—S=N—S=N—S=N—S=N—})_n \quad (\text{—S—N=S=N—S—N=S=N—})_n$$
$$(\text{=S=N—S—N=S=N—S—N=})_n$$

(VIII)

$[SNH]_n$ does not exist in the chain form, but $[SNCH_3]_n$ chains have been prepared by reacting methylamine with sulphur dichloride in hexane and removing methylammonium chloride with methanol[13]. The polymeric residue (IX) was unstable even at room temperature. The gum could be stretched into long threads, but these fractured cleanly.

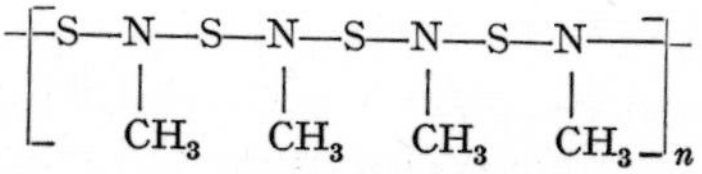

$$\left[\begin{array}{cccccccc} \text{S—} & \text{N—} & \text{S—} & \text{N—} & \text{S—} & \text{N—} & \text{S—} & \text{N—} \\ & | & & | & & | & & | \\ & CH_3 & & CH_3 & & CH_3 & & CH_3 \end{array}\right]_n$$

(IX)

Many derivatives of (VII) are known in which hydrogen is replaced by organic groups[7]. The reaction product of (VII) with tetracyanoethylene is $[S_4(NH)_2N_2C_2(CN)_2]_n$[14], which is probably polymeric.

(ii) Thionyl imide and derivatives

Analogous results are obtained with sulphur in higher oxidation states. $[OSNH]_n$, which corresponds to $[SNH]_n$, is known; it was produced by oxidising $S_4(NH)_4$ with ozone, whereby the eight-membered ring (VII) was apparently opened[14].

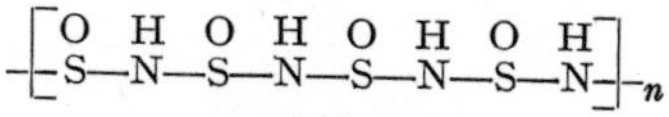

$$\left[\begin{array}{cccccccc} O & H & O & H & O & H & O & H \\ \text{S—} & \text{N—} & \text{S—} & \text{N—} & \text{S—} & \text{N—} & \text{S—} & \text{N—} \end{array}\right]_n$$

(X)

$[OSNH]_n$ was also produced by reacting thionyl chloride with ammonia[15]. Monomeric OSNH was thus formed in the gas phase,

References, p. 136–137

but easily polymerised to the brown, insoluble $[OSNH]_n$, (X). The corresponding products in which hydrogen is replaced by alkyl or aryl groups are monomeric[16].

The product formed by reaction of thionyl fluoride with ammonia is related to these materials. A volatile, ether-soluble amide was first obtained, and this polymerised to a yellow substance.

$$OSF_2 + 2\,NH_3 \longrightarrow OS(F)NH_2 + NH_4F$$

In such polymers, sulphur may have its preferred co-ordination number of four (XI)[17].

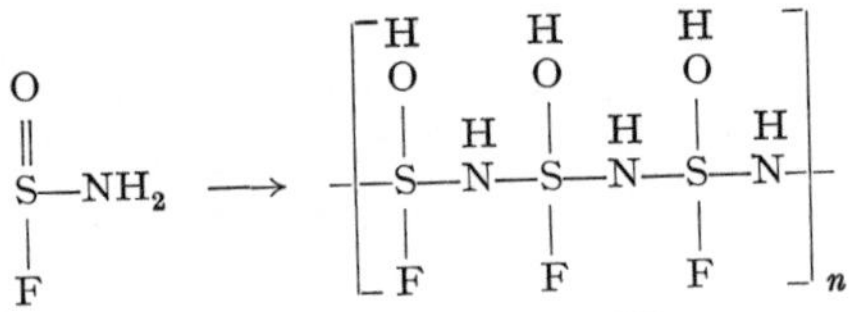

$$O{=}S(F){-}NH_2 \longrightarrow \left[\begin{array}{c} -S(OH)(F)-N(H)-S(OH)(F)-N(H)-S(OH)(F)-N(H)- \end{array}\right]_n \qquad O{=}S(F){-}NR_2$$

(XI) 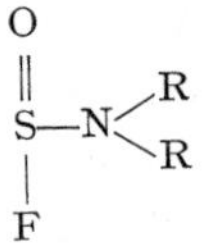 (XII)

In fully-substituted compounds, such as derivatives of the amide (XII), no polymerisation occurs; thus the piperidine derivative, $OS(F)NC_5H_{10}$, is monomeric[17]. Another fluorine-containing polymeric compound, (XXIII), has recently been reported[18a].

In substances with sulphur in the oxidation state +4, the sulphur can be imagined as being replaceable, in a purely formal manner, by carbon. In this sense OSNH and isocyanic acid, (XIII), may be regarded as analogues (H—O—C≡N does not exist).

$$O{=}C{=}N{-}H \longleftrightarrow \overset{-}{O}{-}C{\equiv}\overset{+}{N}{-}H \longleftrightarrow \overset{+}{O}{\equiv}C{-}\overset{-}{N}{-}H$$

(XIII)

Isocyanic acid easily polymerises to cyanuric acid, (XIV).

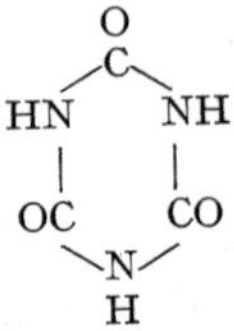

$$\begin{array}{ccc} & O & \\ & C & \\ HN & & NH \\ | & & | \\ OC & & CO \\ & N & \\ & H & \end{array} \qquad \text{(XIV)}$$

Considering now the sulphur-containing material, OSNH also exists as a monomer, not only as (XV) but also as the even more stable tautomer (XVI)[18].

$$\underset{\text{(XV)}}{O{=}S{=}N{-}H} \qquad \underset{\text{(XVI)}}{H{-}O{-}\overset{+}{S}{=}\overset{-}{N}}$$

Nevertheless, OSNH polymerises very easily, just as does isocyanic acid. A trimer corresponding to cyanuric acid is not known, but both a tetramer, $[OSNH]_4$, (XVII)[19], and a polymer, (X), exist.

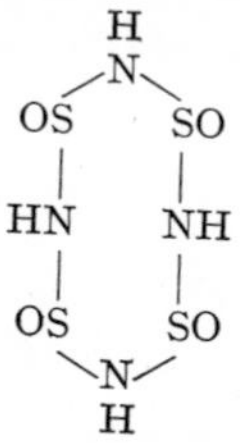

```
       H
      N
   OS    SO
   |      |
   HN    NH      (XVII)
   |      |
   OS    SO
      N
      H
```

(iii) Trithiazyl chloride and derivatives

The derivatives of cyanuric acid are very important as sources of technically-significant organic polymers. Substitution of the chlorine atoms in the acid chloride (XVIII) by amino groups yields melamine, which can be condensed with formaldehyde to form melamine resins.

```
              Cl                         NH2
              C                          C
            N   N                      N   N
(XVIII)     |   ||                     |   ||        (XIX)
           ClC   CCl               H2NC     CNH2
              N                          N
```

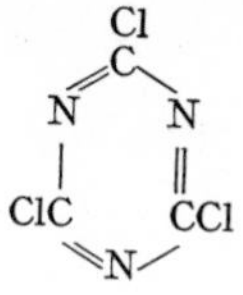

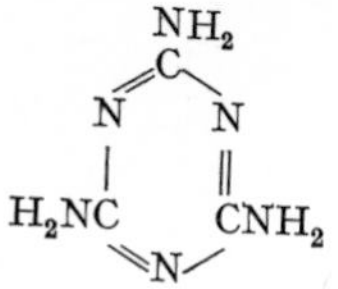

As the sulphur analogue of isocyanic acid is known, it should be possible to synthesise the sulphur analogue of cyanuric chloride, (XVIII), or of melamine, (XIX), and, from these, sulphur-containing melamine resins. The monomers have been synthesised but no polymers have yet been produced.

By chlorination of tetrasulphur tetranitride, the analogue of

References, p. 136–137

cyanuric chloride, trithiazyl chloride, (XX), has been prepared[20]. Furthermore, the chlorine atoms can be replaced by amino groups, (XXI)[21]. However, trithiazylamide is not very stable towards

(XX) 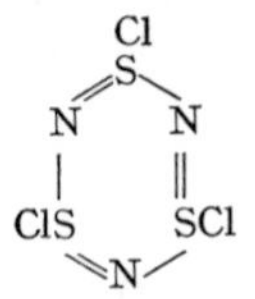 (XXI)

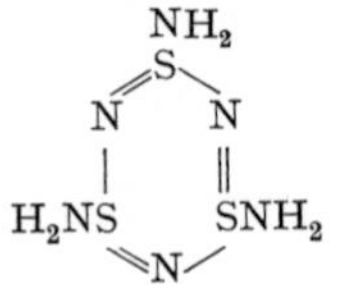

hydrolysis or attack by strongly nucleophilic reagents. Accordingly, the condensation with formaldehyde has not yet been attempted.

(iv) Sulphanuric chloride and derivatives

No useful polymers are likely to be obtained from compounds containing sulphur in the oxidation state +4. Such products are much more sensitive towards hydrolysis than the carbon analogues, because the sulphur atom is susceptible to hydrolytic (nucleophilic) attack by virtue of its available *d*-orbitals. The S—N bond is then severed heterolytically. The problem is to prevent this undesirable effect and so obtain compounds which are stable towards hydrolysis. Monomers must be employed in which as many *d*-orbitals as possible of the sulphur are engaged in bond formation, so that a nucleophilic attack involving participation of *d*-orbitals becomes less

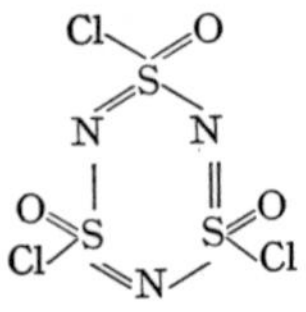

(XXII) 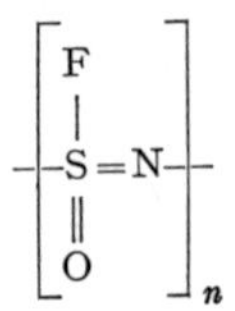 (XXIII) 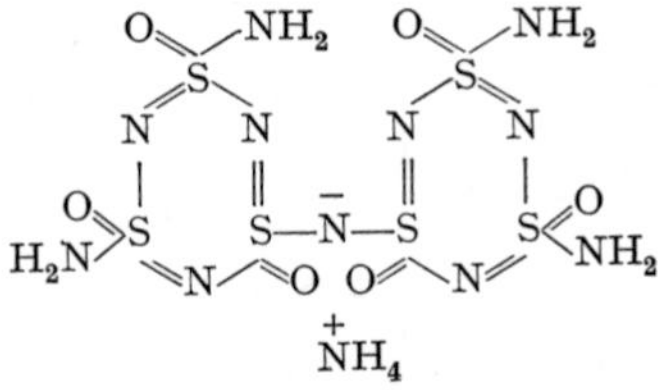 (XXIV)

probable. Furthermore, the co-ordination number should be four in the starting material. Thus attention must be transferred from trithiazyl chloride to a compound such as sulphanuric chloride,

(XXII)[22]. This trimeric chloride may be obtained by the reaction of trithiazyl chloride with sulphur trioxide. Sulphanuric fluoride, which is obtained by the reaction of thionyl tetrafluoride with ammonia, is, however, a polymeric substance, (XXIII)[18].

Substances (XXII) and (XXIII), with sulphur having co-ordination number four, are more stable towards hydrolysis, or other types of nucleophilic attack, than the compounds of sulphur in oxidation state +4, considered above. Sulphanuric chloride reacts with ammonia to produce polymeric substances, and amongst these are analogues, (XXIV), of melam and of melem (a tricyclic condensed compound)[23]. No attempt has yet been made to prepare sulphur analogues of melamine resins because sulphanuric chloride is not readily accessible.

(v) Sulphuryl isocyanate and derivatives

Rather than to proceed from sulphanuric chloride and the sulphur-containing analogues of isocyanic acid, it is simpler to attach the isocyanate group (but not the isothiocyanate group) to sulphur and then use this for the formation of polymers.

$$\mathrm{KOCN} + \mathrm{SO_3} \longrightarrow \mathrm{O{=}C{=}N{-}\overset{O_2}{S}{-}O{-}\overset{O_2}{S}{-}N{=}C{=}O} + \mathrm{K_2S_2O_7}$$

$$\downarrow$$

$$\underset{\text{(XXV)}}{\mathrm{O{=}C{=}N{-}\overset{O_2}{S}{-}N{=}C{=}O}} + \mathrm{SO_3}$$

Potassium cyanate and sulphur trioxide gave potassium pyrosulphate and disulphuryl di-isocyanate, from which sulphur trioxide was eliminated, thus affording sulphuryl isocyanate, (XXV)[24].

Other methods available for the preparation of (XXV) are the reaction of bromine cyanide and sulphur trioxide[25] and the reaction of chlorosulphonyl isocyanate[26] with silver cyanate[27].

$$\mathrm{O{=}C{=}N{-}SO_2{-}N{=}C{=}O} + 2\,\mathrm{H_2O} \longrightarrow \underset{\text{(XXVI)}}{\mathrm{H_2N{-}\overset{O_2}{S}{-}NH_2}} + 2\,\mathrm{CO_2}$$

References, p. 136–137

By complete hydrolysis of disulphuryl di-isocyanate, sulphamide, (XXVI), was produced. However, the hydrolysis apparently proceeds stepwise, as by using smaller amounts of water, an intermediate, the monoisocyanate, (XXVIII), can be isolated. The mechanism can be more readily pictured in terms of the mesomeric form (XXVII)[28].

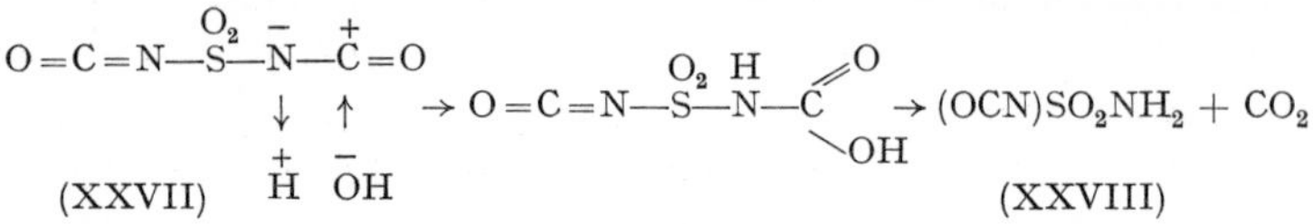

$$\underset{\text{(XXVII)}}{O{=}C{=}N{-}\overset{O_2}{S}{-}\overset{-}{N}{-}\overset{+}{C}{=}O} \quad \begin{matrix}\downarrow & \uparrow \\ \overset{+}{H} & \overset{-}{OH}\end{matrix} \rightarrow O{=}C{=}N{-}\overset{O_2}{S}{-}\overset{H}{N}{-}C\begin{matrix}{\diagup\!\!O} \\ {\diagdown OH}\end{matrix} \rightarrow \underset{\text{(XXVIII)}}{(OCN)SO_2NH_2} + CO_2$$

The monoisocyanate, (XXVIII), can polymerise through the intermolecular reaction of amine and isocyanate groups to produce gel-like materials, (XXIX). These substances form viscous aqueous solutions and hydrolyse slowly[28].

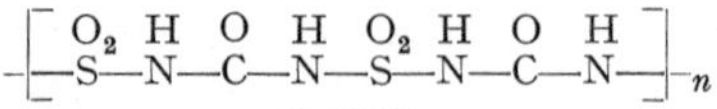

$$\underset{\text{(XXIX)}}{-\left[\overset{O_2}{S}{-}\overset{H}{N}{-}\overset{O}{C}{-}\overset{H}{N}{-}\overset{O_2}{S}{-}\overset{H}{N}{-}\overset{O}{C}{-}\overset{H}{N}{-}\right]_n}$$

In a manner analogous to that of organic isocyanates, polymers can be prepared from the inorganic isocyanate, (XXV), for example, with dihydric alcohols. Thus, in the following reaction scheme, R may be an organic group, or, as in the present case, the sulphuryl group, and R_1 is an organic group.

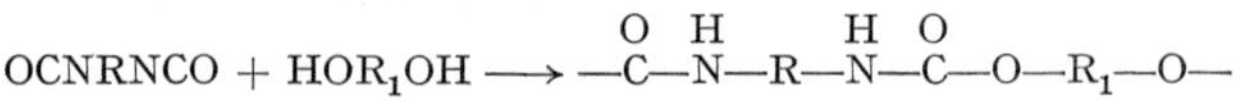

$$OCNRNCO + HOR_1OH \longrightarrow {-}\overset{O}{C}{-}\overset{H}{N}{-}R{-}\overset{H}{N}{-}\overset{O}{C}{-}O{-}R_1{-}O{-}$$

When sulphuryl di-isocyanate was reacted with ethylene glycol, a brittle, horn-like material, (XXX), (m.p. 169°) was obtained[28].

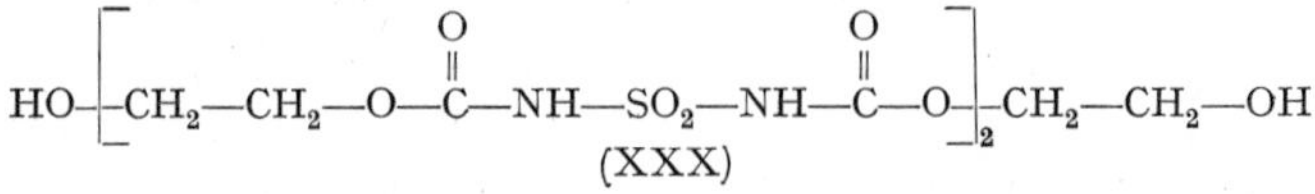

$$\underset{\text{(XXX)}}{HO{-}\left[CH_2{-}CH_2{-}O{-}\overset{\overset{O}{\|}}{C}{-}NH{-}SO_2{-}NH{-}\overset{\overset{O}{\|}}{C}{-}O{-}\right]_2 CH_2{-}CH_2{-}OH}$$

Such compounds are soluble in solvents of high dielectric constant such as dimethylformamide. Substituted glycols can also be used similarly.

Sulphuryl di-isocyanate can also be reacted with diamines such as ethylenediamine to form polyureas, which may be cross-linked. The materials obtained to date are hydrophilic. The product from ethylenediamine and sulphuryl di-isocyanate had m.p. 160°[28].

(vi) *Sulphamide, sulphamic acid, and derivatives*

Polymers with a similar basic structure can also be readily produced in a different way, namely by starting from sulphamide, (XXVI). Pursuing the analogy developed in Section (iv) between compounds of sulphur in oxidation state +6 and of carbon in oxidation state +4, sulphamide may be regarded as the analogue of urea:

$$H_2N{-}\overset{O_2}{S}{-}NH_2 \qquad\qquad H_2N{-}\overset{O}{C}{-}NH_2$$

Since it is known that urea reacts readily with aldehydes to form polymeric substances, the sulphamide/formaldehyde reaction was investigated. Resins having the structural unit (XXXI) were thus obtained[29,30].

A complication for the further utilization of this reaction is that an extremely poisonous by-product of adamantane structure, (XXXII), was also obtained[31].

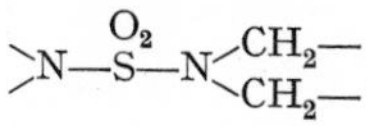

$$>N{-}\overset{O_2}{S}{-}N\begin{matrix}CH_2{-}\\CH_2{-}\end{matrix}$$

(XXXI)

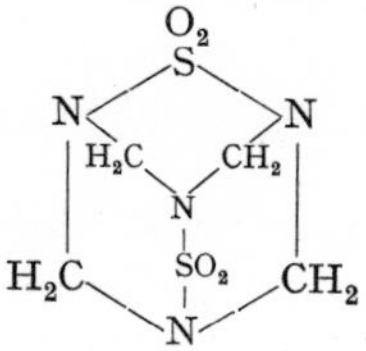

(XXXII)

When, in the reaction with aldehydes, melamine was added, cement-like substances with the basic structure (XXXIII) were obtained[29].

The action of small quantities of sodium hydroxide solution on sulphamide afforded imidodisulphamide, $H_2N{-}SO_2{-}NH{-}SO_2{-}NH_2$[32], with which analogous reactions were carried out;

References, p. 136–137

products containing an —N—C—N—S—N—S—C— chain were formed[29].

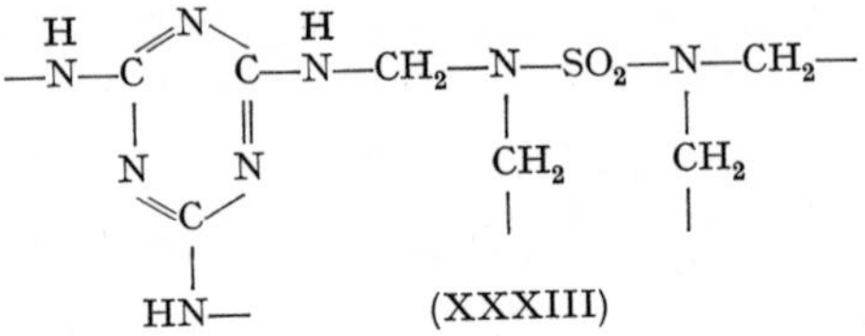

(XXXIII)

It has been shown that ring systems of the triazine type can be built into molecular chains and sulphur-containing analogues can also be produced. Thus, amidosulphonic acid with dicyanogen diamide gave the ring compound (XXXIV), which was condensed with formaldehyde to produce resins[33].

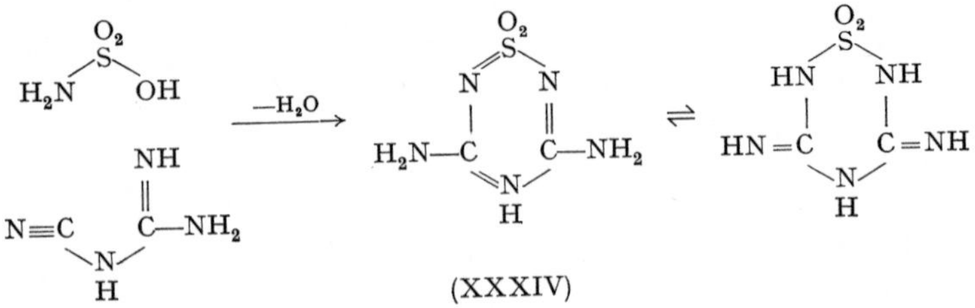

(XXXIV)

When sulphamide was heated, sulphimide or its ammonium salt was formed[34].

$$H_2N{-}SO_2{-}NH_2 \longrightarrow NH_4\,[NSO_2]$$

Sulphimide exists as a trimer[35], (XXXV), or as a tetramer[36], (XXXVI), but not the polymer, $[HNSO_2]_n$. However, polymers with this backbone, (XXXVII), can be prepared, provided there are suitable end-groups.

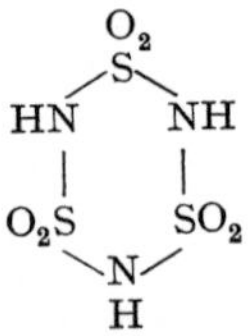

(XXXV) 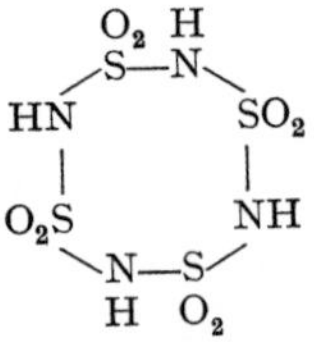 (XXXVI)  (XXXVII)

When sulphur trioxide was reacted with ammonia in nitromethane, a polymeric sulphimidosulphonic acid was produced, together with trimeric and tetrameric sulphimide[36], and the salt $(NH_4)_2S_3O_{10}$.

$$\mathrm{O{=}\overset{\displaystyle O}{\overset{\|}{\underset{\underset{\displaystyle O}{\|}}{S}}} \curvearrowleft \overset{\displaystyle H}{\overset{|}{\underset{\underset{\displaystyle H}{|}}{N}}}{-}H} \longrightarrow [O_2SNH_2]^+$$

$$[O_2SNH_2]^+ + OH^- \begin{cases} \xrightarrow{+SO_3} HO_3S{-}(NH{-}SO_2)_n{-}OH \quad (n = 4\text{–}6) \\ \longrightarrow [O_2SNH]_m + H_2O \quad (m = 3\text{–}4) \end{cases}$$

Polymeric sulphimidosulphonic acid does not possess useful properties, probably because it is too similar to sulphur trioxide, which in the β-modification (the asbestos-like form, Fig. 21) also consists of chains[37a].

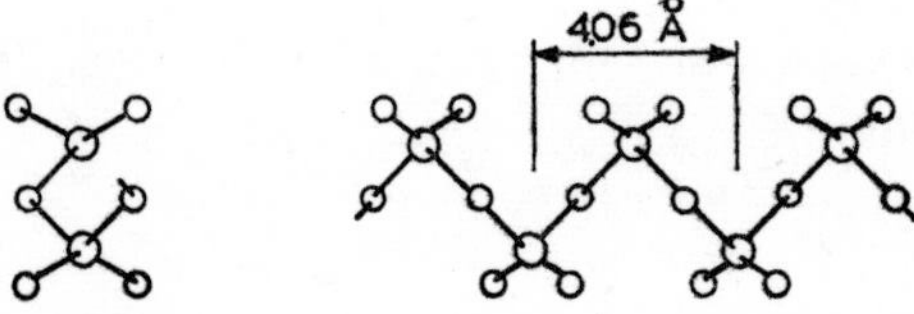

Fig. 21. The structure of sulphur trioxide, $(SO_3)_n$ (asbestos-like form). [Reproduced, with permission, from D. E. C. CORBRIDGE, *Acta Cryst.*, 9 (1956) 308.]

Great care has been taken to prevent the formation of the β-modification and numerous patent specifications deal with this point. These purely inorganic polymers, $(SO_3)_n$ and $HO_3S(NH{-}SO_2)_nOH$, are very sensitive towards hydrolysis.

3. Phosphorus compounds

(i) Polyphosphates and polyphosphimates

Sulphur trioxide and polymeric sulphimide have analogues in phosphorus chemistry, where there are even more polymers which have long been known and some of which are widely used. The

References, p. 136–137

polyphosphates can be mentioned only superficially here and detailed references to the literature are omitted. Comprehensive accounts may be found in Refs. 38 and 39. The polyphosphates *(a)—(d)* are of interest in the present context[39a].

(*a*) Metaphosphates with anionic rings.

$[P_nO_{3n}]^{n-}$, *e.g.*, trimetaphosphate $[P_3O_9]^{3-}$

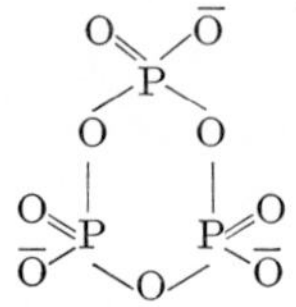

```
      O   Ō
       ⋚P⋛
      /   \
     O     O
     |     |
 O   P     P   O
 Ō  ⟍  O  ⟋   Ō
```

(*b*) Polyphosphates with anionic chains.

$[P_nO_{3n+1}]^{(n+2)-}$ or $[H_2P_nO_{3n+1}]^{n-}$ $n = 1\text{–}10^5$,

e.g., tetraphosphate $[P_4O_{13}]^{6-}$

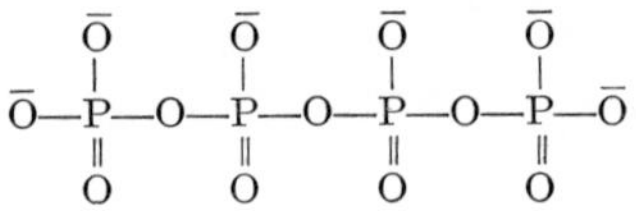

```
    Ō      Ō      Ō      Ō
    |      |      |      |
Ō—P—O—P—O—P—O—P—Ō
    ‖      ‖      ‖      ‖
    O      O      O      O
```

(*c*) Isometaphosphates, with rings having side-chains; only the esters are known[39b].

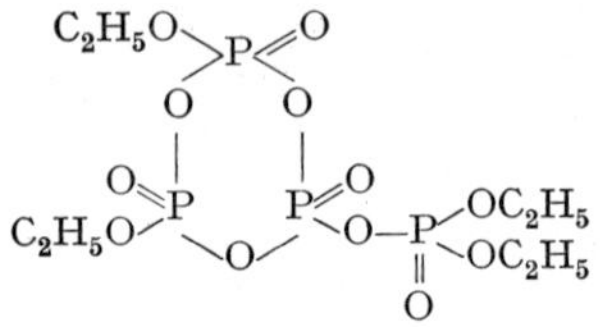

```
      C2H5O>P<O
           O   O
           |   |
        O  P   P  O        OC2H5
  C2H5O ⟍  O ⟋  ⟍ O—P
                     ‖  OC2H5
                     O
```

(*d*) Cross-linked polyphosphates, *e.g.*, with the following skeleton

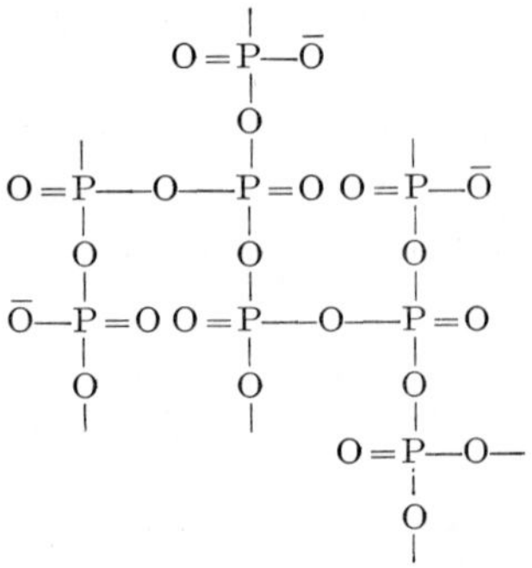

```
               |
          O = P—Ō
               |
               O
     |         |          |
O = P——O——P = O   O = P—Ō
     |         |          |
     O         O          O
     |         |          |
Ō—P = O   O = P——O——P = O
     |         |          |
     O         O          O
     |         |          |
                     O = P—O—
                          |
                          O
                          |
```

In the following scheme, the mode of formation from phosphoric oxide of some polyphosphates is given. Long chains are not formed in the hydrolysis of phosphoric oxide and tetrametaphosphate is the predominant product[40].

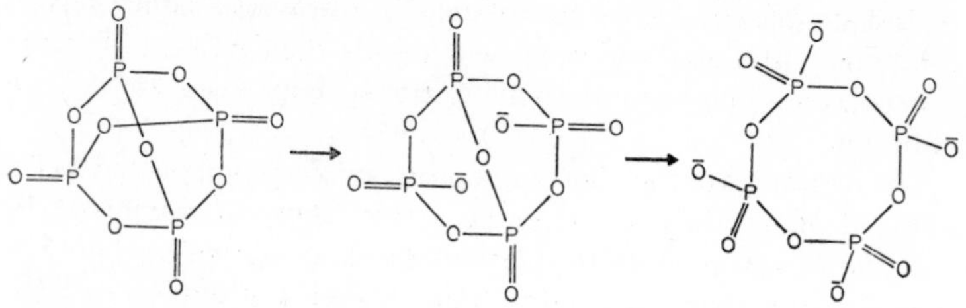

The inter-relation of the various chain polyphosphates is shown below[41]. All these compounds, each of different degree of polymerisation, are formed by heating pyrophosphates to appropriate temperatures.

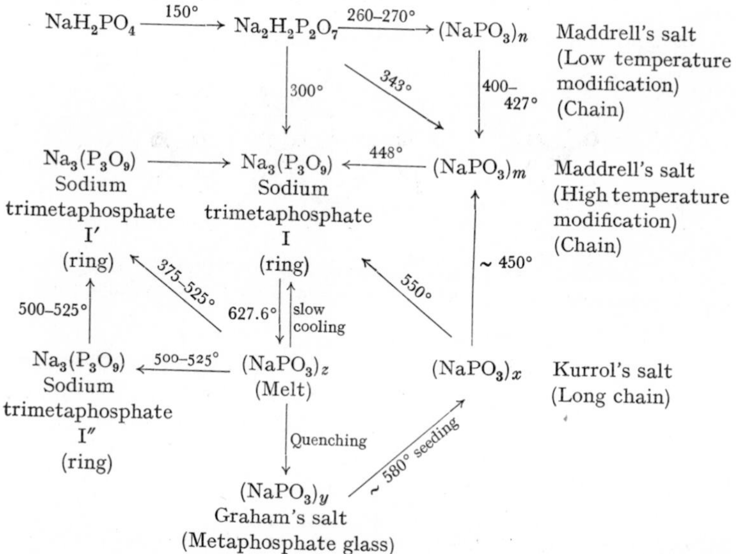

The structure of the metaphosphate glasses is essentially that of the chain phosphates. The anionic chains of PO_4 tetrahedra are of

References, p. 136–137

various lengths consisting of from one to a million units. There is no crystal lattice which can accommodate such a variety of constituents and the glass-like state is therefore preferred[42]. Phosphate glasses are of some technical importance[43]. For example, calcium metaphosphate glass is highly transparent to ultraviolet light; glasses containing titanium and tungsten absorb radioactive radiation; glasses containing cerium remain transparent even to intense radiation.

The structures of the high temperature modification of Maddrell's salt and of Kurrol's salt have been thoroughly investigated[37, 44].

In the present context, the particularly close relationship between the anion of Kurrol's salt and the β-modification of sulphur trioxide is of interest. In both of these substances, and also in the silicates, MO_4 tetrahedra are linked at the apices, but the structures of $(PO_3^-)_n$ and of $(SO_3)_n$ are more closely packed than those of magnesium and sodium metasilicates. The sulphur trioxide (Fig. 21) and the metaphosphate (Fig. 22) chains show spiral arrangements[37], right-handed in $(SO_3)_n$ and left-handed in $(PO_3^-)_n$.

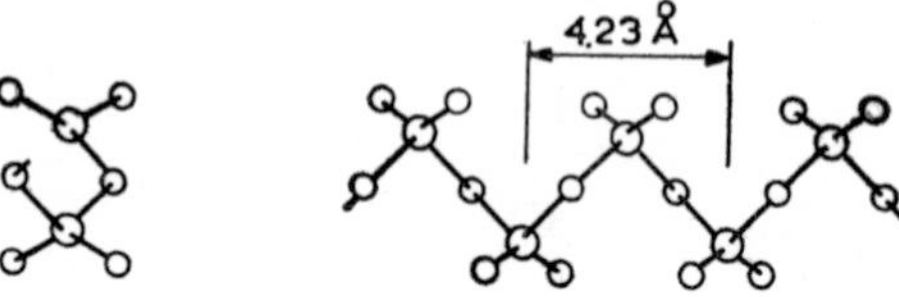

Fig. 22. The structure of the metaphosphate ion $(PO_3^-)_n$. [Reproduced, with permission, from D. E. C. CORBRIDGE, *Acta Cryst.*, 9 (1956) 308.]

In view of the high temperature mode of preparation of polyphosphates, not all polyphosphates can be synthesised in this way. If, for example, ammonium polyphosphate is to be prepared, another

$$\underset{\text{(XXXVIII)}}{\mathrm{HO{-}\overset{\overset{\displaystyle O}{\|}}{\underset{\underset{\displaystyle NH_2}{|}}{P}}{-}OH}} \longrightarrow \underset{\text{(XXXIX)}}{\mathrm{\bar{O}{-}\overset{\overset{\displaystyle O}{\|}}{\underset{\underset{\displaystyle {}^{+}NH_3}{|}}{P}}{-}O{-}H}} \longrightarrow \underset{\text{(XL)}}{\left[\mathrm{\bar{O}{-}\overset{\overset{\displaystyle O}{\|+}}{P}{-}\bar{O}}\right]\overset{+}{\mathrm{N}}\mathrm{H_4}} \longrightarrow \underset{\text{(XLI)}}{\underbrace{[\mathrm{PO_3}]_n^{n-} + n\,\overset{+}{\mathrm{N}}\mathrm{H_4}}}$$

procedure must be employed, such as the thermal rearrangement of amidophosphoric acid, $H_2NP(O)(OH)_2$, which at 110° yields ammonium polyphosphate, (XLI)[45].

This rearrangement may be due to the fact that monoamidophosphoric acid, (XXXVIII), exists, at least in part, as the zwitterion, (XXXIX). The nitrogen atom tends to give up its positive charge to the less electronegative phosphorus. Ammonia is thereby eliminated and forms an ammonium ion (see XL) with the remaining proton of the acid. The ammonium salt then polymerises (see XLI). This polymerisation is interpreted in terms of the tendency of phosphorus to achieve the co-ordination number four. The bonding is based upon sp^3 hybridisation, but each link has some π-character. These polymeric, water-soluble ammonium polyphosphates show a high affinity for calcium ions.

Another method of preparing such ammonium polyphosphates starts from Kurrol's potassium salt[45a]. The free acid was prepared using an ion-exchange resin and the acid was subsequently neutralised with ammonia. Using this latter procedure with diamines in

```
     |                           |                              |
     O                           O                              O
     |   - +                     |   - +                +   -   |
 O=P—O NH3\               O=P—O NH3—(CH2)6—NH3 O—P=O
     |        CH2                |                              |
     O         |                 O                              O
     |   - +  CH2                |   - +                +   -   |
 O=P—O NH3/               O=P—O NH3—(CH2)6—NH3 O—P=O
     |                           |                              |
     O                           O                              O
     |   - +                     |   - +                +   -   |
 O=P—O NH3\               O=P—O NH3—(CH2)6—NH3 O—P=O
     |        CH2                |                              |
     O         |
     |   - +  CH2
 O=P—O NH3/
     |
```

place of ammonia, interesting polymers can be obtained. These may be either insoluble in water if, for example, ethylenediamine is used, or soluble in water if diamines of greater chain length are used[45a].

References, p. 136–137

Polyphosphates which contain the isosteric NH group in place of oxygen can be prepared using the rearrangement method, for

$$\underset{\text{(XLIV)}}{HO{-}\overset{\overset{O}{\|}}{\underset{\underset{NH_2}{|}}{P}}{-}NH_2} \longrightarrow \underset{\text{(XLV)}}{\bar{O}{-}\overset{\overset{O}{\|}}{\underset{\underset{NH_3}{|+}}{P}}{-}\overset{\overset{H}{|}}{N}{-}H} \longrightarrow \underset{\text{(XLVI)}}{\left[\bar{O}{-}\overset{\overset{\bar{O}}{|+}}{P}{=}NH\right]\overset{+}{N}H_4} \longrightarrow$$

$$\underbrace{[O_2PNH]_n^{n-} + n\,\overset{+}{N}H_4}_{\text{(XLVII)}}$$

example, compound (XLVII) from diamidophosphoric acid (XLIV).

The high affinity towards calcium ions of all the above polyphosphates and the imidophosphates, (XLVII), makes them of

P_4O_{10} $\xrightarrow{+2\,NH_3}$ (XLVIII) $\xrightarrow{+2\,NH_3}$ (XLIX) $\xrightarrow{+4\,NH_3}$

$$2\,H_2N{-}\overset{\overset{O}{\|}}{\underset{\underset{\bar{O}\overset{+}{N}H_4}{|}}{P}}{-}O{-}\overset{\overset{O}{\|}}{\underset{\underset{\bar{O}\overset{+}{N}H_4}{|}}{P}}{-}NH_2 \text{ (L)} \xrightarrow{-NH_3} H_2N{-}\overset{\overset{O}{\|}}{\underset{\underset{OH}{|}}{P}}{-}O{-}\overset{\overset{O}{\|}}{\underset{\underset{\bar{O}\overset{+}{N}H_4}{|}}{P}}{-}NH_2 \longrightarrow H_3\overset{+}{N}{-}\overset{\overset{O}{\|}}{\underset{\underset{OH}{|}}{P}}{-}O{-}\overset{\overset{O}{\|}}{\underset{\underset{\bar{O}\overset{+}{N}H_4}{|}}{P}}{-}\bar{N}H$$

$$\xrightarrow{-2\,\overset{+}{N}H_4} \overset{\overset{O}{\|}}{\underset{\underset{\bar{O}}{|}}{\overset{+}{P}}}{-}O{-}\overset{\overset{O}{\|}}{\underset{\underset{O^-}{|}}{P}}{-}\bar{N}H \longrightarrow \left[{-}\overset{\overset{O}{\|}}{\underset{\underset{O^-}{|}}{P}}{-}O{-}\overset{\overset{O}{\|}}{\underset{\underset{O^-}{|}}{P}}{-}\overset{H}{N}{-}\overset{\overset{O}{\|}}{\underset{\underset{O^-}{|}}{P}}{-}O{-}\overset{\overset{O}{\|}}{\underset{\underset{O^-}{|}}{P}}{-}\overset{H}{N}{-}\right]_n^{(4n)-}$$

(LI)

technical importance. In this connection, the reaction of phosphoric oxide and ammonia is of interest.

Although the hydrolysis of this oxide leads predominantly to tetraphosphate[40], the aminolysis can be conducted so that amides of diphosphoric acid, (XLVIII)–(L) are formed. If analogy is made with the rearrangement of amides of phosphoric acid, it becomes understandable that heating amides of diphosphoric acid should produce polymeric substances, (LI), which contain P—O—P and also P—N—P groups. Such substances (LI) are analogues of polyphosphates and have similar properties.

(ii) Phosphoryl amides and derivatives

The main structural unit of the polyphosphates is (LII). In addition, in polyphosphimates, the unit (LIII) is also found.

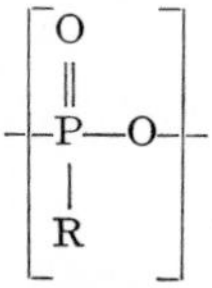

$$\left[-\overset{\overset{\displaystyle O}{\|}}{\underset{\underset{\displaystyle R}{|}}{P}}-O- \right] \quad \text{and} \quad \left[-\overset{\overset{\displaystyle O}{\|}}{\underset{\underset{\displaystyle R}{|}}{P}}-\overset{H}{N}- \right]$$

(LII) (LIII)

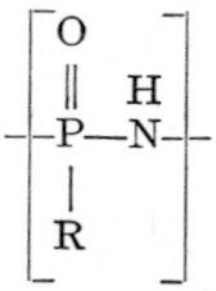

In the polymers just discussed *e.g.*, (LI), R was $-\bar{O}\overset{+}{N}H_4$, but it could alternatively be another group, such as an amino group, as in (LIV) and (LV).

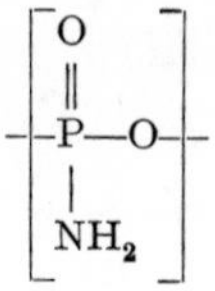

$$\left[-\overset{\overset{\displaystyle O}{\|}}{\underset{\underset{\displaystyle NH_2}{|}}{P}}-O- \right] \qquad \left[-\overset{\overset{\displaystyle O}{\|}}{\underset{\underset{\displaystyle NH_2}{|}}{P}}-\overset{H}{N}- \right]$$

(LIV) 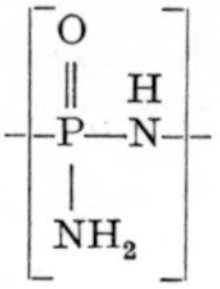 (LV)

A polymeric material based on (LIV) has not yet been described, but compounds containing two phosphorus atoms, namely (LVI)[47] and (L)[46], are known.

A substance based on (LV) was produced by the self-condensation of the triamide of phosphoric acid[48], using hydrochloric acid as an acceptor for ammonia.

References, p. 136–137

At temperatures between —40° and +24°, the tetramide of imidodiphosphoric acid, (LVII), was obtained. Between +28° and +32° a condensation to the pentamide of diamidophosphoric

```
          O       O
          ‖       ‖
    H2N—P—O—P—NH2
          |       |
        NH2     NH2
           (LVI)
```

acid occurred, and at still higher temperatures (up to 180°) the polycondensation resulted finally in the formation of the polymeric phosphamide (LVIII)[49, 50].

```
         O                 O       O                  ┌ O      ┐
         ‖                 ‖   H   ‖                  │ ‖   H  │
2 H2N—P—NH2  ⟶  H2N—P—N—P—NH2  ⟶  H2N—│—P—N—│—H
         |                 |       |                  │ |      │
        NH2               NH2     NH2                 └ NH2    ┘n

                              (LVII)                     (LVIII)
```

The low molecular weight products, such as (LVII), which are first formed, are soluble in water. As the molecular weight increases, the products become increasingly insoluble and have been recommended for use in treatment of paper and textiles[50, 51].

Further thermal condensation of (LVIII) at 300° yielded a cross-linked polymer, (LIX), of empirical formula $P_2O_2N_3H_3$[52].

```
 O       O                           O       O
 ‖   H   ‖   H                       ‖   H   ‖   H
—P—N—P—N—            -NH3         —P—N—P—N—
 |       |            ——→            |       |
NH2     NH2                         HN      NH      O       O
                                     |       |      ‖   H   ‖   H
NH2     NH2     O             O     —P—N—P—N—P—N—P—N—
 |       |      ‖             ‖      ‖   H   ‖   H  |
—P—N—P—N—P—NH2 H2N—P—        O       O      NH
 ‖   H   ‖   H  |             |                     |
 O       O     NH            NH
                |             |                  (LIX)
```

Upon heating these phosphamides up to about 600°, the insoluble and very inert PON was formed, the structure of which has not yet been definitely established[52].

$$P_2O_2N_3H_3 \longrightarrow 2PON + NH_3$$

It is possible that it consists of a three-dimensional cross-linked structure, containing the groups (LX) or (LXI).

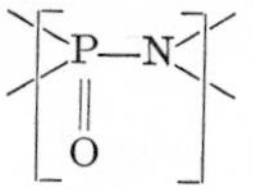

(LX) 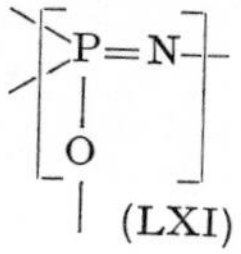 (LXI)

Cross-linked polymers, (LXII), containing boron in the skeleton

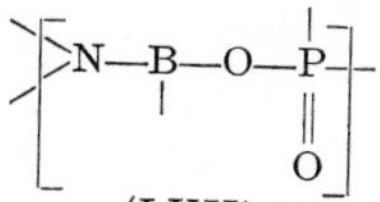

(LXII)

have been prepared and may be considered as related to such phosphoryl nitrides (see Chapter 2, Section 7).

(iii) Phosphonic acids, phosphonic amides, and derivatives

In polymeric substances having repeating units (LIII), R may also be an organic group. A study of the rate of condensation of phenylphosphonic diamide, (LXIII), in the range 200°–300°, indicated that one mole of ammonia was lost per mole of amide, resulting in the formation of a polymer having the probable structure (LXIV)[53].

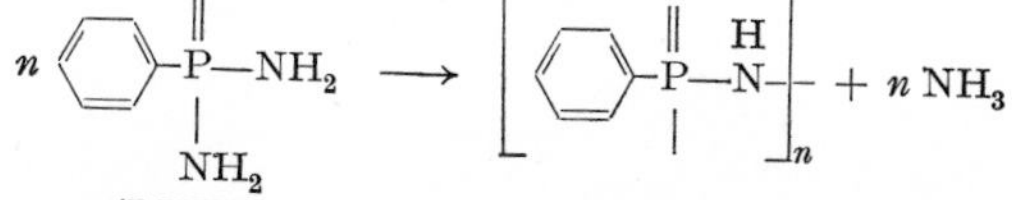

$$n\, C_6H_5\text{-}P(=O)(NH_2)_2 \longrightarrow \left[C_6H_5\text{-}P(=O)\text{-}NH \right]_n + n\, NH_3$$

(LXIII) (LXIV)

Fibres could be drawn from the melt of such polymers, but they were short and brittle. The substances were insoluble in practically

References, p. 136–137

all solvents. These materials may be useful for stabilising polyvinyl chloride against light, and for flame-proofing. Polymers, in which the hydrogen atom located on the nitrogen is substituted by an alkyl group, may also have similar properties[53].

Polymers with a similar skeleton, (LXVI), were obtained[54] by by condensation of phenylphosphonic dichloride, (LXV), with hexamethylenediamine.

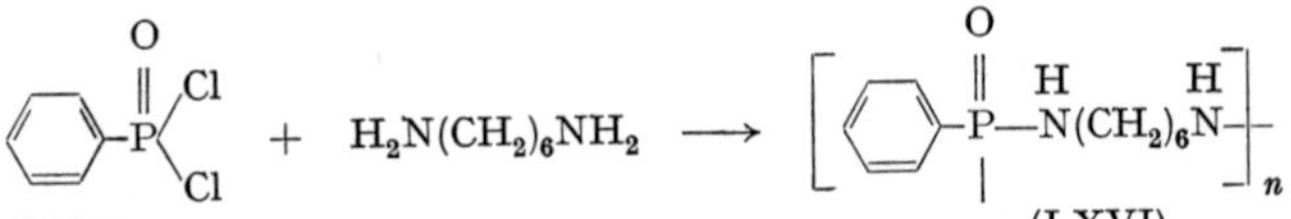

$$C_6H_5\text{-}P(=O)Cl_2 \quad + \quad H_2N(CH_2)_6NH_2 \longrightarrow \left[C_6H_5\text{-}\overset{O}{\overset{\|}{P}}\text{—}\overset{H}{N}(CH_2)_6\overset{H}{N}\text{—} \right]_n$$

(LXV) (LXVI)

Polymeric substances were also formed when piperazine was employed. These materials were reported to be soluble in chloroform but not in water.

The hard, resinous condensation products, (LXVII), of phenylphosphonic diamide, (LXIII), with urea have also been prepared[53].

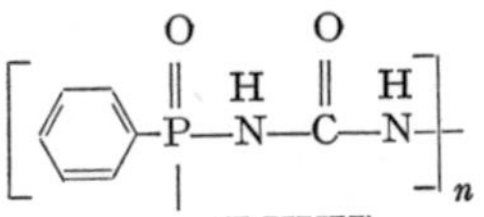

$$\left[C_6H_5\text{-}\overset{O}{\overset{\|}{P}}\text{—}\overset{H}{N}\text{—}\overset{O}{\overset{\|}{C}}\text{—}\overset{H}{N}\text{—} \right]_n \qquad \left[Cl\text{—}CH_2\text{—}\overset{O}{\overset{\|}{P}}\text{—}\overset{H}{N}\text{—}\overset{O}{\overset{\|}{C}}\text{—}\overset{H}{N}\text{—} \right]_n$$

(LXVII) 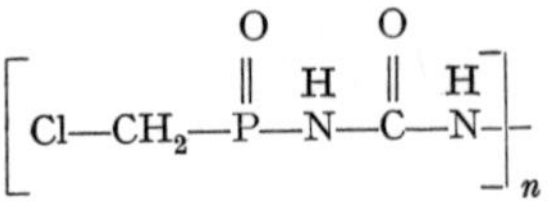 (LXVIII)

A similar reaction between urea and chlorinated methylphosphonic dichloride, affording (LXVIII) has been reported[55].

All these polycondensates contain the groups (LIII) and (LXIX).

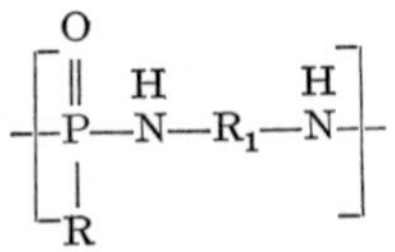

$$\left[\text{—}\overset{O}{\overset{\|}{\underset{R}{\underset{|}{P}}}}\text{—}\overset{H}{N}\text{—}R_1\text{—}\overset{H}{N}\text{—} \right]$$

(LXIX)

Replacement of the imido group by oxygen leads to structures like (LII) and (LXX) in which R can be alkoxy, aryloxy, or phenyl, and in which R_1 represents various bridging groups. The so-called "phoryl resins"[56] have the basic unit (LXX) and have been made by a two-stage process. Phosphoryl chloride was reacted with a

$$\left[-\overset{\overset{\displaystyle O}{\|}}{\underset{\underset{\displaystyle R}{|}}{P}}-O-R_1-O- \right] \quad \text{(LXX)}$$

phenol and the resulting dichloride was condensed with a dihydric phenol.

$$O{=}PCl_3 + ROH \longrightarrow Cl_2\overset{\overset{\displaystyle O}{\|}}{P}OR \xrightarrow{+\ HO\text{–}R_1\text{–}OH} \left[-\overset{\overset{\displaystyle O}{\|}}{P}\begin{matrix} O-R_1-O- \\ OR \end{matrix} \right]$$

The "phoryl resins" melt at temperatures between 60° and 120°, depending on the nature of the phenol. In the solid state, they form glasses which are soluble in organic solvents, such as toluene,

$$C_6H_5P(O)Cl_2 + 2\ HO\text{–}C_6H_4\text{–}OH \xrightarrow{A} HO\text{–}C_6H_4\text{–}O\text{–}P(O)(C_6H_5)\text{–}O\text{–}C_6H_4\text{–}OH \xrightarrow{+\ C_6H_5P(O)Cl_2} \left[-P(O)(C_6H_5)\text{–}O\text{–}C_6H_4\text{–}O- \right]_n$$

$$2\ C_6H_5P(O)Cl_2 + HO\text{–}C_6H_4\text{–}OH \xrightarrow{B} Cl\text{–}P(O)(C_6H_5)\text{–}O\text{–}C_6H_4\text{–}O\text{–}P(O)(C_6H_5)\text{–}Cl \xrightarrow{+\ HO\text{–}C_6H_4\text{–}OH} \left[-P(O)(C_6H_5)\text{–}O\text{–}C_6H_4\text{–}O- \right]_n$$

chloroform, and alcohols. It has been suggested that any useful potential applications arise because of their good adhesive power to

References, p. 136–137

a wide range of materials, low moisture permeability, and resistance to acids, salts, and dilute alkalis.

Another group of polymers based on the unit (LXX) was obtained by reacting phenylphosphonic dichloride with dihydric phenols, for example, hydroquinone. The reaction, for which magnesium chloride may be used as a catalyst, proceeded with the evolution of hydrogen chloride. Two reaction routes (A and B, above) are possible.

All polymers of this type are flame-resistant[57].

(iv) Phosphonitrilic imide and derivatives

Polymers not containing oxygen may be obtained by reactions involving other phosphorus halides, such as phosphorus pentachloride.

In 1811, Sir Humphrey Davy heated phosphorus pentachloride with ammonia at about 400°. A substance named "phospham", of empirical formula PN_2H was obtained, together with ammonium chloride. Thus "phospham", now known as phosphonitrilic imide, is a compound which has long been known; it is polymeric and extremely inert.

This reaction merits examination in greater detail. It is clear that phosphorus pentachloride and ammonia (or ammonium chloride, which may function as a source of ammonia) do not react

$$NH_3 + [\overset{+}{P}Cl_4]\,[\overset{-}{P}Cl_6] \longrightarrow HCl + [H_2N\overset{+}{P}Cl_3]\,[\overset{-}{P}Cl_6]$$

$$\downarrow$$

$$NPCl_2 \xleftarrow{-HCl} HN{=}PCl_3 + \overset{+}{H} + [\overset{-}{P}Cl_6]$$

$$\nearrow_{-2PCl_5} \qquad \nwarrow^{-2PCl_5} \qquad \downarrow + PCl_5$$

$$[Cl_3\overset{+}{P}{-}N{=}PCl_2{-}N{=}PCl_3]\overset{-}{P}Cl_6 \xleftarrow[-HCl]{+HN=PCl_3} [Cl_3\overset{+}{P}{-}N{=}PCl_3]\,[\overset{-}{P}Cl_6] + 2\,HCl$$

to form phosphonitrilic imide in a single step. Apparently phosphonitrilic chlorides are involved (see also Chapter 4).

Under mild conditions, phosphorus pentachloride is said to react with ammonia, so that two hydrogen atoms of the ammonia are substituted by the $>PCl_3$ group. It seems certain that this occurs by an ionic mechanism. The action of an excess of phosphorus pentachloride produces the chloride P_3NCl_{12}[58]. Further action of phosphorus pentachloride and ammonia forms another chloride, $P_4N_2Cl_{14}$. Phosphonitrilic chloride is then formed by elimination of phosphorus pentachloride from this material. If phosphorus pentachloride, in excess, is allowed to react with ammonia at higher temperatures, only phosphonitrilic chlorides are produced, whereas at lower temperatures P_3NCl_{12} is the main product.

The procedure for the preparation of phosphonitrilic chlorides has been improved[58a].

$$n\,PCl_5 + n\,NH_4Cl \xrightarrow{150\text{–}200°} (NPCl_2)_n + 4n\,HCl$$

Phosphonitrilic chlorides of various degrees of polymerisation are obtained by this method (see Chapter 4), but the crystalline trimer and tetramer predominate. Oily phosphonitrilic chlorides, with a degree of polymerisation of the order of eleven, and gums, waxes, and so-called inorganic rubbers with a high degree of polymerisation can also be obtained. It is believed that in the reaction with an excess of ammonia, the phosphonitrilic chlorides are amidated, and that upon heating to 300° the resulting phosphonitrilic diamides, $[NP(NH_2)_2]_n$, condensation to phosphonitrilic imides (such as LXXIII and LXXIV) takes place. The reaction intermediates for each of the proposed steps have now been isolated[59]. The amides (LXXI) and (LXXII) were prepared by careful amidation in benzene of trimeric and tetrameric phosphonitrilic chlorides, in the presence of an ammonia acceptor, such as hydrogen chloride[60].

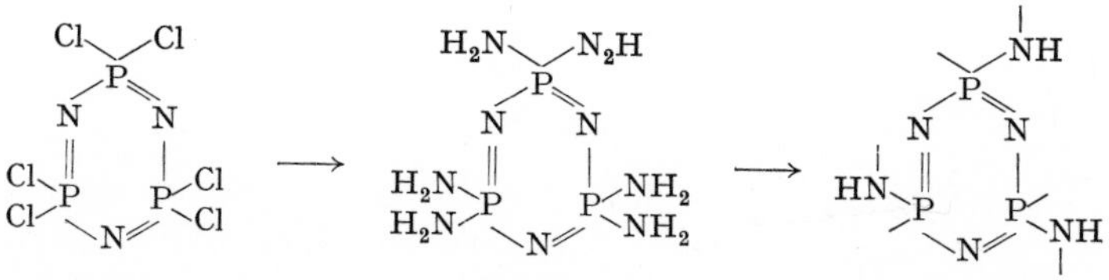

(LXXI)

(LXXIII)

References, p. 136–137

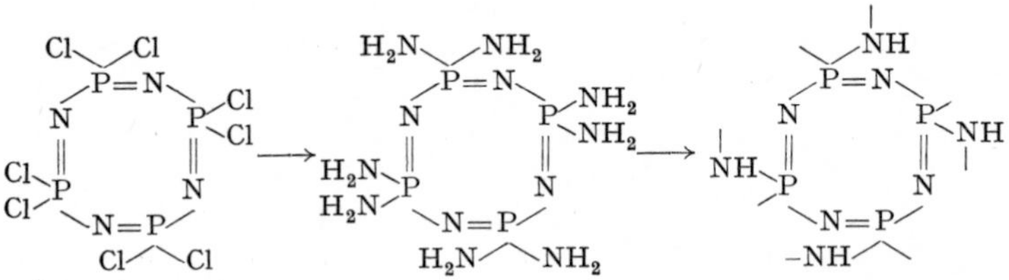

```
   Cl   Cl                 H2N   NH2                      NH
     P=N                     P=N                         P=N
   N     P-Cl              N     P-NH2                 N     P-NH
   ||    | Cl    ---->     ||    || NH2    ---->    NH-P     ||
Cl-P     N            H2N-P      N                   |       N
Cl   N=P              H2N   N=P                        N=P
   Cl   Cl                H2N   NH2                 -NH
                         (LXXII)                     (LXXIV)
```

It appears that the properties of the phosphonitrilic imides are largely dependent upon the condensation temperature. When the reaction was carried out using hydrogen chloride at $-80°$, ammonium chloride was formed together with a product which was very readily soluble in water. An attempt to sublime the ammonium chloride out of this product led merely to the phosphonitrilic imide becoming insoluble and exhibiting typical inertness. If, on the other hand, the reaction was carried out at about 150°, the product could be separated from ammonium chloride by extracting with liquid ammonia. It was no longer soluble in water and had an empirical formula NPNH. However, treatment with water at 50° led to hydrolysis and the production of phosphamide, $HNP(O)NH_2$. When condensation was carried out at still higher temperatures the product was not only insoluble in water, but also not hydrolysed.

It is believed that in the reaction with ammonia, the ring systems of the phosphonitrilic chlorides remain intact, that the amides then condense, and that no low-molecular-weight ring systems arise.

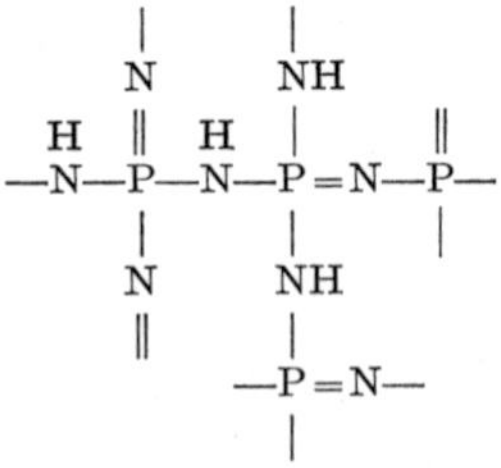

```
        |     |
        N     NH
   H    ||  H |      ||
  —N—P—N—P=N—P—
        |     |      |
        N     NH
        ||    |
            —P=N—
              |
```

(LXXV)

The reactivity of the phosphonitrilic imide depends upon its degree of polymerisation. The skeletal structure of the original constituents units, (LXXIII) and (LXXIV), should remain intact, at least in the low-temperature products, but the number of these units is variable. Various possibilities for cross-linking exist, such as shown in (LXXV)[61].

Polymeric cross-linked substances, with the structural unit (LXXVI), which resemble phosphonitrilic imide in some degree, have also been obtained[62].

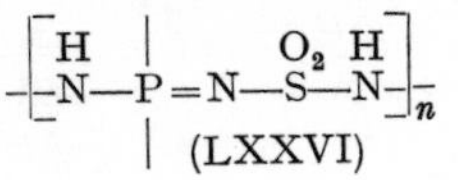

```
 ┌H   |      O2 H┐
─┤N—P=N—S—N├─
 └    |          ┘n
      |  (LXXVI)
```

All these products are non-inflammable.

(v) Polymers with phosphorus in a lower oxidation state

In the reaction of phosphorus trichloride and ammonia, polymeric HN=P—NH_2 and PN were readily formed[63]. When dialkylamino-phosphorus dichlorides were reacted with ammonia, similar polymeric substances were also produced. These can be formulated as shown in (LXXVII).

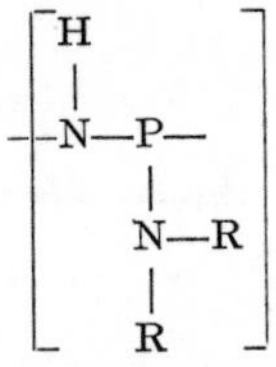

```
 ┌H        ┐         ┌H         ┐
 │|        │         │|  |_     │
─┤N—P—     │        ─┤N—P—      │
 │   |     │         │   |+     │
 │   N—R   │         │ —N—R     │
 │   |     │         │   |      │
 └   R     ┘         └   R      ┘
 (LXXVII)            (LXXVIII)
```

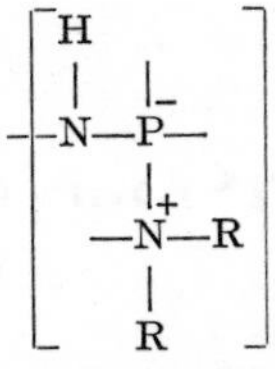

However, they may be substances in which phosphorus possesses the co-ordination number four (LXXVIII). All these substances containing phosphorus in the oxidation state +3 are unstable. They decompose in moist air, releasing phosphine, PH_3.

In this review no attempt has been made to cover exhaustively the literature concerning polymeric sulphur and phosphorus compounds. Further details will be found in the cited references. The work discussed should give a good impression of the substantial effort already put into this field and also of some of the many remaining problems.

References, p. 136–137

REFERENCES

[1] D. P. Craig, *Chem. Soc. Spec. Publ.*, 12 (1958) 343.

[2] G. Gee, *Science Progress*, 170 (1955) 193, *Chem. Soc. Spec. Publ.*, 12 (1958) 247.

[3] P. W. Schenk and K. Thümmler, *Z. Elektrochem.*, 63 (1959) 1002.

[4] D. M. Gardner and G. K. Fraenkel, *J. Am. Chem. Soc.*, 76 (1954) 5891; 78 (1956) 3279.

[5] J. Donohue and A. Caron, *J. Polymer Sci.*, 50 (1961) 17.

[6] J. Donohue, A. Caron and E. Goldish, *Nature*, 182 (1958) 518.

[7] M. Becke-Goehring, *Advances in Inorganic Chemistry and Radiochemistry*, Eds. H. J. Emeléus and A. G. Sharpe, Vol. 2, Academic Press, New York, 1960, p. 159.

[8] J. Weiss, *Z. anorg. Chem.*, 305 (1960) 190.

[9] E. W. Lund and S. R. Svendsen, *Acta Chem. Scand.*, 11 (1957) 940.
R. L. Sass and J. Donohue, *Acta Cryst.*, 11 (1958) 497.

[10] M. Becke-Goehring, *Progress in Inorganic Chemistry*, Ed. F. A. Cotton, Vol. 1, Interscience Publishers, New York, 1959, p. 207.

[11] D. Clark, *J. Chem. Soc.*, (1952) 1615.

[12] M. Goehring and D. Voigt, *Naturwiss.*, 40 (1953) 482; *Z. anorg. Chem.*, 285(1956) 181.

[13] B. D. Stone and M. L. Nielsen, *J. Am. Chem. Soc.*, 81 (1959) 3580.

[14] M. Becke-Goehring and S. Saliba, unpublished work.

[15] P. W. Schenk, *Chem. Ber.*, 75 (1942) 94.

[16] Houben-Weyl, *Methoden der Organischen Chemie*, Vol. XI/2, Georg Thieme Verlag, Stuttgart, 1958, p. 738.

[17] M. Goehring and G. Voigt, *Chem. Ber.*, 89 (1956) 1050.

[18] M. Goehring and J. Messner, *Z. anorg. Chem.*, 268 (1952) 47.
M. Becke-Goehring, R. Schwarz and W. Spiess, *Z. anorg. Chem.*, 293 (1957) 294. 18a F. Seel u G. Simon Angew. Chem. 72 (1960) 709

[19] E. Fluck and M. Becke-Goehring, *Z. anorg. Chem.*, 292 (1957) 229.

[20] W. Muthmann and E. Seitter, *Chem. Ber.*, 30 (1897) 627.

[21] See Ref. 7, p. 175.

[22] A.V. Kirsanov, *Izvest. Akad. Nauk S.S.S.R., Otdel. Khim. Nauk*, (1950) 426.
A. V. Kirsanov, *Zhur. Obshcheĭ Khim.*, 22 (1952) 81.
M. Goehring, J. Heinke, H. Malz and G. Roos, *Z. anorg. Chem.*, 273 (1953) 200.
M. Goehring and H. Malz, *Z. Naturforsch.*, 9b (1954) 567.

[23] M. Becke-Goehring and G. Fries, unpublished work.

[24] R. Appel and H. Gerber, *Angew. Chem.*, 70 (1958) 271.

[25] R. Graf, *German Patent*, 940,351 (1956).

[26] R. Graf, *Chem. Ber.*, 89 (1956) 1071.

[27] R. Appel and H. Gerber, *Chem. Ber.*, 91 (1958) 1200.

[28] H. Gerber, *Dissertation*, Heidelberg, 1960.

[29] F. L. Scott and H. O. Smith, *136th Meeting American Chemical Society*, New Jersey, Sept. 1959, p. 21N.

[30] A. M. Paquin, *Angew. Chem.*, A 60 (1948) 316.

[31] G. Hecht and H. Hennecka, *Angew. Chem.*, 61 (1949) 365.

[32] A. V. Kirsanov and Yu. M. Zolotov, *Zhur. obshcheĭ Khim.*, 20 (1950) 1790.

[33] H. A. Walter, *U.S.P.*, 2,449,520 (1948).

[34] W. TRAUBE, *Chem. Ber.*, 25 (1892) 2472.
G. HEINZE and A. MEUWSEN, *Z. anorg. Chem.*, 275 (1954) 49.
[35] H. HANTZSCH and A. HOLL, *Chem. Ber.*, 34 (1901) 3430.
[36] R. APPEL and M. GOEHRING, *Z. anorg. Chem.*, 271 (1953) 171.
[37] D. E. C. CORBRIDGE, *Acta Cryst.*, 9 (1956) 308.
[37a] R. WESTRIK and C. H. MACGILLAVRY, *Acta Cryst.*, 7 (1954) 764.
[38] J. R. VAN WAZER, *Phosphorus and its Compounds*, Vol. 1, Interscience Publishers, New York, 1958.
[39] E. THILO, *Angew. Chem.*, 63 (1951) 508; *Chem. Tech. (Berlin)*, 4 (1952) 345; *Angew. Chem.*, 67 (1955) 141; *Chem. Tech. (Berlin)*, 10 (1958) 70.
[39a] E. THILO, *Chem. Tech. (Berlin)*, 8 (1956) 251.
[39b] R. RÄTZ and E. THILO, *Ann.*, 572 (1951) 173.
E. THILO and H. WOGGON, *Z. anorg. Chem.*, 277 (1954) 17.
[40] E. THILO and W. WIEKER, *Z. anorg. Chem.*, 277 (1954) 27.
[41] E. THILO, *Forsch. u. Fortschr.*, 26 (1950) 284; Ref. 38, p. 607.
[42] See, for example, E. THILO, *Silikat Tech.*, 6 (1955) 278; *Forsch. u. Fortschr.*, 29 (1955) 161; *Chem. Tech. (Berlin)*, 10 (1958) 70.
[43] A survey is given in Ref. 38, p. 796.
[44] K. PLIETH and C. W. WURSTER, *Z. anorg. Chem.*, 267 (1951) 49.
K. DORNBERGER-SCHIFF, F. LIEBAU and E. THILO, *Acta Cryst.*, 8 (1955) 752.
[45] M. GOEHRING and J. SAMBETH, *Chem. Ber.*, 90 (1957) 232.
[45a] R. KLEMENT and R. POPP, *Chem. Ber.*, 93 (1960) 156.
[46] M. BECKE-GOEHRING and J. SAMBETH, *Z. anorg. Chem.*, 297 (1958) 287. Further references are listed there.
[47] M. GOEHRING and K. NIEDENZU, *Chem. Ber.*, 89 (1956) 1771.
R. KLEMENT and L. BENEK, *Z. anorg. Chem.*, 287 (1956) 12.
[48] R. KLEMENT and O. KOCH, *Chem. Ber.*, 87 (1954) 333.
[49] M. GOEHRING and K. NIEDENZU, *Chem. Ber.*, 89 (1956) 1771.
J. TRUHLAR and A. A. PANTSIOS, *U.S.P.* 2,528,181 (1952).
[50] J. E. MALOWAN and F. R. HURLEY, *U.S.P.* 2,596,935 (1952).
[51] J. TRUHLAR and A. A. PANTSIOS, *U.S.P.* 2,582,181 (1952).
J. E. MALOWAN, *U.S.P.* 2,661,264 (1953).
[52] P. R. BLOOMFIELD, *Symposium on High Temperature Resistance and Thermal Degradation of Polymers*, London, 1960; S.C.I. Monograph No. 13, London, 1961, p. 89.
[53] H. W. COOVER, R. L. MCCONNELL and N. H. SHEARER, *Ind. Eng. Chem.*, 52 (1960) 412.
[54] M. L. NIELSEN, personal communication.
[55] A. C. HAVEN, *U.S. P.* 2,716,639 (1955).
[56] See H. ZENFTMAN and H. R. WRIGHT, *Brit. Plastics*, 25 (1952) 374.
[57] H. W. COOVER, R. L. MCCONNELL and M. A. MCCALL, *Ind. Eng. Chem.*, 52 (1960) 409.
[58] M. BECKE-GOEHRING and W. LEHR, unpublished work.
[58a] H. N. STOKES, *Am. Chem. J.*, 19 (1897) 782.
[59] L. F. AUDRIETH, *17th IUPAC Congress*, Munich, 1959.
[60] M. GOEHRING, *German Patent* 1,015,777 (1956).
[61] E. STEGER, *Angew. Chem.*, 69 (1957) 145.
[62] TH. MANN, *Dissertation*, Heidelberg, 1960.
[63] M. BECKE-GOEHRING and J. SCHULZE, *Chem. Ber.*, 91 (1958) 1188.

Chapter 6

Some Recent Advances in Silicone Chemistry

by

J. S. HUGHES

1. Introduction

The field of silicone chemistry and technology is of ever increasing importance in scope, both commercially and in the volume of publications appearing. The purpose of this review is to indicate how recent research has led to significant progress in process methods and in product and application development. Examples are also given to illustrate the growing intensity of research in the realm of organosilicon and silicone chemistry. The period covered is that of approximately four years up to July 1960, but only selected topics, consistent with the previously stated purpose, are discussed.

It may be as well for those as yet unfamiliar with the silicones to outline very briefly the basic structure, preparation, and properties of this group of compounds. This has been expanded later where it has been felt necessary to clarify the purpose of some of the work. Details of the processes, properties, etc., are adequately described elsewhere[1–5].

2. Structure, preparation, and properties of silicones

Chemically, silicones are based on the siloxane structure and may have the following general linear or cross-linked formulae:

```
   R       R       R
   |       |       |
 —Si—O—Si—O—Si—O—
   |       |       |
   R       R       R
```

```
   |       |
 —Si—O—Si—O—
   |       |
   O       O
R  |       |  R
  >Si      Si<
R  |       |  R
   O       O       R
   |       |       |
 —Si—O—Si—O—Si—O—
   |       |       |
   R       R
```

where R may be a monovalent hydrocarbon group (such as alkyl, alkenyl, or aryl) or a functional group (such as methoxy, ethoxy, hydroxy, or hydrogen). The linear siloxanes are fluids varying from a viscosity of 0.65 cS (mol. weight, 162) to a gum (mol. weight, 2,000,000). The branched-chain siloxanes are fluids (in the simplest cases) or complex resinous solids of varying degrees of brittleness.

The Si—O—Si link is made by the hydrolysis of the chlorine compounds of silicon, the chlorosilane sometimes being dissolved in an organic solvent, such as toluene, to effect separation of the hydrolysis product.

```
     R              R               R      R
     |              |               |      |
Cl—Si—Cl  ——→  HO—Si—OH  ——→  HO—Si—O—Si—
     |              |               |      |
     R              R               R      R
```

The alkyl or aryl chlorine compounds of silicon are prepared by passing the corresponding alkyl or aryl chloride over silicon at 200—300°. Alternatively, the Grignard reagent of the alkyl or aryl chloride may be reacted with silicon tetrachloride.

References, p. 159–161

$$Si + 2RCl \longrightarrow R_2SiCl_2$$

$$SiCl_4 + 2RMgCl \longrightarrow R_2SiCl_2 + 2MgCl_2$$

In practice, a variety of substituted chlorosilanes are produced by both these methods, so that an essential preparative step is that of high fractionation[6]. The purified intermediates are then mixed as required and the mixture hydrolysed and/or polymerised to yield the desired fluid, resin, or rubber gum.

The commercially-available silicones, usually methyl- or phenyl-substituted siloxanes, have five properties, (a)–(e), which make them widely applicable in a large number of industries.

(a) They possess heat stability and they maintain their particular physical properties over a wide range of temperature (—70° to 250° or even 300°.) Thus the rubbers remain flexible over this temperature range.

(b) They are resistant to oxidation and exhibit general chemical inertness.

(c) They exhibit water-repellency. This is due in part to their ability to bond themselves to a wide range of materials so that the water-shedding alkyl groups are exposed.

(d) They have excellent dielectric properties.

(e) They exhibit certain specific surface-active effects that give rise to applications such as antifoaming. Also of interest is their ability to release certain materials such as rubber from metal moulds, their adhesion to other substrates, and their use in polishes.

Phenyl groups, partly because of their innate heat-stability and partly because of the ionic character of the silicon–phenyl bond, have an effect on the heat stability of the siloxanes similar in magnitude to that of methyl groups. As it was their heat stability that first attracted attention to the silicones, it is not surprising that the most commonly encountered silicones are methyl- and phenyl-substituted siloxanes.

As the alkyl group increases in size to ethyl, propyl, etc., or as substituent groups are introduced on the phenyl nucleus, the Si—R bond becomes more polar. The heat-stability of the compound is decreased and the Si—R bond becomes more susceptible to attack by acids, alkalis, and other nucleophilic or electrophilic agents. However, heat-stability is not necessarily the only one of the five properties to be considered. For example, water-repellency, the ability to adhere to a variety of surfaces, specific surface-activity, or the dielectric properties may be of prime importance. A large research effort has, therefore, been applied in the recent past to the preparation and examination of compounds containing organo-functional and more polar substituent groups. These compounds are usually known as "carbon functional silicones". They are either used unmodified for specific applications or they are used to prepare copolymers with organic materials, where the benefits of "both worlds" are required.

3. Production of chlorosilane intermediates

Before considering the advances that have been made in the silicone products themselves, some developments and improvements in the processes used to produce the chlorosilane intermediates will be discussed. Some of these have only been used on the laboratory-scale, but they serve to show how silicone research has been directed to the improvement of the primary processes.

It has already been mentioned that phenylchlorosilanes are prepared by the reaction of chlorobenzene and silicon or silicon tetrachloride. Another route to these intermediates is by reaction of trichlorosilane and benzene in the presence of suitable catalysts, *e.g.*, boron compounds[7]. Moderately high temperatures (300°) and pressures (1,000 p.s.i.—the autogenous pressure) are used.

$$SiHCl_3 + C_6H_6 \rightleftharpoons C_6H_5SiCl_3 + H_2$$

This reaction is most useful for the preparation of the substituted phenylchlorosilanes, *e.g.*, tolyltrichlorosilane and diphenylyltrichlorosilane (xenyltrichlorosilane). These compounds may also be prepared by the reaction of the chlorophenyl derivative and trichlorosilane.

$$Cl{\cdot}C_6H_4{\cdot}CH_3 + 2\ SiHCl_3 \rightleftharpoons CH_3C_6H_4{\cdot}SiCl_3 + SiCl_4 + H_2$$

References, p. 159–161

There are a number of isomers produced by this type of reaction and of interest to the kineticist is the proposition that this reaction proceeds via a siliconium ion.

The reaction between trichlorosilane and benzene may be represented as an H—Si≡ addition to a double bond of the benzene ring, under the influence of boron trichloride as a catalyst.

$$C_6H_6 + HSiCl_3 \xrightarrow{BCl_3} \left[\text{(H)(H)}C_6H_4\text{(SiCl}_3\text{)(H)} \right] \longrightarrow \begin{cases} H_2 + PhSiCl_3 \\ HSiCl_3 + C_6H_6 \end{cases}$$

The reactivity of the hydrogen atom attached to silicon has also been utilised in two other ways.

The first, a major advance in synthetic organosilicon chemistry, was the discovery of the addition between olefinic hydrocarbons and compounds containing silicon–hydrogen bonds. Commercial applications of this reaction are given later, but the range of the utility of the reaction may be judged from the type of olefins that will take part in the reaction:

$$\equiv Si{-}H + CH_2{=}CH{\cdot}X \longrightarrow \equiv SiCH_2CH_2{\cdot}X$$

Acetylene, ethylene, propylene, butylene, halogeno- and cyano-alkenes, styrene, and α-methylstyrene are examples of unsaturated compounds that have been used successfully. Many substituted ethylenes are not reactive, possibly because the addition product itself is relatively unstable. Silanes and siloxanes containing ≡Si—H may be used. Platinum is the usual catalyst recommended[8–10], but amines, iron pentacarbonyl[11], chromic chloride, and tungsten hexachloride are among a long list of others used.

Another useful reaction of an ≡Si—H group, especially on the laboratory-scale, is that with a Grignard reagent in tetrahydrofuran[12]. The oversubstitution difficulties encountered when the chlorides are used are obviated. The reactivity of an ≡Si—H group in the presence of a Grignard reagent decreases with increasing alkyl, aryl, or alkaryl substitution on the silicon atom. Thus, the

$\equiv$Si—H group in phenylsilane will react more easily than that in triphenylsilane. Grignard reagents in tetrahydrofuran are more reactive with $\equiv$Si—H groups than in ethereal solution. The metallic alkyls (*e.g.*, phenylsodium, lithium alkyls) are powerful substituting agents. Thus, by suitable choice of solvent and reagent, specific substitution can be achieved.

$$PhSiH_3 + RMgX \xrightarrow{THF} PhRSiH_2$$

$$PhRSiH_2 + R'MgX \xrightarrow{THF} PhRR'SiH$$

$$PhRR'SiH + R''Li \xrightarrow{Ether} PhRR'R''Si$$

The reaction with alkylsilanes is slower than that with phenylsilanes.

One manufacturing problem is that the primary reactions mentioned above often do not produce the chlorosilanes in the ratio required by the silicone manufacturer. Of interest, therefore, is the use of metal halogenoaluminates, $MAlX_4$[13,14], or aluminium chloride and a silicon-bonded hydrogen silane as catalysts[15] in the disproportionation reaction:

$$R_3SiCl + RSiCl_3 \rightleftharpoons 2R_2SiCl_2$$

Temperatures of 250–350° are usually necessary. The relative intermolecular migratory power in this reaction is in the order $H > C_6H_5 > C_2H_5$. It is possible, therefore, that the mechanism of the reaction is by virtue of nucleophilic attack on the silicon atom and electrophilic attack on the hydrogen or carbon atom.

Another manufacturing difficulty is the production of polysilanes in the silicon/methyl chloride reaction. These polysilanes may, however, be reacted with hydrogen chloride to produce useful monomers.

$$R_2ClSi—SiClR_2 \xrightarrow{HCl} R_2ClSiH + R_2SiCl_2$$

Alternatively, the polysilanes may be refluxed with quaternary ammonium or quaternary phosphonium compounds[16].

Other methods of making halogenosilanes are always worthy of

References, p. 159–161

research effort and among recent interesting published work is an account of the reaction of alkyl halides, aluminium alkyls, and silica[17]. Silica is, of course, one of the most commonly occurring minerals. Another readily available silicon compound is silicon tetrafluoride, which is the by-product of many industrial processes. Chlorofluorosilanes have been made by reaction of:

(a) silicon, silicon tetrafluoride, and hydrogen chloride at 385–525°[18]; and

(b) silicon, silicon tetrafluoride, and an alkyl chloride.

These chlorofluorosilanes have been suggested as intermediates for siloxane manufacture. A disadvantage, however, is that the silicon–fluorine bond is very resistant to hydrolysis.

4. Thermal properties of silicones

Reference has already been made to the heat-stability of the silicones. Generally speaking, they have a satisfactory life at 250° and are capable of intermittent operation at 300°. There is an increasing interest in the preparation of high-temperature polymers for application in high velocity aircraft, rockets, etc. Consequently, there has been much research activity, directed towards preparing "inorganic" polymers containing other elements such as boron, phosphorus, nitrogen, aluminium, silicon, etc. Concurrently, the silicone chemist has been trying to find out what happens when siloxanes degrade thermally[19–23]. Perhaps from this will arise silicones which are even more stable to heat.

In the absence of oxygen, and at temperatures greater than 350°, linear siloxanes fairly readily yield volatile cyclic materials, $(Me_2SiO)_{3-9}$. The analysis of both the starting materials and the by-products corresponds to Me_2SiO. In addition, there is an absence of a charred coloration from the product, thus suggesting the stability of the Si—C and C—H linkages at 350°. Branched-chain polysiloxanes indicate no Si—C cleavage at temperatures in excess of 400°, while tetramethylsilane is stable in the vapour phase above 600°. In the absence of oxygen, therefore, it appears that degradation occurs by cleavage of an Si—O bond. When a commercial silicone fluid is heated at temperatures in excess of 400°, there is a marked rise in the rate of weight loss until about 20% of the product has been lost, when the rate decreases. It has been suggested that this is due to ionic impurities in the fluid, 0.05% Ba, 0.01% Pb, and 0.005% Al being found. It has been proposed that the impurity metal atoms become concentrated in the shorter chains and the relative rate of volatilisation of impurities is greater than in the pure polymer.

$$-\overset{R}{\underset{R}{Si}}-O-M-O-\overset{R}{\underset{R}{Si}}- \longrightarrow -\overset{R}{\underset{R}{Si}}-O-\overset{+}{M} + \overset{-}{O}-\underset{(I)}{\overset{R}{\underset{R}{Si}}}-$$

$$\underset{(I)}{-O-\overset{R}{\underset{R}{Si}}-O-\overset{R}{\underset{R}{Si}}}\left\langle\begin{matrix}\overset{-}{O}-SiR_2\\ O-SiR_2\end{matrix}\right\rangle O \longrightarrow -O-\overset{R}{\underset{R}{Si}}-\overset{-}{O} + (R_2SiO)_3$$

Whatever the mechanism, the sensitivity of siloxanes to silicon–oxygen bond cleavage by ionic impurities has been confirmed.

The thermal stability of tetraphenylsilane in the presence of oxygen has been known for some time. Examination of polydimethylsiloxanes and polyphenylmethylsiloxanes under oxidative conditions has confirmed the greater stability of the silicon–phenyl bond relative to that of the silicon–methyl bond. Silicon–methyl cleavage occurs with subsequent cross-linking of the polymer under conditions in which no phenyl cleavage occurs, as viscosity measurements and infrared examination of the products show. This has been confirmed by oxygen absorption measurements of a phenylmethylsiloxane polymer. At 400° in the presence or absence of oxygen (at 300–700 mm pressure) a similar degradation occurred, with only a small amount of oxygen consumed.

The thermal degradation of a methylphenylsilicone resin has also been studied and the nett apparent activation energy for the degradation in air has been recorded as about 6 kcal lower than for the degradation reaction occurring *in vacuo*.

Summarising present knowledge, therefore, it may be said that:

References, p. 159–161

(a) the oxidative degradation reaction occurs at lower temperatures than the polymer rearrangement reaction;

(b) the phenylsiloxanes are more stable to oxidative degradation than the methylsiloxanes; and

(c) the polymer rearrangement reaction which takes place is very much dependent on the presence of ionic impurities.

These remarks apply to the pure polymers. In application, of course, other factors become important. For example, in a weight loss *versus* time study of a methylphenylsiloxane resin at 200°, a steady state was reached after about 50–60 hours. If the surface was then abraded with sand and the sample re-heated at 200°, a sharp increase in the weight loss occurred before a steady state was again reached[21]. Some factor associated with the physical state of the surface is obviously involved. In the case of silicone rubbers, it is even more difficult to interpret heat-stability data. Here, in addition to the physical state of the material, the complex nature of the compounded rubber is an important factor.

Various heat-stability additives have been suggested for extending the life of silicones at 250° under oxidative conditions. Among the additives which have been suggested are compounds of iron[24], phosphorus (phosphites)[25], tin, and cerium. Cerium is especially effective in the presence of a chelating compound such as disalicylalpropylenediamine[26]. Many of these have proved extremely useful in certain applications, but their mode of action is not known. As would be expected, these additives are less effective when used with the phenylmethylsiloxanes—the effectiveness decreasing with increasing phenyl content.

It has already been said that the silicon–oxygen bond is susceptible to attack by ionic reagents or impurities. This is a major factor in the thermal degradation of the silicones in non-oxidative conditions. However, it has been the practice to prepare the siloxane polymers by using polar reagents, either by acid hydrolysis of chlorosilanes and subsequent polymerisation:

$$R_2SiCl_2 \xrightarrow{HOH} R_2Si(OH)_2 \xrightarrow{HCl} (R_2SiO)_n$$

or by alkaline (or acid) cleavage and polymerisation of cyclic tetramer:

$$(R_2SiO)_4 \xrightarrow{KOH} HO(R_2SiO)_4K \longrightarrow (R_2SiO)_n$$

In either case, low-molecular-weight siloxanes (cyclic and linear) remain in equilibrium with the polymer. If the polymerisation catalyst is left in the polymer and the polymer heated under conditions in which the low-molecular-weight fraction is removed (the cyclic tetramer boils at 160–170°) then the high polymer degrades. It is essential, therefore, to remove the ionic catalysts and this has been done by washing, neutralisation, or deactivation and filtration.

More recently, however, the use of "transient" catalysts has been recommended[27]. The operating principle of these catalysts is that they are sufficiently active to cause polymerisation at, say, 100°, but when heated, to say, 150°, they decompose and are rendered inactive. Examples of suitable catalysts are quaternary ammonium and quaternary phosphonium bases. Tetramethylammonium hydroxide functions at 70–120° and is deactivated at 130°.

$$(CH_3)_4N \cdot OH \longrightarrow (CH_3)_3N + CH_3OH$$

Tetra-*n*-butylphosphonium hydroxide functions satisfactorily at 110° and is decomposed at 140°.

$$R_4P \cdot OH \longrightarrow R_3PO + RH$$

In order to make the quaternary bases more compatible, they can be converted into the silanolates.

$$4R_4POH + (Me_2SiO)_4 \longrightarrow 4R_4POSi(Me_2)OH$$

$$2R_4POSi(Me_2)OH \longrightarrow R_4POSi(Me_2)OSi(Me_2)OPR_4$$

The use of "transient" catalysts makes possible the development of continuous methods of polymerisation. After polymerisation in a coil (or jacketted pipe) the liquid is merely heated to a higher temperature in another coil to deactivate the catalyst. The equilibrium mixture is distilled to remove the volatile low-molecular-weight siloxanes and the high polymer is discharged continuously.

The silicone chemists and chemical engineers are continually

References, p. 159–161

looking for new methods of hydrolysis and polymerisation, so that more processes can be put on a continuous and fully-automated basis. Thus, aluminium alkyls, and metal hydroxides in polar solvents, have been suggested as catalysts to induce faster polymerisation[28]. All these efforts have resulted in a lowering of the world prices for silicones by about 25% in the last three to four years.

Considering now the siloxane products, it should be emphasised that when silicone resins, certain silicone fluids, and silicone rubbers are used, an essential part of the applicational technique to produce optimum physical properties is curing by heat treatment. The temperature of this cure is usually from 150 to 250°. Silicones could not, therefore, be used with heat-sensitive materials, or in locations where the use of these temperatures was not possible. The past years have seen the development of products requiring lower curing temperatures. The lines of investigation have involved the use of more reactive polymers or of active polymerisation catalysts. Results so far have been very encouraging and several products are now being marketed which can be cured without the application of any heat whatsoever.

Apart from these and other general types of research, development work has been directed to the preparation of products with improved properties, or for specific new applications, and there have also been extensive investigations of further uses for the wide range of siloxanes already available.

5. Silicone rubbers

Silicone rubbers consist of a mixture of a long-chain siloxane gum, an inorganic filler, and an oxidising agent such as benzoyl peroxide. The filler is introduced to obtain the required reinforcement and affects physical properties such as tensile strength, tear strength, and hardness. The object of the peroxide is to induce cross-linking of the siloxane molecules by oxidation of the alkyl side-chain when the "uncured" rubber is heated to 150–250°. The cross-linking imparts the "rubbery" texture to the finished product.

An obvious filler to use with siloxane gums is, of course, finely-divided silica. This is chemically inert, unaffected by heat and also, as a result of some bonding that takes place between the siloxane and the silica, has good reinforcing properties. This results in the production of rubbers of high tension strength. The control of this polymer/filler interaction has led to the development of silica fillers yielding rubbers of tensile strengths of 1500–2000 p.s.i. This should be compared with the 500–1000 p.s.i. of only a few years ago.

The polymer/silica filler interaction has, however, one serious disadvantage. It causes a phenomenon known as "structure". When the rubber is freshly-made it is quite soft and workable. However, after several days (or even hours), the uncured rubber gives all the appearance of being cured. It is hard and has high tensile strength. The material becomes difficult (if not impossible) to soften by milling. Many attempts have been made to reduce this tendency to "structure" by introducing various compounds into the rubber formulation. Examples are octamethylcyclotetrasiloxane, hydroxylated siloxanes, or silanes[29], and hydroxylated carbon compounds, such as pinacol[30, 31]. Alternatively, the silica filler has been treated with different compounds. Silanes, silicates and, even, sulphur dioxide gas have been suggested. The mode of action of the various treatments is not fully understood. It seems likely that it is due to many factors, among which is the reaction of the additive with free hydroxyl groups on the silica, which thus limits the interaction with the siloxane polymer. In other cases, the formation of a physical barrier after thorough wetting of the filler is a possible explanation.

There have been two outstanding advances in the rubber field in recent years. Firstly, the curing temperature has been reduced, so that there are two basic types of rubber which cure at room temperature, and, secondly, oil and solvent resistant rubbers have been developed.

In the first type of cold-curing rubber, a catalyst is mixed with the polymer/filler mixture, the fluid product is then applied in the required manner and allowed to stand for periods which may be varied from a few minutes to many hours to achieve the cure. The fundamental cross-linking reaction involved is between hy-

References, p. 159–161

droxyl groups on the polymer and alkoxyl groups on a cross-linking agent:

$$\equiv Si—OH + RO—\overset{|}{\underset{|}{Si}}—OR + HO—Si\equiv$$

$$\longrightarrow \equiv Si—O—\overset{|}{\underset{|}{Si}}—O—Si\equiv + 2ROH$$

Organotin compounds or a wide variety of other compounds can be used as catalysts to aid reaction[32, 33, 34].

A compound containing a silicon–hydrogen bond may also be introduced to increase the rate of cure. In this case, hydrogen is one of the products of the reaction.

The second type of cold-curing rubber is that which is kept in an enclosed container, such as a tube. When the uncured material is exposed to the air, curing takes place as a result of hydrolysis of acyloxysilicon groups by atmospheric moisture. The reaction involved here is:

$$\equiv Si—O\cdot COR + H\cdot OH \longrightarrow \equiv Si—OH$$

This hydroxyl group is then available for cross-linking[35, 36]. Alternatively, the acyloxysilicon compound can be used to cross-link polymers on the same principle as explained earlier for the alkoxy-type cross-linking agent.

The "cold-curing" rubbers have opened up many new fields of application and they are used as sealants, potting compounds, and for making rubber moulds. Modification of these basic reactions enable rubbers that cure at temperatures intermediate between 25° and 150° to be made.

The second significant advance in the rubber field is that of the development of solvent-resistant and oil-resistant rubbers.[37–40] The alkyl- and aralkyl-siloxanes are swollen by aromatic and aliphatic hydrocarbons. If, however, the side-chain is modified so that it contains a perfluoroalkyl or cyanoalkyl group, then the solvent- and oil-resistance is greatly increased. This is one important application of the "carbon functional" research referred to earlier.

It has been made possible by the use of the established Grignard reaction, and also by the discovery of the addition reaction that takes place between olefinic compounds and siloxanes or silanes containing an $\equiv$Si—H group. Various catalysts such as dialkyl-cyanamides (R_2N—CN), "hindered" trisubstituted phenols, platinum, and alkylphosphorus halides have been recommended. The basic reaction is:

$$R(Cl_2)SiH + CH_2 = CH(CH_2)_nCN \longrightarrow R(Cl_2)\cdot SiCH_2CH_2(CH_2)_nCN$$

$$R(Cl_2)SiH + CH_2 = CH(CH_2)_nCF_3 \longrightarrow R(Cl_2)\cdot SiCH_2CH_2(CH_2)_nCF_3$$

or

$$R(Cl_2)SiCl + ClMg\cdot CH_2(CH_2)_nCN \longrightarrow R(Cl_2)SiCH_2(CH_2)_nCN$$

The chlorides are hydrolysed and polymerised according to the standard techniques.

The —CN and —CF_3 intermediates are made as follows:

$$CH_2{=}CH_2 \xrightarrow{HOCl} HO\cdot CH_2CH_2Cl \xrightarrow{KCN}$$
$$HO\cdot CH_2CH_2CN \xrightarrow{HCl} Cl\cdot CH_2CH_2CN$$

$$CF_2Br_2 + CH_2{=}CH_2 \longrightarrow CF_2Br\cdot CH_2CH_2Br \xrightarrow{HF}$$
$$CF_3CH_2\cdot CH_2.Br \xrightarrow{KOH} CF_3\cdot CH{=}CH_2$$

Silicones can now be used for gaskets and seals where resistance to solvents and oils at temperatures of up to 250° is required. Other developments in the rubber field have been the preparation of flame-resistant rubbers, of more easily processed stocks, of stocks for roller covering, and of an interesting self-adhering rubber tape[41].

6. Silicone fluids

The silicone fluids are usually linear polysiloxanes. They are inert materials that have found application as polish additives, dielectrics, liquid springs, high temperature lubricants, antifoaming compounds, textile treatments, etc. Perhaps the most disappointing

References, p. 159–161

aspect of the application of these fluids is their poor metal/metal lubrication when under heavy load. It has been said that this is due primarily to the poor adherence of the silicone film to the metal under these conditions. Successful attempts have been made to improve the lubricity by the introduction of polar side groups on the siloxane chain. Chlorophenyl groups have been so used. It is also possible that these chlorophenylsiloxanes function by virtue of the increased cohesion that occurs between the silicone molecules.

Of interest is the use of extreme pressure additives such as tricresyl phosphate and dialkyl acid phosphites[42]. The improvement conferred on the ester-type lubricants is well known. The extreme pressure (E.P.) additives also improve the lubrication properties of silicones. It is significant that they improve the properties of the chlorophenylsiloxanes more than those of the dialkyl- and dialkaryl-siloxanes.

Reference has already been made to the use of cerium soaps and chelating compounds to increase the oxidative resistance of the bulk fluid. Advances of this type are of significance in hydrodynamic lubrication.

Another method of improving the lubricating properties of silicones is to use organometallic additives, such as tetraethyllead, (methylcyclopentadienyl)manganese tricarbonyl, and di-*n*-butyltin sulphide. The additives are considered effective in boundary lubrication because of their thermal breakdown during rubbing which produces a compound with the metal surface. Alternatively, a film may be deposited on the surface. Of the three compounds mentioned, dibutyltin sulphide (5%) was the most effective in reducing wear in a four-ball tester over the 1–20 kg range[43].

Theories have been advanced to account for the relatively poor lubricity of silicones under heavy load, and although improvements have been made, much has yet to be done.

Allied to the lubricating application is the use of silicones and silicates as aviation hydraulic fluids and as heat-transfer fluids. Here alkoxy-groups attached to silicon atoms in a siloxane or in monosilane have the disadvantage of hydrolytic instability. This has been partially overcome by the use of tertiary alkoxy- or long-chain hydrocarbonoxy-groups attached to the silicon atom[44]. If one alkyl group is also introduced per silicon atom, the hydrolytic stability is further improved.

Siloxanes and silanes adhere very well to glass surfaces and the use of vinylsilane glass-cloth sizes has been known for some time. The silane adheres to the glass surface and presents the vinyl group for reaction with the organic resin which is to be used with the glass. In this way a firm bond is made, the silane acting as a linking agent from the glass to the organic resin. Two products containing functional side-groups based on a similar principle are recent introductions for the treatment of glass. One is employed to treat glass-fibre and glass-wool used for heat insulation. By this means, greater mechanical strength and moisture resistance are imparted to the insulation. The other product is employed as an "anchor" between the glass-cloth and dyes used in the manufacture of coloured curtains made from glass cloth.

Yet another application of silicones is as diffusion pump fluids. For this, a heat stable liquid is required with closely defined vapour pressure/temperature characteristics. A specific low-molecular-weight siloxane has been developed for this duty, pressures down to 2×10^{-6} mm mercury being obtained[45].

The siloxane used for the treatment of textiles relies on the formation of a resinous film on the fibre, as the result of the reaction of a polymethylsiloxane, $(MeSiHO)_n$. It is now known, as the result of gas evolution studies[46,47], that this proceeds by the base-catalysed reaction:

$$\equiv Si{-}H + H_2O \longrightarrow \equiv Si{-}OH + H_2$$

Condensation of two silanol groups or of one silanol group and a silicon-hydrogen group follows.

$$\equiv SiOH + \equiv SiOH \longrightarrow \equiv SiOSi \equiv + H_2O$$

$$\equiv SiOH + \equiv SiH \longrightarrow \equiv SiOSi \equiv + H_2$$

The reaction is catalysed by salts of metals such as tin, zinc, and lead with organic acids such as octanoic and oleic. Presumably, in the presence of water the salt is partially hydrolysed to a base which is effective as a catalyst. It is of interest that stannous octanoate,

References, p. 159–161

for example, differs in its effect from the octanoates of zinc and lead. The latter give rise to a smooth evolution of hydrogen, and gelation occurs after a volume of hydrogen, corresponding with one cross-link per polymer molecule, has been evolved. In the case of stannous octanoate, gelation occurs more rapidly, before, in fact, sufficient hydrogen corresponding with one cross-link per molecule has been evolved. Thereafter, the expected hydrogen evolution occurs. Further, stannous salts (but not those of zinc and lead) can cause gelation even under anhydrous conditions, although in this case there may have been some ≡Si—OH present on a polymer incompletely end-blocked with alkyl groups. It is evident from this, that stannous salts can act by a different mechanism from those of zinc, causing rapid formation of a solid siloxane. An interesting characteristic of both catalysts, however, is that they continue to promote the hydrolysis of ≡Si—H with slow formation of a more highly cross-linked film. This gives rise to a gradual increase in water-repellency when a fabric, freshly-treated with a polymethylsiloxane, is stored.

Reference has been made to the development of room-temperature-curing rubbers. Similar systems have been used in the textile field, wherever a treatment is required which does not need heat to produce the excellent water-repellent effect. One criticism levelled at the silicone treatment is that the water-repellency is not truly permanent, although it is "more permanent" than any other known water-repellent finish. A recent announcement has been made in the U.S.A. of a permanent treatment for cotton. This involves the preparation of a so-called "silicone alloy" by the reaction of tetravinylsilane and a siloxane containing silicon-bonded hydrogen[48]. Peroxide is used as a catalyst for the addition reaction. It is too early yet to assess the value of these claims.

As has been mentioned, the siloxane used for the treatment of textiles relies on the formation of a resinous film, by the hydrolysis of siloxanes containing silicon-bonded hydrogen.

$$\equiv\text{Si—H} \longrightarrow \equiv\text{Si—OH} \longrightarrow \equiv\text{Si—O—Si}\equiv$$

The same system is used in the treatment of paper to impart release properties when the paper is used with sugar confectionery, adhesives, bitumen, etc. In some conditions, the silicone film was found to "migrate" with loss of releasing efficiency. An investigation of the curing mechanism has led to the development of a faster and more complete curing system for this important field of application.

7. Silicone resins

The resins are solvent solutions of branched-chain siloxanes containing residual hydroxyl groups. The solutions are applied, for example, as paints or electrical varnishes. After solvent evaporation, the resin is heated so as to effect condensation of the residual hydroxyl groups to produce a cured resinous film.

In the resin field, too, attempts have been made to reduce the temperature and time of cure. One difficulty is that the cured resin has to withstand temperatures of up to 250°. Thus, if an "active" catalyst is introduced, it will tend to cause crazing of the film on prolonged exposure at high temperatures, due to the continuing condensation of silanol groups. However, catalysts, such as salts of indium and cerium, have been successfully used at curing temperatures of 150°, and these do not cause undue crazing of the film at 250°[49].

Reference has been made to the use of solvent as a carrier for the silicone resin. This is necessary because the resin, even before cure, is a solid, though often a "tacky" solid. The necessity of removing solvent, and the evolution of the water produced by the curing action, is disadvantageous in many systems, as, for example, when thick resinous casts are prepared. Here, a two-component system has been developed. This is sufficiently fluid for application without recourse to solvents, and there is no volatile by-product of the curing technique. The cross-linking system relies on the addition of silicon-bonded hydrogen groups to silicon-bonded vinyl groups[50].

$$\equiv \mathrm{Si{-}H} + \mathrm{CH_2{=}CH{-}Si}\equiv \longrightarrow \equiv \mathrm{Si{-}(CH_2)_2{-}Si}\equiv$$

The vinyl-group can be linked to a silicon atom in the resin–siloxane-polymer and the silicon-hydrogen grouping can be incorporated in the cross-linking agent.

References, p. 159–161

In some applications, a foamed resin structure, which will withstand temperatures of 250°, is needed. An example would be as an insulating pad between metal surfaces operating at high temperature, *e.g.*, in aircraft. A disadvantage of using conventional "blowing agents" is that the organic residue has a deleterious effect on the high-temperature stability. If, however, use is made of the reaction:

$$\equiv\text{Si—OH} + \equiv\text{Si—H} \longrightarrow \equiv\text{Si—O—Si}\equiv + H_2$$

a foamed structure results which does not suffer from this disadvantage. The reaction is catalysed by metallic hydroxides, quaternary ammonium silanolates, and tin or lead carboxylates[51].

8. "Carbon functional" silicones and copolymers

Reference has been made to "carbon functional" silicones and in the rubber field two important results of this basic research have been given. Much use has been made of the silicon-hydrogen/olefin reaction and examples have been given to illustrate the very useful function of the ≡Si—H group in silicone research. It can be converted to ≡Si—Cl, ≡Si—OH, ≡Si—O—Si≡, ≡Si—Ar, and ≡Si—R very easily. Alkoxyl groups can also be substituted by reaction with compounds containing a carbonyl group.

$$\equiv\text{Si—H} + \begin{matrix}R\\R\end{matrix}\!\!>\!C{=}O \longrightarrow \equiv\text{Si—O—CHR}_2$$

Another useful starting-point for the preparation of "carbon functional" silicones is the chloromethylsilicon group, $\equiv$Si—CH_2Cl. This is made by controlled chlorination of $\equiv$Si—CH_3.

An excellent review of "carbon functionals" has been published[52]. Examples of the preparation of some "carbon functionals" are shown below. These "carbon functional" silicones are of use in their own right, or they may be used to make co-polymers with organic materials. Thus, co-polymers with a wide variety of organic resins are possible. Paint alkyds and solventless polyester-styrene copolymers have been made[53–60]. The resultant products are of a heat-stability intermediate between the organic and silicone components, but here again, heat-stability need not be the only property to consider.

Acrylates

$$\equiv Si{-}CH_2Cl \xrightarrow[\text{in presence of acid acceptors}]{\text{Sodium methacrylate}} \equiv Si{-}CH_2{\cdot}O{\cdot}CO.C(CH_3){=}CH_2$$

Epoxides

$$\equiv Si{-}H + \underset{\text{allyl glycidyl ether}}{H_2C{=}CH{\cdot}CH_2{\cdot}O{\cdot}CH_2{\cdot}\overset{O}{CH{\cdot}CH_2}} \xrightarrow{Pt}$$

$$\equiv Si{\cdot}CH_2{\cdot}CH_2{\cdot}CH_2{\cdot}O{\cdot}CH_2{\cdot}\overset{O}{CH{\cdot}CH_2}$$

Acids

$$\equiv Si{-}H + H_2C{=}C\,(Me){\cdot}CO{\cdot}OMe \longrightarrow \equiv Si{\cdot}CH_2{\cdot}CH(Me)CO{\cdot}OMe$$

Hydrolysis produces the acid

Esters and alcohols

$$\equiv Si{-}H + CH_2{=}CH{\cdot}CH_2OCOCH_3 \longrightarrow \equiv Si{-}CH_2{\cdot}CH_2{\cdot}CH_2OCOCH_3$$

Hydrolysis with sulphuric acid produces the alcohol

The paints find application because of their weather-resistance and use is made of the curing of the organic portion of the molecule to provide a cured resin film.

A recent introduction of a surfactant in the preparation of polyurethane-foamed rubbers is another example of the use of a silicone co-polymer with an organic molecule[61–63]. The first method used to make a polyurethane foam was termed the "prepolymer process". In this method, toluene di-isocyanate and a poly(glycol ether) [*e.g.*, poly(propylene glycol)] are reacted together (100–120°, 4–8 hr.) and allowed to stand. The polymer develops linearly:

$$HO{\sim\sim}OH + OCN{-}C_6H_3(CH_3)(NCO) + HO{\sim\sim}OH$$

$$\downarrow$$

$$HO{\sim\sim}O{\cdot}CO{\cdot}NH{-}C_6H_3(CH_3)(NH{\cdot}CO{\cdot}O{\sim\sim}OH)$$

References, p. 159–161

and also by cross–linking, via the reactive imide-group.

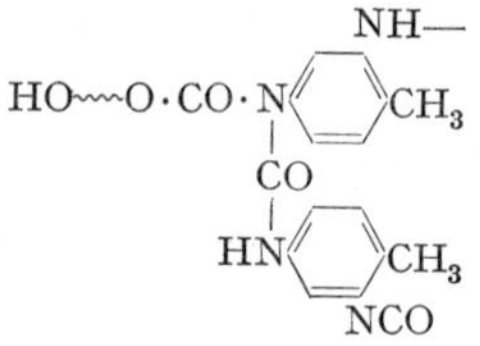

$$HO\sim\sim O\cdot CO\cdot N\text{-}C_6H_3(CH_3)\text{-}NH\text{—}$$
$$|$$
$$CO$$
$$|$$
$$HN\text{-}C_6H_3(CH_3)\text{-}NCO$$

The prepolymer consists of a cross-linked material with some free isocyanate groups. In application, the prepolymer is mixed with water in the presence of a tertiary nitrogen base, when carbon dioxide is produced and more cross-linking takes place.

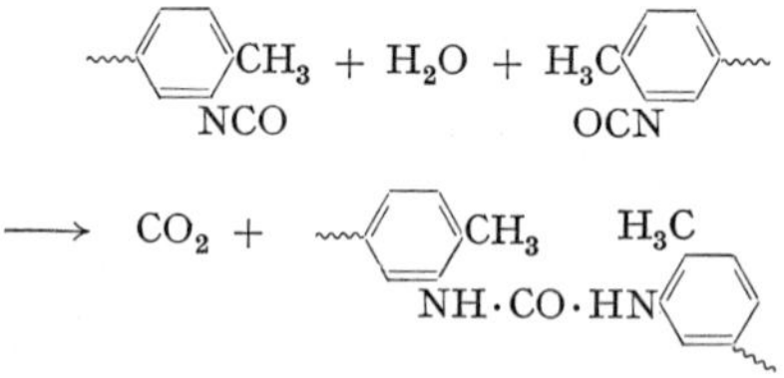

$$\sim C_6H_3(CH_3)(NCO) + H_2O + H_3C(OCN)C_6H_3\sim$$
$$\longrightarrow CO_2 + \sim C_6H_3(CH_3)\text{-}NH\cdot CO\cdot HN\text{-}C_6H_3(CH_3)\sim$$

The evolution of the carbon dioxide causes the bubbles in the foam, and a polydimethylsiloxane of about 50 cS (mol. weight about 3000) is used as foam stabiliser and pore size controller. The silicone acts possibly by virtue of its concentration at the water-amine/prepolymer interface, thus causing emulsification and also slowing down the rate of reaction.

A more recent method of making the foam is by the "one shot" process. In this method, heavy metal catalysts are added to speed up the polymerisation process, so that it becomes possible to mix the toluene di-isocyanate, poly(glycol ether), amine, and water. The foam is produced in "one shot". However, the dimethylsiloxane is not effective as a foam stabiliser in this method. It is necessary to use a co-polymer of the siloxane and a poly(glycol ether)[64–66] *e.g.*,

$$\text{—}(Me_2SiO)_n\text{—}(C_xH_{2x}O)_m\text{—}$$

It is of interest that this material is not effective in the prepolymer process. The mechanism is not understood. It is apparent, however, that the surfactant in the "one shot" process needs to have some solubility in the glycol ether.

This is one example of the application of siloxane-organic co-polymers where heat-stability is not required. There will undoubtedly be many more in the future in the pharmaceutical, agricultural, and surfactant fields.

Chemical co-polymerisation is not the only method that can be used. Graft polymerisation has been used to prepare co-polymers with halogenoethylenes. A siloxane polymer and an olefinic monomer have been polymerised with a free-radical initiator, such as an organic peroxide, or an azo-compound[67].

9. Future aspects

Some of the recent advances in silicone chemistry have been described, particularly as applied to the established processes and finished products. Much work has been done, too, in the study of the structure of siloxanes by application of flow measurement studies, nuclear magnetic resonance, etc.[68,69]. The silicone chemist is being made increasingly aware of the function of molecular configuration and properties of the polymer. He is also increasingly aware of his lack of understanding of what are, to him, familiar processes. One can therefore, expect much information in the next years on molecular structure, physical characteristics, and polymerisation, as well as other syntheses of organosilicon compounds and siloxanes.

There is also an ever-increasing research activity in the preparation of polymers containing silicon and elements other than oxygen. An increasing amount of work on Si—O—Al, Si—O—Ti, Si—O—Sn, and Si—O—B polymers is being published (see Chapters 7 and 8). The next few years will certainly see a great expansion in the organic chemistry and polymer chemistry of silicon and the silicones.

REFERENCES

1 E. G. Rochow, *Introduction to the Chemistry of the Silicones*, 2nd. Ed., Wiley & Sons, New York, 1951.
2 R. R. McGregor, *Silicones and their Uses*, McGraw-Hill, New York, 1954.
3 R. N. Meals and F. M. Lewis, *Silicones*, Rheinhold, New York, 1959.

4 C. Eaborn, *Organosilicon Compounds*, Butterworth, London, 1960.
5 S. Fordham, Ed., *Silicones*, Newnes, London, 1960.
6 D. B. Whitehouse, *Chem. & Process Eng.*, 41 (1960) 501.
7 A. J. Barry, J. W. Gilkey and D. E. Hook, *Ind. Eng. Chem.*, 51 (1959) 131.
8 G. H. Wagner and C. O. Strother (to Linde Air Products Co.), *British Patent*, 670,617 (1952).
9 Midland Silicones, Ltd., *British Patent*, 804,097 (1958).
10 G. H. Wagner and W. G. Whitehead (to Union Carbide Corp.), *British Patent*, 822,830 (1959).
11 R. K. Freidlina, E. T. Chukovskaya and I. Tsao, *Doklady Akad. Nauk S.S.S.R.*, 127 (1959) 352.
12 H. Gilman and E. A. Zuech, *J. Am. Chem. Soc.*, 81 (1959) 5925.
13 General Electric Co., *British Patent*, 756,677 (1956).
14 General Electric Co., *British Patent*, 790,351 (1958).
15 General Electric Co., *British Patent*, 822,561 (1959).
16 General Electric Co., *British Patent*, 794,086 (1958).
17 R. C. Anderson and G. J. Sleddon, *Chem. & Ind. (London)*, (1960) 1335.
18 F. T. Fitch (to W. R. Grace and Co.), *British Patent*, 804,068 (1958).
19 C. M. Murphy, C. E. Saunders and D. C. Smith, *Ind. Eng. Chem.*, 42 (1950) 2462.
20 L. E. Scala, W. M. Hickam and M. H. Loeffler, *J. Appl. Polymer Sci.*, 2 (1959) 297.
21 C. D. Doyle, *J. Polymer Sci.*, 31 (1958) 95.
22 C. W. Lewis, *J. Polymer Sci.*, 33 (1958) 153.
23 C. W. Lewis, *J. Polymer Sci.*, 37 (1959) 425.
24 Midland Silicones Ltd., *British Patent*, 799,067 (1958).
25 A. R. Gilbert (to General Electric Co.), *U.S.P.*, 2,717,902 (1955).
26 H. R. Baker and C. R. Singleterry, *U.S. Government Research Reports*; PB 161449.
27 A. R. Gilbert and S. W. Kantor, *J. Polymer Sci.*, 40 (1959) 35.
28 Kali-Chemie, A.-G., *British Patent*, 797,235 (1958).
29 G. M. Konkle, J. A. McHard and K. E. Polmanteer (to Dow Corning Corp.), *U.S.P.*, 2,890,188 (1959).
30 N. New (to I.C.I., Ltd.), *British Patent*, 792,580 (1958).
31 R. A. Hall and N. New (to I.C.I., Ltd.), *British patent*, 800,554 (1958).
32 Midland Silicones, Ltd., *British Patent*, 764,246 (1956).
33 Wacker Chemie, G.m.b.H., *British Patent*, 841,825 (1960).
34 A. Zappel (to Farbenfabriken Bayer A.-G.), *British Patent*, 851,575 (1960).
35 Midland Silicones Ltd., *British Patent*, 862,576 (1961).
36 Cie des Usines chem. Rhone-Poulenc, *British Patent*, 851,578 (1960).
37 O. R. Pierce, G. W. Holbrock, O. K. Johannson, J. C. Saylor and E. D. Brown, *Ind. Eng. Chem.*, 52 (1960) 783.
38 Midland Silicones, Ltd., *British Patent*, 832,488 (1960).
39 Midland Silicones, Ltd., *British Patent*, 786,020 (1957).
40 T. C. Williams, R. A. Pike and F. Fekete, *Ind. Eng. Chem.*, 51 (1959) 939.
41 M. Wick, *Kunststoffe*, 50 (1960) 433.
42 E. E. Klaus, E. J. Tewkesbury and M. R. Fenske, *J. Chem. Eng. Data*, 6 (1961) 99.
43 M. Antler, *Ind. Eng. Chem.*, 51 (1959) 753.
44 R. L. Peeler and S. A. Kovacich, *Ind. Eng. Chem.*, 51 (1959) 749.

[45] A. R. Huntress, A. R. Smith, D. B. Power and N. T. M. Dennis, *4th National Symposium on Vacuum Technology, Boston*, 1957, p. 104 (published 1958).
[46] J. A. C. Watt, *J. Textile Inst.*, 48 (1957) T175.
[47] J. A. C. Watt, *J. Textile Inst.*, 51 (1960) T1.
[48] C. J. Connor, *Chem. Eng. News*, 37 (October 26, 1959) 46.
[49] Midland Silicones, Ltd., *British Patent*, 797,318 (1958).
[50] Midland Silicones, Ltd., *British Patent*, 814,927 (1959).
[51] Midland Silicones, Ltd., *British Patent*, 809,497 (1959).
[52] P. D. George, M. Prober and J. R. Elliot, *Chem. Revs.*, 56 (1956) 1065.
[53] Westinghouse Electric International Co., *British Patent*,788, 230 (1957).
[54] Midland Silicones, Ltd., *British Patent*, 798,140 (1958).
[55] Midland Silicones, Ltd., *British Patent*, 766,627 (1957).
[56] Midland Silicones, Ltd., *British Patent*, 810,284 (1959).
[57] Midland Silicones, Ltd., *British Patent*, 771,843 (1957).
[58] Midland Silicones, Ltd., *British Patent*, 765,642 (1957).
[59] Midland Silicones, Ltd., *British Patent*, 801,529 (1958).
[60] Westinghouse Electric International Co. *British Patent*, 804,158 (1958).
[61] H. K. Frensdorf, *Rubber Age*, 83 (1958) 812.
[62] E. A. Packer and J. F. Wood, *Rubber & Plastics Age*, 41 (1960) 1174.
[63] Goodyear Tire and Rubber Co., *British Patent*, 825,896 (1959).
[64] J. M. Buist, R. Hurd and A. Lowe, *Chem. & Ind. (London)*, (1960) 1544.
[65] J. H. Saunders and T. G. Gemeinhardt (to Mobay Chemical Co.), *Belgian Patent*, 582,362 (1959).
[66] G. Loew (to Farbenfabriken Bayer and Mobay Chemical Co.), *Belgian Patent*, 582,363 (1959).
[67] Midland Silicones, Ltd., *British Patent*, 806,582 (1958).
[68] H. Kusumoto, I. J. Lawrenson and H. S. Gutowsky, *J. Chem. Phys.*, 32 (1960) 724.
[69] J. G. Powles, *Polymer*, 1 (1960) 219.

Chapter 7

Polymetallosiloxanes. Part I. Introduction and Synthesis of Metallosiloxanes

by

J. IDRIS JONES

1. Introduction

Of all the elements in the Periodic Table, carbon stands out for its capacity for forming long homochain polymers. Catenation of elements other than carbon is restricted to a few of the non-metals[1,2]. Among the inorganic polymers, heterochain high-molecular structures predominate[3,4]. A notable feature of the chemistry of silicon is its inability to form multiple bonds. Only recently has the first compound containing Si=C bond been reported[137]*, and no silicon analogues of the olefins, containing the Si=Si bond (which could form addition polymers) exist. However, catenation of silicon atoms has been encountered to a limited extent in systems such as the saturated silicon hydrides up to Si_6H_{14}, and halides such as $Si_{10}Cl_{22}$, but the Si—Si bonds are not particularly strong[1]. Similarly, no structures containing the Si=O bond have been authenticated, but the tendency to form polymeric structures containing a sequence of Si—O linkages is very pronounced as evidenced by the abundance and variety of the naturally-occurring silicates and the wide range of synthetic silicones which are directly related to them. The ability to form heterochain polymers by linking through oxygen

* This claim is now believed to be specious.

atoms is shared by a number of other elements, both metals and non-metals. The polymeric forms of formaldehyde[5] and acetaldehyde[6] have a backbone of alternating carbon and oxygen atoms. An extended chain of sulphur–oxygen linkages occurs in the polymeric modifications of sulphur trioxide[7–9] (Chapter 5). In the case of the metals, the polymeric structures as a class are known as polymetalloxanes. Typical examples of such heterochain polymers are those whose molecular chains consist of aggregates of metalloxane units such as (I)–(VI).

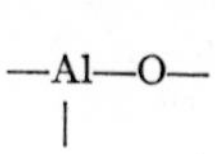

```
                   |             |
—Al—O—          —Ti—O—        —Sn—O—
 |                 |             |
 (I)              (II)          (III)

                   |
—As—O—          —Ge—O—        —Ga—O—
 |                 |             |
 (IV)             (V)           (VI)
```

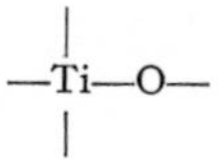

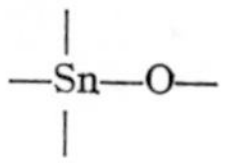

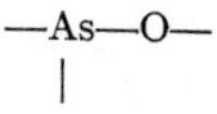

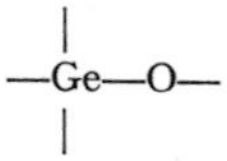

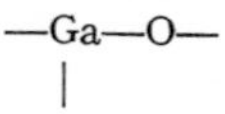

Among the other elements known to give similar macromolecular structures are boron, phosphorus, selenium, bismuth, magnesium, cadmium, mercury, lead, beryllium, tellurium, zirconium, antimony, vanadium, chromium, molybdenum, tungsten, indium, uranium, and thorium[4]. Some of these systems are wholly inorganic and include oxides, hydrous oxides, oxyhalides, condensed oxyacids, and the polyionic complexes formed by cationic and anionic aggregation in solution[10–12]. When the elements are capable of forming stable bonds with carbon, polyorganometalloxanes can be

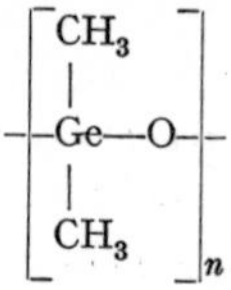

$$\left[\begin{array}{c} CH_3 \\ | \\ -Ge-O- \\ | \\ CH_3 \end{array}\right]_n \qquad \left[\begin{array}{c} C_6H_5 \\ | \\ -Ge-O- \\ | \\ C_6H_5 \end{array}\right]_n$$

(VII) 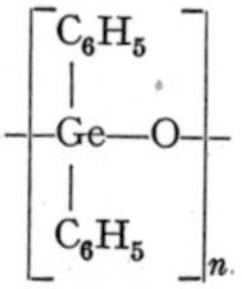 (VIII)

formed. Thus, germanium behaves like silicon in giving polyorganogermanoxanes[13,14], like (VII) and (VIII).

Organotin oxides, *e.g.*, dimethyltin oxide, are known to be poly-

References, p. 195–199

meric[15]. Metalloxane chains, bearing alkoxy- and triorganosiloxy-groups on the metal atoms, have also been characterised[16]. Many of the metal alkoxides have been found to be polymeric in character[17].

Further, some mixed polymetalloxane systems are known wherein two or more different elements are linked through oxygen atoms to form the structural unit; typical units in such polymeric species are (IX)–(XI)[18], (XII)[19], (XIII)[20], (XIV), and (XV)[11].

P—O—B—O (IX)

P—O—As—O (X)

P—O—Al—O (XI)

As—O—Sn—O (XII)

Zr—O—S—O (XIII)

P—O—Mo—O (XIV)

P—O—W—O—V—O—W (XV)

Where the one element is silicon, the systems are generally known as polymetallosiloxanes although, in some instances, the other element can hardly be classed as a "metal". Here again, the systems may be wholly inorganic as in the aluminosilicates, borosilicates, or in zircon, (XVI).

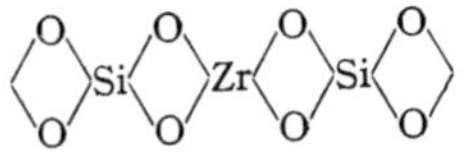

(XVI)

In appropriate cases, organic groups may be attached to form polyorganometallosiloxanes. This latter group forms the subject of this contribution, and our knowledge of these polymers is derived largely from the work of Soviet researchers, in particular, that of Professor K. A. Andrianov and his school at the Institute of Elemento-Organic Compounds, Moscow[16,134]. Two types of polymetallosiloxanes need to be distinguished, the first, wherein the basic metallosiloxane unit Si—O—M—O (where M represents the "metal") is regularly repeated in the polymeric chain and the second, wherein only isolated metallosiloxane linkages exist in a polysiloxane structure. Most of the Russian investigations have been devoted to the latter system. The polymetallosiloxanes to be described contain the structural units (XVII)–(XXXIV).

—Si—O—Al—O—
(XVII)

—Si—O—Ti—O—
(XVIII)

—Si—O—Sn—O—
(XIX)

—Si—O—Sn—O—
(XX)

—Si—O—B—O—
(XXI)

—Si—O—P—O—
(XXII)

—Si—O—As—O—
(XXIII)

—Si—O—As—O—
(XXIV)

—Si—O—Sb—O—
(XXV)

—Si—O—Ge—O—
(XXVI)

—Si—O—Co—O—
(XXVII)

—Si—O—Ni—O—
(XXVIII)

—Si—O—Mg—O—
(XXIX)

—Si—O—Pb—O—
(XXX)

—Si—O—S—O—
(XXXI)

—Si—O—Cr—O—
(XXXII)

—Si—O—Zr—O—
(XXXIII)

—Si—O—Al—O—P—O—
(XXXIV)

References, p. 195–199

Reference should also be made to polydimethylsilylformal[21]

$$\left[-\overset{\displaystyle CH_3}{\underset{\displaystyle CH_3}{\overset{|}{\underset{|}{Si}}}}-O-CH_2-O-\right]_n ,$$

the only known representative of the carbosiloxane polymers, which was synthesised from $(CH_3)_2Si(OC_2H_5)_2$ and $(CH_3COO)_2CH_2$.

By the subtle expedient of surrounding the metal atoms in a metalloxane chain with organosiloxy-groups, Andrianov[16] has been able to synthesise a novel group of linear organometallic polymers, known as polyorganosiloxymetalloxanes, *e.g.*, (XXXV)–(XXXVII), which are readily soluble in organic solvents. Particular interest attaches to the use of R_3SiO groups to surround metals such as aluminium and titanium which, normally, do not form stable bonds with organic groups. Polyorganosiloxysiloxanes, (XXXVIII), may be regarded as unique representatives of this class of polymers.

$$-\underset{\displaystyle OSiR_3}{\underset{|}{Al}}-O-\underset{\displaystyle OSiR_3}{\underset{|}{Al}}-O-\underset{\displaystyle OSiR_3}{\underset{|}{Al}}-O-$$

(XXXV) Polyorganosiloxyaluminoxanes

$$-\overset{\displaystyle OSiR_3}{\underset{\displaystyle OSiR_3}{\overset{|}{\underset{|}{Ti}}}}-O-\overset{\displaystyle OSiR_3}{\underset{\displaystyle OSiR_3}{\overset{|}{\underset{|}{Ti}}}}-O-\overset{\displaystyle OSiR_3}{\underset{\displaystyle OSiR_3}{\overset{|}{\underset{|}{Ti}}}}-O-$$

(XXXVI) Polyorganosiloxytitanoxanes

$$-\overset{\displaystyle OSiR_3}{\underset{\displaystyle OSiR_3}{\overset{|}{\underset{|}{Sn}}}}-O-\overset{\displaystyle OSiR_3}{\underset{\displaystyle OSiR_3}{\overset{|}{\underset{|}{Sn}}}}-O-\overset{\displaystyle OSiR_3}{\underset{\displaystyle OSiR_3}{\overset{|}{\underset{|}{Sn}}}}-O-$$

(XXXVII) Polyorganosiloxystannoxanes

$$-\overset{\displaystyle OSiR_3}{\underset{\displaystyle OSiR_3}{\overset{|}{\underset{|}{Si}}}}-O-\overset{\displaystyle OSiR_3}{\underset{\displaystyle OSiR_3}{\overset{|}{\underset{|}{Si}}}}-O-\overset{\displaystyle OSiR_3}{\underset{\displaystyle OSiR_3}{\overset{|}{\underset{|}{Si}}}}-O-$$

(XXXVIII) Polyorganosiloxysiloxanes

2. The synthesis of metallosiloxanes

Before discussing the different preparative approaches to polymetallosiloxanes and polysiloxymetalloxanes, it is pertinent to consider the various methods available for the synthesis of simple metallosiloxanes since, in many instances, these form the intermediates for polymer synthesis and the reactions by which they are formed, when applied to polyfunctional intermediates, lead to polymer formation.

Carbosiloxanes, like alkoxy- and acyloxy-silanes, often figure in the synthesis of metallosiloxanes. For a full discussion of their synthesis and reactions readers are referred to various standard works on organosilicon compounds[22,23].

3. Alkali metal silanolates

The alkali metal silanolates can be regarded as the simplest type of metallosiloxane. Because of their monofunctionality, they cannot form an integral part of a polymeric chain. Their main utility is as starting materials for the synthesis of other metallosiloxanes, both simple and polymeric. There is a good deal of evidence, both chemical and physical, that trialkylsilanols are stronger acids than the corresponding carbinols[23]. Thus, lithium, sodium, and potassium react readily with trimethylsilanol, even when the latter is in solution in organic solvents. Treatment of trimethylsilanol with aqueous sodium hydroxide also affords sodium trimethylsilanolate[24] and even in alkaline methanol–isopropanol solutions the silanolates are formed[25]. The physical evidence is based on studies of the relative donor properties, in hydrogen-bond formation, of silanols and the corresponding carbinols and also on spectral data[23]. Since silicon is more electropositive than carbon, the silanols might be expect to be lower in acidity than the carbinols; the observed enhancement of acidity must therefore be attributed to d_π—p_π bonding between the silicon and oxygen atoms. Triarylsilanols are far stronger acids than the trialkylsilanols. Indeed, triphenylsilanol may be titrated against tetrabutylammonium hydroxide in pyridine solution[26]. It is a rather weaker protonic acid than most

References, p. 195–199

phenols but somewhat stronger than *p*-nitroaniline. Trialkylsilanols and alkyl- or aryl-carbinols cannot be titrated under these conditions.

The simplest and generally most satisfactory method of preparing the alkali metal silanolates is by direct reaction of the pure alkali metal with the silanols, usually in the presence of an inert solvent, such as ether, petroleum ether, or benzene[24,27–29].

$$2(CH_3)_3SiOH + 2Li \longrightarrow 2(CH_3)_3SiOLi + H_2$$

$$2(C_2H_5)_3SiOH + 2Na \longrightarrow 2(C_2H_5)_3SiONa + H_2$$

$$2(C_6H_5)_3SiOH + 2Na \longrightarrow 2(C_6H_5)_3SiONa + H_2$$

Some of the silanolates thus prepared have been isolated as solids and characterised in both solvated and unsolvated forms[30]. They are hygroscopic and hydrolyse readily to the hydroxide and the silanol. In the case of sodium trimethylsilanolate this reaction is evidently reversible, since its formation from trimethylsilanol and 12*M* sodium hydroxide has been reported[24]. Triorganosilanols with larger alkyl groups do not form silanolates with alkali hydroxide. Addition of trimethylsilanol to a saturated solution of lithium hydroxide yields no precipitate, while use of solid lithium hydroxide results only in intermolecular dehydration of the silanol to give hexamethyldisiloxane[30]. Although the action of a strong base on hexamethyldisiloxane leads to silanolate formation, the competing demethylation reaction makes it impossible to separate the products in a pure state[31]. When hexaphenyldisiloxane is boiled with potassium hydroxide in ethanol[32], or with sodium hydroxide in aqueous acetone[33], a solution of the triphenylsilanolate is obtained. If care is taken completely to remove the water formed during the alkali cleavage of hexaorganodisiloxanes in an alcoholic medium, then the solid alkali metal silanolates can be prepared in a pure state[25]. By this process, hexamethyldisiloxane gives a low yield of the silanolate. A more successful method is to treat the disiloxane with sodium in liquid ammonia, or sodium oxide in pyridine–methanol[25].

$$(C_6H_5)_3Si—O—Si(C_6H_5)_3 + 2\ NaOH \longrightarrow 2\ C_6H_5—Si(C_6H_5)_2—ONa + H_2O$$

$$C_6H_5—Si(CH_3)_2—O—Si(CH_3)_2—C_6H_5 + 2\ NaOH \longrightarrow 2\ C_6H_5—Si(CH_3)_2—ONa + H_2O$$

$$2(CH_3)_3Si—O—Si(CH_3)_3 + 2NaNH_2 \longrightarrow 2(CH_3)_3SiONa + 2(CH_3)_3SiNH_2$$

$$2(CH_3)_3Si—O—Si(CH_3)_3 + Na_2O \longrightarrow 2(CH_3)_3SiONa$$

Hexaorganodisiloxanes are also cleaved by organolithium reagents in boiling ether[33].

$$(C_6H_5)_3Si—O—Si(C_6H_5)_3 + C_6H_5Li \longrightarrow (C_6H_5)_4Si + (C_6H_5)_3SiOLi$$

A distinctive property of the silanols is the ease with which they condense to siloxanes:

$$2\ {\equiv}Si—OH \longrightarrow {\equiv}Si—O—Si{\equiv} + H_2O$$

For a given group R, the tendency to undergo this intermolecular dehydration increases in the series $R_3SiOH < R_2Si(OH)_2 < RSi(OH)_3$. Polymeric siloxanes result from the condensation of silanediols and triols. As would be expected, most organosilanediols dissolve directly in aqueous alkali (though the solubility may be low). The stabilities of the solutions vary with the nature and size of the organic groups present and eventually polymers form. Some silanols, *e.g.*, phenylsilanetriol[34] and dimethylsilanediol[35], are very sensitive to traces of alkalis (and acids). In the hydrolysis or organic di- and tri-chlorosilanes, or of other hydrolysable silicon compounds with concentrated aqueous alkali, alkali metal silanolates are initially formed and remain in solution. Even some polysiloxane mixtures, obtained by hydrolysis of appropriate di- and

References, p. 195–199

tri-functional silicon compounds, will dissolve in strong aqueous, aqueous-alcoholic, or alcoholic alkali, presumably because some silanol linkages persist in the structures. Some solid silanolates, sometimes solvated, have been isolated from solution and characterised[36–41]. Examples are:

$$[C_6H_5Si(ONa)O]_n,\ [C_6H_5\cdot CH_2Si(ONa)O]_n,\ [C_6H_5\cdot(C_2H_5)\cdot Si(ONa)]_2O,$$

$$[CH_3Si(ONa)O]_n,\ C_6H_5Si(ONa)_3,\ C_6H_5Si(OH)_2ONa,$$

$$NaOSi(CH_3)_2OSi(CH_3)_2ONa,\ C_2H_5Si(OH)_2ONa,\ \text{and}$$

$$NaO[Si(C_6H_5)(CH_3)O]_3Na.$$

The alkali metal silanolates are usually employed as solutions in the solvents in which they are prepared. They react readily with the halides of metals and non-metals. The reaction with silicon halides constitutes an important route to many organo di- and poly-siloxanes not readily obtained by hydrolysis procedures, particularly unsymmetrical and branched compounds[23]. Typical of the reactions with carbon halides are the following[42, 43]:

$$4(C_6H_5\cdot CH_2)_3SiONa + CCl_4 \longrightarrow 4[(C_6H_5\cdot CH_2)_3SiO]_4C + 4NaCl$$

$$(C_6H_5)_3SiONa + CH_3COCl \longrightarrow (C_6H_5)_3SiOCOCH_3 + NaCl$$

As will be seen later, the exchange reaction between alkali metal silanolates and metallic halides is an important method, of almost general application, for the synthesis of metallosiloxanes, both simple and polymeric.

4. Organosiloxymagnesium compounds

In 1947, Andrianov discovered that organosilicon polymeric compounds containing silanol groups react not only with elements of the 1st Group, but also with those of the 2nd and 3rd Groups of the Periodic Table, forming complex polymers, the molecular chains of which contain not only silicon and oxygen, but also metal atoms[16,44]. This constituted the first synthesis of polyorgano-metallosiloxanes. Thus, both magnesium and aluminium were found to react with silanols with evolution of hydrogen.

Triorganosiloxymagnesium compounds are formed when polysiloxanes are treated with excess of a Grignard reagent at high temperatures (usually near 200°)[45]. The main utility of this reaction is for the synthesis of triorganosilanols, since the magnesium siloxanes hydrolyse with extreme ease. In fact, this was one of the first methods discovered for preparing trimethylsilanol[46].

$$[(CH_3)_2SiO]_n + CH_3MgI \longrightarrow (CH_3)_3SiOMgI \xrightarrow{H_2O} (CH_3)_3SiOH$$

$$(C_6H_5 \cdot SiO_{1.5})_n + C_6H_5MgBr \longrightarrow (C_6H_5)_3SiOMgBr \xrightarrow{H_2O} (C_6H_5)_3SiOH$$

Siloxane linkages in hexaorganodisiloxanes do not cleave with Grignard reagents[45]. Similarly, no cleavage occurs when hexachlorodisiloxane is treated with phenylmagnesium bromide, but some reaction occurs with the hexabromo-analogue[47].

$$(Br_3Si)_2O + C_6H_5MgBr \longrightarrow (C_6H_5)_4Si + (C_6H_5)_3SiOMgBr$$

sym-Diphenyldisiloxane undergoes both the normal reaction:

$$(C_6H_5H_2Si)_2O + RMgX \longrightarrow C_6H_5H_2SiR + C_6H_5H_2SiOMgX$$

and another, involving production of phenylsilane and a magnesium derivative in which an Si—H bond has been replaced by an Si—R bond[48]:

$$(C_6H_5H_2Si)_2O + RMgX \longrightarrow C_6H_5SiH_3 + C_6H_5HRSiOMgX$$

Siloxene, its oxidation products, and even ignited silica gel and quartz powder, have also been reported to enter into these reactions with Grignard reagents[49].

Hornbaker and Conrad[50] found that a magnesium siloxane polymer is formed when diphenylsilanediol is treated with diethylmagnesium, but it decomposes rather easily upon heating, to give a cyclic diphenylsiloxane and magnesium oxide.

References, p. 195–199

5. Organosiloxyaluminium compounds

A number of compounds containing the Si—O—Al linkage have been synthesised. These have played a prominent role in the development of the polyorganoaluminosiloxanes and polyorganosiloxyaluminoxanes. Tris(triethylsiloxy)aluminium, a crystalline solid, m.p. 159°, was obtained by Andrianov[44,51,52] in 88% yield, and by Wiberg and Kanzler[53] by direct reaction of aluminium with triethylsilanol, in the presence of a little mercuric chloride.

$$6(C_2H_5)_3SiOH + 2Al \longrightarrow 2[(C_2H_5)_3SiO]_3Al + 3H_2$$

Treatment of the sodium salt of triphenylsilanol with aluminium chloride has been reported to give tris(triphenylsiloxy)aluminium[54].

$$3(C_6H_5)_3SiONa + AlCl_3 \longrightarrow [(C_6H_5)_3SiO]_3Al + 3NaCl$$

This compound is a white solid, soluble in acetone and insoluble in ether. It decomposes around 300°, but has m.p. ~ 485°. By mass spectrometer studies, the degradation at 300° was found to be due to rupture of the silicon–carbon bond, thus confirming the essential thermal stability of the Al—O—Si linkage. The preparation of tris(trimethylsiloxy)aluminium from sodium trimethylsilanolate and aluminium chloride has been studied[55].

A reaction which has proved of considerable interest and value in the synthesis of aluminosiloxanes and other metallosiloxanes, both simple and polymeric, is the alkoxide–acyloxide reaction. This reaction has been largely exploited by American workers. Thus, by reaction of trimethylsilyl acetate with aluminium tri-isopropoxide, di-isopropoxy(trimethylsiloxy)aluminium and tris(trimethylsiloxy)-aluminium were obtained[56].

$$(CH_3)_3SiOCOCH_3 + Al(OC_3H_7^i)_3 \longrightarrow (CH_3)_3SiOAl(OC_3H_7^i)_2 + CH_3COOC_3H_7^i$$

$$3(CH_3)_3SiOCOCH_3 + Al(OC_3H_7^i)_3 \longrightarrow [(CH_3)_3SiO]_3Al + 3CH_3COOC_3H_7^i$$

By the same heterofunctional condensation, di-isopropoxy(triphenylsiloxy)aluminium has been obtained in vitreous form. The thermal stability of these aluminosiloxanes has been examined and the products of pyrolysis identified[57,58]. Crystalline di-isopropoxy-(trimethylsiloxy)aluminium decomposes at 260° with formation of propylene, isopropyl alcohol, isopropoxytrimethylsilane, and a residue, insoluble in benzene. On heating to 260–280°, tris(trimethylsiloxy)aluminium formed hexamethyldisiloxane and a benzene-soluble resin (mol. weight 1200).

Trialkylsilyl halides were obtained when hexa-alkyldisiloxanes and polysiloxanes of the type $R_3Si[OSiR_2]_nOSiR_3$ were treated with aluminium chloride, bromide, or iodide[59,61]. The reaction is believed to proceed in stages:

$$(R_3Si)_2O + AlCl_3 \longrightarrow (R_3Si)_2\overset{+}{O} - \overset{-}{Al}Cl_3$$

$$(R_3Si)_2\overset{+}{O} - \overset{-}{Al}Cl_3 \longrightarrow R_3SiCl + R_3SiOAlCl_2$$

$$R_3SiOAlCl_2 \longrightarrow R_3SiCl + AlOCl$$

The intermediate $R_3SiOAlX_2$ compounds are surprisingly stable[60,61]. Thus, (trimethylsiloxy)aluminium dichloride, m.p. 87–88°, can be distilled *in vacuo* (b.p. 102°/4 mm). (Triethylsiloxy)aluminium dibromide has b.p. 181°/3 mm. Disproportionation occurs when they are heated to higher temperatures. Cyclic polydiorganosiloxanes are also cleaved by aluminium chloride on prolonged heating, to give cyclic aluminosiloxanes[62,63], as shown below for the ethyl derivatives.

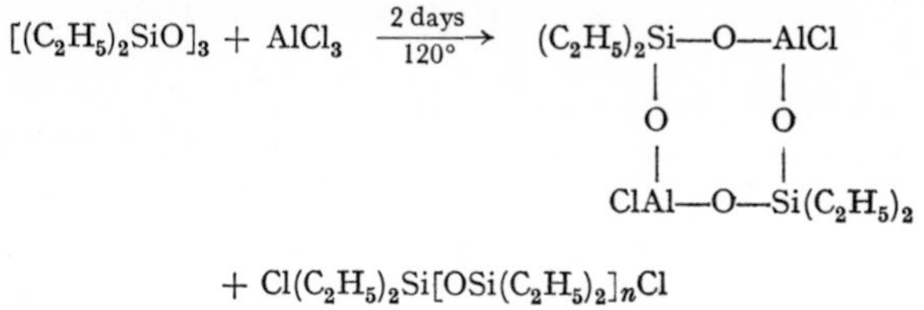

$$[(C_2H_5)_2SiO]_3 + AlCl_3 \xrightarrow[120^\circ]{2\text{ days}} \begin{array}{ccc} (C_2H_5)_2Si & - O - & AlCl \\ | & & | \\ O & & O \\ | & & | \\ ClAl & - O - & Si(C_2H_5)_2 \end{array}$$

$$+ Cl(C_2H_5)_2Si[OSi(C_2H_5)_2]_nCl$$

Petree[64] has reported a simple synthesis of pure aluminosiloxanes by reaction of trialkylaluminium compounds with polydialkylsiloxanes.

$$R_3Al + \frac{n}{4}\left[R'_2SiO\right]_4 \longrightarrow R_2Al - \left[OSiR'_2\right]_n - R$$

References, p. 195–199

Examples of this reaction are:

$$4(CH_3)_3Al + [(CH_3)_2SiO]_4 \longrightarrow 4(CH_3)_2AlOSi(CH_3)_3$$

$$(C_2H_5)_3Al + [(CH_3)_2SiO]_4 \longrightarrow (C_2H_5)_2AlOSi(CH_3)_2 \text{-}[OSi(CH_3)_2]_3\text{-} C_2H_5$$

Products of different polysiloxane chain-length are obtained by varying the reactant ratio.

The scope of the metathetic alkyl halide-elimination reaction

$$RMX + R'OM' \longrightarrow R'X + RMOM',$$

where X = halogen, M = metal, M′ = metalloid and R and R′ are alkyl groups, has also been investigated[64]. In the following example, the reaction proceeds in high yield with almost complete absence of side reactions.

$$2(C_2H_5)_2AlCl + (C_2H_5)_2SO_4 \longrightarrow 2C_2H_5Cl + [(C_2H_5)_2Al]_2SO_4$$

However, in other cases, there is competition from possible alternative reaction paths. Certain trends have been noted for the extent of this competition in systems involving different metals and metalloid anions, but no details are available for those systems where either M or M′ = Si.

6. Organosiloxytitanium compounds

In recent years, considerable attention has been devoted to the synthesis of titanosiloxanes. The methods of synthesis are generally similar to those used in the preparation of other metallosiloxanes. Tetrakis(trimethylsiloxy)titanium is formed to the extent of 15% in the following reaction[65]:

$$4(CH_3)_3SiOH + TiCl_4 \xrightarrow{NH_3} [(CH_3)_3SiO]_4Ti + 4HCl$$

Some related compounds have also been prepared by this route[66,67]. Metathetical reactions between titanium tetrachloride and alkali metal silanolates have given greatly improved yields[52]:

$$4R_3SiONa + TiCl_4 \longrightarrow (R_3SiO)_4Ti + 4NaCl$$

If carefully conducted, the exchange reaction:

$$4(CH_3)_3SiOH + Ti(OC_3H_7^i)_4 \longrightarrow [(CH_3)_3SiO]_4Ti + 4C_3H_7^iOH$$

is capable of giving a quantitative yield of tetrakis(trimethylsiloxy)titanium[68,69]. In view of the ease with which the silanol condenses to siloxane, the published experimental directions need to be followed closely. The procedure involves slow addition of the silanol and the continuous removal by distillation of the azeotrope of isopropyl alcohol and benzene used as a solvent. The tetraethoxy- and butoxy-derivatives of titanium[66,67,70] have also been successfully used in the same reaction, and advantage has been taken of the catalytic activity of sodium. The tendency to siloxane formation is not so marked with triethyl- or triphenyl-silanol and, accordingly, the reaction is easier to carry out.

$$4(C_6H_5)_3SiOH + Ti(OC_4H_9^n)_4 \longrightarrow [(C_6H_5)_3SiO]_4Ti + 4C_4H_9^nOH$$

Bradley and Thomas[69] found that quantitative yields of tetrakis-(trialkylsiloxy)titanium are obtained by the silanolysis of tetrakis-(trimethylsiloxy)titanium with higher alkylsilanols in boiling hexamethyldisiloxane, *e.g.*

$$[(CH_3)_3SiO]_4Ti + 4(C_2H_5)_3SiOH \longrightarrow [(C_2H_5)_3SiO]_4Ti + 4(CH_3)_3SiOH$$

Tetrakis(triphenylsiloxy)titanium is also obtained when triphenylsilanol is heated with condensed titanium esters, the Ti—O—Ti bonds in the latter being broken[66]. Contrary to expectations, a bicyclic compound, (XXXIX), rather than a polymer, resulted from the reaction of diphenylsilanediol and tetra-*n*-butyl titanate.

```
(C6H5)2Si—O—Si(C6H5)2—O          O—Si(C6H5)2—O—Si(C6H5)2
    |                    \      /                  |
    O                     Ti                       O
    |                    /      \                  |
(C6H5)2Si—O—Si(C6H5)2—O          O—Si(C6H5)2—O—Si(C6H5)2
```

(XXXIX)

References, p. 195–199

By controlling the stoicheiometry of the reaction between trimethylsilanol and tetraisopropoxytitanium, Danforth[71] was able to prepare partially-substituted (trimethylsiloxy)titanium esters,

$$(CH_3)_3SiOTi(OC_3H_7^i)_3, \text{ and } [(CH_3)_3SiO]_2Ti(OC_3H_7^i)_2,$$

as well as the tetraester. Similarly, Andrianov and Astakhin[72] claim that in the case of triethylsilanol the reaction proceeded according to the equation:

$$Ti(OR)_4 + n(C_2H_5)_3SiOH \xrightarrow{Na} [(C_2H_5)_3SiO]_nTi(OR)_{4-n} + nROH$$

where R = C_3H_7 or C_4H_9, and n = 1, 2, 3, or 4. In the course of the study of this reaction, tris(triethylsiloxy)butoxytitane (46%), bis(triethylsiloxy)dibutoxytitane (34%), and bis(triethylsiloxy)-dipropoxytitane (21%) were obtained and their stabilities towards hydrolysis were studied.

From the isopiestic method[73], there is evidence that the di-n-propyloxy- and di-isobutoxy-titanium oxides, $(RO)_2TiO$, are substantially monomeric in dilute benzene solutions (up to 0.1%), thus indicating the presence of a Ti = O linkage. Some confirmation of this was obtained from the following addition reactions.

$$(C_3H_7O)_2TiO + Si(OC_3H_7)_4 \longrightarrow (C_3H_7O)_3Ti{-}O{-}Si(OC_3H_7)_3$$

$$2(C_3H_7O)_2TiO + Si(OC_3H_7)_4 \longrightarrow (C_3H_7O)_3Ti{-}O{-}\underset{\displaystyle OC_3H_7}{\overset{\displaystyle OC_3H_7}{\overset{|}{\underset{|}{Si}}}}{-}O{-}Ti(OC_3H_7)_3$$

Using the alkoxide-acyloxide reaction, Bradley and Thomas[69,74] obtained a 95% yield of tetrakis(trimethylsiloxy)titanium from (trimethyl)acetoxysilane and tetraisopropyl titanate.

$$4(CH_3)_3SiOCOCH_3 + Ti(OC_3H_7^i)_4 \longrightarrow [(CH_3)_3SiO]_4Ti + 4CH_3COOC_3H_7^i$$

On the other hand, Andrianov and Ganina[75] have reported that a similar heterofunctional condensation reaction between (trimethyl)-acetoxysilane and tetra-n-butyl titanate afforded, instead of the expected tetrakis(trimethylsiloxy)titanium, solid, infusible substances. Among the products isolated and characterised were (XL) and (XLI).

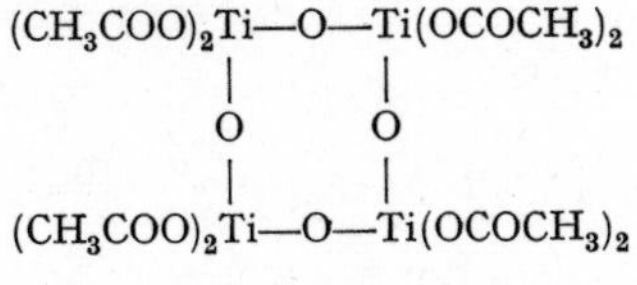

$$\begin{array}{c} (CH_3COO)_2Ti\text{—}O\text{—}Ti(OCOCH_3)_2 \\ | \quad\quad | \\ O \quad\quad O \\ | \quad\quad | \\ (CH_3COO)_2Ti\text{—}O\text{—}Ti(OCOCH_3)_2 \end{array} \qquad \text{(XL)}$$

$$\begin{array}{c} (CH_3COO)_2Ti\text{—}O\text{—}Ti(OCOCH_3)_2 \\ | \quad\quad | \\ O \quad\quad O \\ | \quad\quad | \\ CH_3COO\text{—}Ti\text{—}O\text{—}Ti(OCOCH_3)_2 \\ | \\ OSi(CH_3)_3 \end{array} \qquad \text{(XLI)}$$

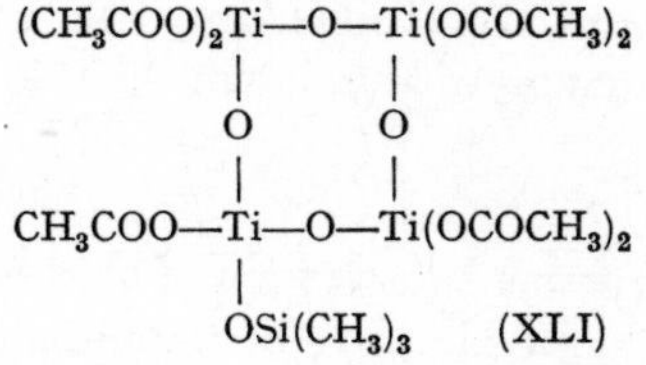

This apparent anomaly has recently been resolved by Rust, Takimoto and Denault[76]. In the first place, the earlier results of Bradley and Thomas[69] were fully confirmed. Furthermore, by ensuring that their starting materials were of high purity and by controlling the proportions of reactants as well as the order of addition, it was possible to prepare the pure compounds, $[(CH_3)_3SiO]_{4-n}Ti(OCOCH_3)_n$, in high yields. In their experiment leading to (XL) and (XLI) Andrianov and Ganina[75] used a 6 to 1 molar ratio of trimethylacetoxysilane to tetrabutoxytitanium, whereas the required stoicheiometry for formation of tetrakis-(trimethylsilyloxy)titanium would have required a ratio of 4 to 1. The order of addition was also such that the latter reagent was in considerable excess at all times. Finally, Bradley and Thomas have further shown[69] that tetrakis(trimethylsiloxy)titanium reacts with trimethylacetoxysilane to give a solid product containing acetoxy-groups. This suggests that the following reaction takes place readily:

$$\text{—}\overset{|}{\underset{|}{Ti}}\text{—}OSi(CH_3)_3 + (CH_3)_3SiOCOCH_3 \longrightarrow \text{—}\overset{|}{\underset{|}{Ti}}\text{—}OCOCH_3 + [(CH_3)_3Si]_2O$$

Clearly, the conditions of reaction used by the Russian workers were such as to favour the formation of Ti—$OCOCH_3$ compounds, to the point of exclusion of tetrakis(trimethylsiloxy)titanium.

Rust and his co-workers[76] have also investigated the reaction of tetrakis(trimethylsiloxy)titanium with acetic anhydride. Replacement of the siloxy-groups by acetoxy-groups occurred as follows:

$$\text{—}\overset{|}{\underset{|}{Ti}}\text{—}OSi(CH_3)_3 + (CH_3CO)_2O \longrightarrow \text{—}\overset{|}{\underset{|}{Ti}}\text{—}OCOCH_3 + (CH_3)_3SiOCOCH_3$$

References, p. 195–199

A series of trialkylsiloxytitanium halides of the type $(R_3SiO)_nTiX_{4-n}$ (where $n = 1$ or 2, and X = Cl or Br) has recently been reported[77,78]. These compounds were obtained by reaction of hexa-alkyldisiloxanes with titanium tetrahalides, using a small amount of aluminium chloride as catalyst.

$$nR_3SiOSiR_3 + TiX_4 \xrightarrow{AlX_3} (R_3SiO)_nTiX_{4-n} + nR_3SiX \quad (\text{where } n = 1 \text{ and } 2)$$

Further substitution of halogen atoms does not occur. Use of ferric chloride in place of aluminium chloride leads to complete cleavage of the disiloxane.

$$2R_3SiOSiR_3 + TiCl_4 \xrightarrow{FeCl_3} 4R_3SiCl + TiO_2$$

Andrianov and Dulova[79] obtained tris(trimethylsiloxy)titanium chloride and trimethylsiloxytitanium trichloride by the exchange reaction:

$$n(CH_3)_3SiONa + TiCl_4 \longrightarrow [(CH_3)_3SiO]_nTiCl_{4-n} + nNaCl \quad (n = 1 \text{ and } 3)$$

Attempts to prepare the dichloro-derivative by this method were not successful (evidently owing to disproportionation); this compound was, however, obtained by the action of titanium tetrachloride on tetrakis(trimethylsiloxy)titanium[52].

$$Ti[OSi(CH_3)_3]_4 + TiCl_4 \longrightarrow 2[(CH_3)_3SiO]_2TiCl_2.$$

In a review[78] of organotitanium compounds a number of other organotitanosiloxanes are also listed. Available physical constants are shown in Table 10.

TABLE 10

PHYSICAL PROPERTIES OF SOME TITANOSILOXANES

Compound	*B.p.*	*M.p.*	n_D	*Ref.*
$[(CH_3)_3SiO]_4Ti$	125°/8 mm	—	1.4283 (25°)	76
	110°/10 mm	—	1.4275 (20°)	70
$[(C_2H_5)_3SiO]_4Ti$	193°/3.5 mm	99–101°		70
$[(C_6H_5)_3SiO]_4Ti$	—	501–505°		66
$[(CH_3)_3SiO]Ti(OC_3H_7^i)_3$	91°/5 mm	—	1.4509 (25°)	76
$[(CH_3)_3SiO]_2Ti(OC_3H_7^i)_2$	103°/9 mm	—	1.4378 (25°)	76
$[(CH_3)_3SiO]_3Ti(OC_3H_7^i)$	107°/8 mm	—	1.4321 (25°)	76

Tetrakis(trimethylsiloxy)titanium is hydrolysed by water, but less readily than alkyl titanates, $(RO)_4Ti$[68]. It has been claimed to be useful for rendering textiles water-repellent[80]. When applied to a steel surface and then baked, a continuous film is formed which is said to withstand bright red heat[65].

7. Organosiloxyboron compounds

Several methods have been described for the preparation of borosiloxanes. Silanes, chlorosilanes, silanols and alkali metal silanolates, alkoxy- and acetoxy-silanes, and siloxanes have variously been used as starting materials.

The following reaction, in which nickel(II) chloride was used as catalyst, serves to illustrate the formation of a borosiloxane from a silane[81].

$$3(C_5H_{11}^i)_2(C_2H_5)SiH + B(OH)_3 \longrightarrow [(C_5H_{11}^i)_2(C_2H_5)SiO]_3B + 3H_2$$

Chlorosilanes also react with boric acid and its esters[82].

$$3(CH_3)_3SiCl + B(OH)_3 \longrightarrow [(CH_3)_3SiO]_3B + 3HCl$$

$$3(C_2H_5)_3SiCl + B(OC_4H_9^n)_3 \longrightarrow [(C_2H_5)_3SiO]_3B + 3C_4H_9^nCl$$

Ferric chloride was used as catalyst in the latter reaction. A low yield of the bis(triethylsilyl) ester, (XLII), of benzeneboronic acid, has been obtained from the boronic acid and triethylbromosilane[83].

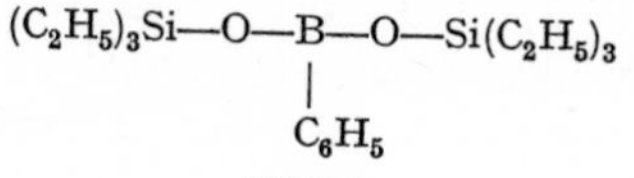

$$\begin{array}{c} (C_2H_5)_3Si\text{—}O\text{—}B\text{—}O\text{—}Si(C_2H_5)_3 \\ | \\ C_6H_5 \end{array}$$

(XLII)

Tris(trialkylsiloxy)boranes are obtained in good yield by transesterification between silanols and borates, using a trace of sodium as catalyst[82].

$$3(C_2H_5)_3SiOH + B(OC_4H_9^n)_3 \longrightarrow [(C_2H_5)_3SiO]_3B + 3C_4H_9^nOH$$

Boric acid and silanols reacted in a similar way[135].

References, p. 195–199

Boron halides and alkylboron halides react readily with alkali metal silanolates[84,128].

$$3(C_2H_5)_3SiONa + BBr_3 \longrightarrow [(C_2H_5)_3SiO]_3B + 3NaBr$$

$$2(C_2H_5)_3SiONa + CH_3BBr_2 \longrightarrow [(C_2H_5)_3SiO]_2BCH_3 + 2NaBr$$

A low yield of tris(trimethylsiloxy)borane was obtained by condensation of trimethylmethoxysilane with boric acid in the presence of *p*-toluenesulphonic acid[82,85]. This reaction proceeds more readily with triethylmethoxysilane. Tris(trimethylsiloxy)borane was also prepared from trimethylethoxysilane and boron trioxide, and from the silanol and tris(dimethylamino)borane[135].

Borosiloxanes are also formed by cleavage of disiloxanes with boron trioxide[82].

$$3[(CH_3)_3Si]_2O + B_2O_3 \longrightarrow 2[(CH_3)_3SiO]_3B$$

Boron halides and alkylboron halides convert hexa-alkyldisiloxanes into the corresponding trialkylsilyl halides[84]. The reactions proceed stepwise, with formation of borosiloxane intermediates, which can be isolated.

$$[(CH_3)_3Si]_2O + BBr_3 \longrightarrow (CH_3)_3SiOBBr_2 + (CH_3)_3SiBr$$

$$(CH_3)_3SiOBBr_2 \longrightarrow (CH_3)_3SiBr + BBrO$$

$$3BBrO \longrightarrow B_2O_3 + BBr_3$$

$$2[(C_2H_5)_3Si]_2O + BBr_3 \longrightarrow [(C_2H_5)_3SiO]_2BBr + 2(C_2H_5)_3SiBr$$

A stable trimethylsiloxyborane is obtained by direct reaction of dimethylbromoborane with hexamethyldisiloxane.

$$[(CH_3)_3Si]_2O + (CH_3)_2BBr \longrightarrow (CH_3)_3SiOB(CH_3)_2 + (CH_3)_3SiBr$$

A series of well-defined steps has also been recognised in the reaction of boron trichloride with cyclic siloxanes, $(R_2SiO)_n$; certain borosiloxane intermediates were isolated[86].

$$(R_2SiO)_n + nBCl_3 \longrightarrow nR_2ClSiOBCl_2$$

$$3R_2ClSiOBCl_2 \longrightarrow (R_2ClSiO)_3B + 2BCl_3$$

Of the siloxanes studied, the order of decreasing reactivity towards boron trichloride was:

$$[(CH_3)_2SiO]_3 > [(CH_3)_2SiO]_4 > [(C_2H_5)_2SiO]_3 > [(C_2H_5)_2SiO]_4$$

Whereas boron trichloride and *n*-butoxysilanes undergo stepwise replacement of alkoxyl by chlorine, with a noticeable fall in rate for each successive step, another mode of fission occurs with tetra-*s*-butoxysilane and tetra-1-phenylethoxysilane[87]. Here, the overall reaction sequences were rather complex, but alkyl-oxygen fission was clearly indicated in the case of *s*-butoxytrichlorosilane which gave the novel trichlorosilyl borate[88].

$$(C_4H_9^nO)_4Si + BCl_3 \longrightarrow (C_4H_9^nO)_3SiCl + C_4H_9^nO\cdot BCl_2$$

$$Cl_3Si\cdot OC_4H_9^s + BCl_3 \longrightarrow (Cl_3SiO)_3B + C_4H_9^sCl$$

In the synthesis of borosiloxane polymers using di- and trifunctional silicon intermediates, the reactions of organosilicon acetates with alkoxyboranes, and of organosilicon alkoxides with acetoxyboranes have been studied[89,90]. These reactions proceed in a stepwise manner and simple borosiloxane intermediates have been recognised. Thus, the first stage in such reactions is:

$$(CH_3)_2Si(OCOCH_3)_2 + B(OC_2H_5)_3 \rightarrow CH_3COOC_2H_5 + CH_3COO\text{–}\overset{\overset{\displaystyle CH_3}{|}}{\underset{\underset{\displaystyle CH_3}{|}}{Si}}\text{–}O\text{–}B(OC_2H_5)_2$$

$$(CH_3)_2Si(OC_4H_9)_2 + B(OCOCH_3)_3 \rightarrow CH_3COOC_4H_9 + C_4H_9O\text{–}\overset{\overset{\displaystyle CH_3}{|}}{\underset{\underset{\displaystyle CH_3}{|}}{Si}}\text{–}O\text{–}B(OCOCH_3)_2$$

The isolation of an interesting cyclic borosiloxane has been reported, but no details are available[91].

$$B\begin{array}{l} \diagup O\text{—}Si(C_6H_5)_2\text{—}O \diagdown \\ \text{—}O\text{—}Si(C_6H_5)_2\text{—}O\text{—} \\ \diagdown O\text{—}Si(C_6H_5)_2\text{—}O \diagup \end{array}B$$

(XLIII)

References, p. 195–199

Organosiloxyboron compounds generally are very susceptible to hydrolysis. Trialkylsilylmetaborates have been prepared from trialkylsilyl borates and boron trioxide[135].

8. Organosiloxytin compounds

By a series of metathetical reactions between the alkali metal silanolates and the appropriate tin chlorides, Rochow and Tatlock[30] have prepared the crystalline bis(trimethylsiloxy)tin, tetrakis-(trimethylsiloxy)tin, and bis(trimethylsiloxy)dimethyltin.

$$2(CH_3)_3SiONa + SnCl_2 \longrightarrow [(CH_3)_3SiO]_2Sn + 2NaCl$$

$$4(CH_3)_3SiOK + SnCl_4 \longrightarrow [(CH_3)_3SiO]_4Sn + 4KCl$$

$$2(CH_3)_3SiOK + (CH_3)_2SnCl_2 \longrightarrow [(CH_3)_3SiO]_2Sn(CH_3)_2 + 2KCl$$

Both the tin(II) and tin(IV) derivatives hydrolyse fairly readily in water. Dimethylbis(triphenylsiloxy)tin is formed in good yield by the reaction of triphenylsilanol with dimethyltin oxide in boiling dioxan or xylene[16b,92]. It is likely that other reactions (such as the alkoxide–acyloxide reaction), which have been successfully used in the synthesis of polystannosiloxanes[93–95] could, if applied to monofunctional intermediates, be equally successful in the preparation of simple organosiloxy-tin compounds. Further, there is no doubt that the reactions leading to polymer formation proceed initially through simple stannosiloxanes.

9. Organosiloxyarsenic compounds

The quest for siloxane derivatives possessing pesticidal properties led Kary and Frisch[96] to explore the possibilities of certain compounds of arsenic(V), containing Si—O—As linkages. By the interaction of both alkyl- and aryl-chlorosilanes (2 moles) with either alkyl- or aryl-arsonic acids (1 mole), a series of compounds of this type was successfully synthesised. Thus, from methylarsonic acid and dimethyldichlorosilane, bis(dimethylchlorosilyl) methylarsonate was obtained. Similarly, bis(methyldichlorosilyl) methylarsonate was prepared from methyltrichlorosilane. Bis(diphenylchlorosilyl) and bis(phenyldichlorosilyl) phenylarsonates were made from phenylarsonic acid and diphenyldichlorosilane and phenyltrichlorosilane, respectively, essentially by the same method. In the synthesis of bis(triphenylsilyl) phenylarsonate, pyridine was used as hydrohalogen acceptor.

$$2Cl{-}Si(CH_3)_2{-}Cl + HO{-}As(=O)(CH_3){-}OH \longrightarrow Cl{-}Si(CH_3)_2{-}O{-}As(=O)(CH_3){-}O{-}Si(CH_3)_2{-}Cl + 2HCl.$$

$$2Cl{-}Si(Cl)(CH_3){-}Cl + HO{-}As(=O)(CH_3){-}OH \longrightarrow Cl{-}Si(Cl)(CH_3){-}O{-}As(=O)(CH_3){-}O{-}Si(Cl)(CH_3){-}Cl + 2HCl.$$

$$2(C_6H_5)_3Si{-}Cl + HO{-}As(=O)(C_6H_5){-}OH \rightarrow (C_6H_5)_3Si{-}O{-}As(=O)(C_6H_5){-}O{-}Si(C_6H_5)_3 + 2\,HCl$$

Both aliphatic and aromatic chlorosilyl arsonates hydrolyse readily to give polymeric materials.

More recently, Chamberland and MacDiarmid[97] have prepared and characterized monomers and polymers containing Si—O—As(III) and Si—O—As(V) linkages. Tris(triphenylsilyl) arsenite, m.p. 190.5°, was prepared as indicated.

$$AsCl_3 + 3(C_6H_5)_3SiOH + 3NH_3 \longrightarrow [(C_6H_5)_3SiO]_3As + 3NH_4Cl$$

$$AsCl_3 + 3(C_6H_5)_3SiONa \longrightarrow [(C_6H_5)_3SiO]_3As + 3NaCl$$

$$AsCl_3 + 3(C_6H_5)_3SiCl + 3H_2O \xrightarrow{NH_3} [(C_6H_5)_3SiO]_3As + 6HCl$$

Tris(triphenylsilyl) arsenate, m.p. 240–242°, was prepared in 87% yield by treating an ethereal solution of triphenylchlorosilane (in

References, p. 195–199

excess) with potassium dihydrogen arsenate at room temperature. Although the intermediate species could not be isolated, the reaction is believed to have occurred in two stages:

$$KH_2AsO_4 + (C_6H_5)_3SiCl \longrightarrow (C_6H_5)_3Si{-}O{-}\overset{\overset{\displaystyle O}{\|}}{\underset{\underset{\displaystyle OH}{|}}{As}}{-}OH + KCl$$

$$3(C_6H_5)_3SiOAs(O)(OH)_2 \longrightarrow [(C_6H_5)_3SiO]_3AsO + 2H_3AsO_4$$

Both tris(triphenylsilyl) arsenite and tris(triphenylsilyl) arsenate were hydrolysed only very slightly when dissolved in acetone–water solutions. The former distilled unchanged *in vacuo* at 351° but decomposed at 420°. Tris(triphenylsilyl) arsenate could not be distilled and decomposed at 290°.

Instead of the expected polymeric species, a cyclic arsenosiloxane was found to be the predominant product from the co-hydrolysis of arsenic(III) chloride and diphenyldichlorosilane. The principal reaction is:

$$2AsCl_3 + 3(C_6H_5)_2SiCl_2 + 6H_2O \longrightarrow As[OSi(C_6H_5)_2O]_3As + 12HCl$$

The same compound, m.p. 194–195°, was also obtained by interaction of arsenic(III) chloride with diphenylsilanediol (in the presence of ammonia or triethylamine as acid acceptor). Its structure, which has been postulated as (XLIV), recalls that of the analogous boron compound, (XLIII)[91].

$$\begin{array}{c} \diagup O{-}Si(C_6H_5)_2{-}O\diagdown \\ As{-}O{-}Si(C_6H_3)_2{-}O{-}As \\ \diagdown O{-}Si(C_6H_5)_2{-}O\diagup \end{array}$$

(XLIV)

From the reaction of arsenic(III) chloride with the silanediol, another substance of composition corresponding to $As[OSi(C_6H_5)_2\text{-}OSi(C_6H_5)_2O]_3As$, was isolated, but not fully characterised. Although the compound (XLIV) does not suffer any measurable hydrolysis even in boiling acetone–water solutions, its melting point is depressed, which suggests that ring-opening reactions may be taking place, with formation of polymeric species.

Further studies[98] of Si—O—As compounds are illustrated by the following equations:

$$C_6H_5AsI_2 + 2(C_6H_5)_3SiONa \longrightarrow C_6H_5As[OSi(C_6H_5)_3]_2 + 2NaI$$

$$2C_6H_5AsI_2 + 2(C_6H_5)_2Si(OH)_2 + 4NH_3 \longrightarrow$$

$$C_6H_5As[OSi(C_6H_5)_2O]_2AsC_6H_5 + 4NH_4I$$

$$Ag_3AsO_4 + 3(C_6H_5)_3SiCl \longrightarrow [(C_6H_5)_3SiO]_3AsO + 4AgCl$$

Schmidt and Schmidbaur[99] have described the preparation of tris(trimethylsilyl) arsenate from trimethylchlorosilane and anhydrous silver arsenate in inert organic solvents. The arsenate ester hydrolyses readily to give arsenic acid and hexamethyldisiloxane.

For comparison with the Si—O—As compounds, analogous compounds containing the Sn—O—As linkage have also been synthesised[19].

10. Organosiloxyphosphorus compounds

The first recorded synthesis of an alkylsilyl phosphate was by Sauer in 1944[100]. Slow distillation of hexamethyldisiloxane with phosphorus pentoxide or phosphoric acid resulted in cleavage of the siloxane bond with formation of tris(trimethylsilyl) phosphate. This reaction was later studied by Voronkov[101].

$$3[(CH_3)_3Si]_2O + P_2O_5 \longrightarrow 2[(CH_3)_3SiO]_3PO$$

Since 1955, a large number of alkylsilyl esters of phosphoric acid, alkylphosphonic acids, phosphorous acid, and thiophosphoric acid have been prepared and investigated, largely by Voronkov and his school[101–104], and by Fehér and co-workers[105–107]. In addition to the Sauer reaction, the following methods have been applied to the synthesis of tris(trialkylsilyl) phosphates:

(a)[102] $3R_3SiOR' + (HO)_3PO \longrightarrow (R_3SiO)_3PO + 3R'OH$

(b)[103] $3R_3SiOR' + (HO)_2PHO + \frac{1}{2}O_2 \longrightarrow (R_3SiO)_3PO + 3R'OH$

References, p. 195–199

(c)[108] $$6R_3SiOR' + P_2O_5 \longrightarrow 2(R_3SiO)_3PO + 3R'_2O$$

(d)[102] $$3R_3SiCl + (HO)_3PO \longrightarrow (R_3SiO)_3PO + 3HCl$$

(e)[102, 109] $$3R_3SiX + (R'O)_3PO \longrightarrow (R_3SiO)_3PO + 3R'X \ (X = Cl \text{ or } Br)$$

(f)[99] $$3R_3SiCl + Ag_3PO_4 \longrightarrow (R_3SiO)_3PO + 3AgCl \ (R = CH_3)$$

(g)[107] $$R_2SiHCl + (R'O)_2P(O)OH \longrightarrow (R_2SiHO)P(O)(OR')_2 + HCl$$

(h)[107] $$2R_2SiHCl + (R'O)P(O)(OH)_2 \longrightarrow (R_2SiHO)_2P(O)(OR') + 2HCl$$

Reaction (a) furnished good yields of the esters, obtained as colourless, readily-hydrolysed liquids. In reaction (e), anhydrous iron(III) chloride was added as catalyst (when chlorosilanes were used). Tris(trimethylsilyl) phosphate had b.p. 232°/760 mm, and the triethylsilyl compound distills unchanged at reduced pressures, but the higher alkylsilyl esters undergo decomposition on attempted distillation, even at 1 mm pressure[101].

By chlorination of diethylsilyl diethyl phosphate, $[(C_2H_5)_2SiHO]$-$P(O)(OC_2H_5)_2$, and subsequent condensation with triethylsilanol, the compound $(C_2H_5)_3SiOSi(C_2H_5)_2OP(O)(OC_2H_5)_2$ was obtained[107]. An alternative preparation is from the disiloxane $(C_2H_5)_3SiOSi$-$(C_2H_5)_2Cl$ and diethyl hydrogen phosphate.

Trimethylsilyl dihydrogen phosphate, m.p. 66–66.5°, has been prepared by the following reaction[110] in ethereal solution.

$$(CH_3)_3SiCl + KH_2PO_4 \longrightarrow (CH_3)_3SiOPO(OH)_2 + KCl$$

The corresponding triethylsilyl ester was obtained as an undistillable oil. Both esters hydrolyse readily, as do the phosphonates.

Bis(trialkylsilyl) phosphonates have similarly been derived from phosphorous acid[103].

$$2(CH_3)(C_2H_5)_2SiOCH_3 + H_3PO_3 \longrightarrow [(CH_3)(C_2H_5)_2SiO]_2PHO + 2CH_3OH$$

$$2(CH_3)_3SiCl + H_3PO_3 \longrightarrow [(CH_3)_3SiO]_2PHO + 2HCl$$

When triethylbromosilane is treated with triethyl phosphite (an Arbusov-type reaction), a triethylsilyl ester of ethylphosphonic acid is formed[111,112].

$$(C_2H_5)_3SiBr + P(OC_2H_5)_3 \longrightarrow C_2H_5 \cdot PO(OC_2H_5)[OSi(C_2H_5)_3] + C_2H_5Br$$

Phosphorus halides serve as useful reagents for the conversion of alkoxytrialkylsilanes to the silyl halides. With silanols and siloxanes they give tris(trialkylsilyl) phosphites[104].

$$3R_3SiOH + PBr_3 \xrightarrow{ZnCl_2} (R_3SiO)_3P + 3HBr$$

$$3(R_3Si)_2O + PBr_3 \longrightarrow (R_3SiO)_3P + 3R_3SiBr$$

Phosphoryl chloride and bromide also convert trimethylsilyl alkoxides into chloro- or bromo-silanes, but an unusual reaction was encountered between phosphoryl chloride and 1-phenylethoxytrimethylsilane[113]. This led to the formation of trimethylsilyl phosphorodichloridate. A similar reaction was observed with diphenylmethoxytrimethylsilane.

$$(CH_3)_3SiOCH(CH_3)(C_6H_5) + POCl_3 \longrightarrow (CH_3)_3SiOPOCl_2 + ClCH(CH_3)C_6H_5$$

$$(CH_3)_3SiOCH(C_6H_5)_2 + POCl_3 \longrightarrow (CH_3)_3SiOPOCl_2 + ClCH(C_6H_5)_2$$

Other methods for the synthesis of trimethylsilyl phosphorodichloridate have recently been described[114]. These include the reaction of phosphoryl or pyrophosphoryl chloride with hexamethyldisiloxane, and the disproportionation reaction of tris(trimethylsilyl) phosphate with phosphoryl chloride.

$$POCl_3 + [(CH_3)_3Si]_2O \longrightarrow (CH_3)_3SiCl + (CH_3)_3SiOPOCl_2$$

$$Cl_2OPOPOCl_2 + [(CH_3)_3Si]_2O \longrightarrow 2(CH_3)_3SiOPOCl_2$$

$$POCl_3 + [(CH_3)_3SiO]_3PO \longrightarrow 3(CH_3)_3SiOPOCl_2$$

With water or alcohols, the ester is readily solvolysed.

$$2(CH_3)_3SiOPOCl_2 + 5H_2O \longrightarrow [(CH_3)_3Si]_2O + 4HCl + 2H_3PO_4$$

11. Organosiloxysulphur compounds

Although organosilyl bisulphates have never been isolated, there is considerable evidence, based on cryoscopic measurements, for their

References, p. 195–199

formation in the reactions of sulphuric acid with silanols, ethoxysilanes, disiloxanes, and cyclosiloxanes[115, 116].

$$(C_2H_5)_3SiOH + 2H_2SO_4 \longrightarrow (C_2H_5)_3SiHSO_4 + H_3\overset{+}{O} + HS\overset{-}{O}_4$$

$$(C_2H_5)_3SiOEt + 3H_2SO_4 \longrightarrow (C_2H_5)_3SiHSO_4 + C_2H_5HSO_4 + H_3\overset{+}{O} + HS\overset{-}{O}_4$$

$$(R_3Si)_2O + 3H_2SO_4 \longrightarrow 2R_3SiHSO_4 + H_3\overset{+}{O} + HS\overset{-}{O}_4$$

$$[(CH_3)_2SiO]_4 + 12H_2SO_4 \longrightarrow 4(CH_3)_2Si(HSO_4)_2 + 4H_3\overset{+}{O} + 4HS\overset{-}{O}_4$$

There is close correspondence between the expected and observed Van't Hoff factors in all cases. Thus, in the last reaction, which should give rise to a factor of 12, the value observed was 12.6, which is consistent with the formation of a bis(hydrogen sulphate). It seems likely that the bisulphates which are formed, for example, on mixing a disiloxane with sulphuric acid, are in equilibrium with a small proportion of the normal sulphate since, on extraction with solvent, the normal sulphate is obtained. Bis(trimethylsilyl) sulphate, $[(CH_3)_3Si]_2SO_4$, a solid of m.p. 56–58°, was thus obtained by extracting with dry pentane the white crystalline slurry resulting from the treatment of hexamethyldisiloxane with concentrated sulphuric acid[117,118]. The liquid triethyl ester has been obtained in a similar manner[117]. The preparation of bis(trimethylsilyl) sulphate by treating trimethylchlorosilane[119] or trimethylvinylsilane[120] with sulphuric acid has also been reported. Organosilicon sulphates generally are immediately hydrolysed by water.

Cleavage of methyl groups from certain organosilicon compounds readily occurs with sulphuric acid. In the process, organosilicon bisulphates are formed as intermediates[23]. Addition of water results in hydrolysis and formation of disiloxanes. By treating the bisulphates with hydrogen halides or inorganic halides, organosilicon halides are formed.

Schmidt and Schmidbaur[121] have recently succeeded in synthesising a cyclic, dimeric dimethylsilyl sulphate, (XLV). This crystalline material was obtained in high yields from dimethyldichlorosilane and sulphuric acid, and from polydimethylsiloxane and sulphur trioxide. It reacts vigorously with water and methanol, giving polydimethylsiloxane, and with hydrogen chloride to give dimethyldichlorosilane.

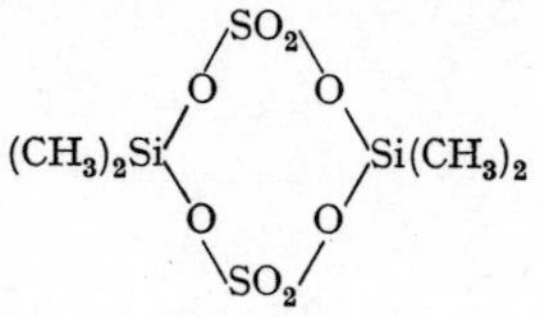

```
            SO2
           /   \
          O     O
         /       \
(CH3)2Si           Si(CH3)2
         \       /
          O     O
           \   /
            SO2
```

(XLV)

12. Other organosiloxymetal compounds

Organosiloxyantimony compounds have received some attention. Heating trimethylethoxysilane with antimony(III) chloride at 240° under pressure in presence of zinc chloride for 12 hours, was claimed to afford tris(trimethylsiloxy)antimony [tris(trimethylsilyl) antimonite][16b].

$$3(CH_3)_3SiOC_2H_5 + SbCl_3 \longrightarrow [(CH_3)_3SiO]_3Sb + 3C_2H_5Cl$$

Other methods for the synthesis of tris(trialkylsilyl) antimonites include: (a)[122] azeotropic distillation of water from a mixture of trialkylsilanol and antimony trioxide (70% yield):

$$6R_3SiOH + Sb_2O_3 \rightleftharpoons 2(R_3SiO)_3Sb + 3H_2O$$

(b)[122] transesterification of trialkyl antimonites and triorganosilanols (90% yield):

$$(R'O)_3Sb + 3R_3SiOH \rightleftharpoons (R_3SiO)_3Sb + 3\,R'OH$$

and (c)[130] exchange reaction between the chloride and sodium silanolates:

$$3(C_2H_5)_3SiONa + SbCl_3 \longrightarrow [(C_2H_5)_3SiO]_3Sb + 3NaCl$$

Henglein, Lang and Scheinost[123] have described the synthesis of a polyantimonosiloxane, by treating triethyl antimonite with di-

References, p. 195–199

methyldiacetoxysilane (see p. 234) and they speculate on the possible formation of a cyclic antimonosiloxane (XLVI) as an intermediate. However, the products were not well characterised and the existence of (XLVI) was not substantiated.

$$\mathrm{Sb}\begin{cases} \mathrm{O{-}Si(CH_3)_2{-}O} \\ \mathrm{O{-}Si(CH_3)_2{-}O} \\ \mathrm{O{-}Si(CH_3)_2{-}O} \end{cases}\mathrm{Sb}$$

(XLVI)

A siloxy-derivative of molybdenum(III) has been isolated and characterised[124]. The isolation of tris(triphenylsiloxy)molybdenum was achieved, rather unexpectedly, by the reaction of two moles of sodium triphenylsilanolate and one mole of molybdenyl(VI) chloride. The reaction had been anticipated to proceed as follows:

$$MoO_2Cl_2 + 2(C_6H_5)_3SiONa \longrightarrow [(C_6H_5)_3SiO]_2MoO_2 + 2NaCl.$$

However, analysis corresponded to the formula $[(C_6H_5)_3SiO]_3Mo$. Attempts to form this compound by direct reaction of sodium triphenylsilanolate (3 moles) and molybdenum(III) chloride (1 mole) failed.

Trimethylsilanol and the appropriate metal alkoxide afford[68,69] tetrakis(trimethylsiloxy)zirconium (m.p. 151°, yield 60%) and pentakis(trimethylsiloxy)tantalum (m.p. 80°, yield 74%).

$$4(CH_3)_3SiOH + Zr(OC_3H_7^i)_4 \longrightarrow [(CH_3)_3SiO]_4Zr + 4C_3H_7^iOH$$

$$5(CH_3)_3SiOH + Ta(OC_3H_7^i)_5 \longrightarrow [(CH_3)_3SiO]_5Ta + 5C_3H_7OH$$

The corresponding reactions with triethylsilanol were quantitative. This reflects less competition from the side reaction involving siloxane formation from the silanol. In the case of niobium, there was evidence of the formation of an unstable pentakis(trimethylsiloxy)-derivative, but attempts to purify it by vacuum sublimation caused it to break down, giving octakis(trimethylsiloxy)-diniobium oxide, $[(CH_3)_3SiO]_4NbONb[OSi(CH_3)_3]_4$.

Favourable conditions were also found for the silanolysis of metal trimethylsiloxides.

$$M[OSi(CH_3)_3]_n + nR_3SiOH \longrightarrow M[OSiR_3]_n + n(CH_3)_3SiOH$$

These reactions were carried out in hexamethyldisiloxane as a solvent, because the latter forms a convenient minimum-boiling azeotrope with trimethylsilanol. It is noteworthy that all the reactions investigated gave practically quantitative yields, in spite of the fact that the reactive trimethylsilanol was liberated in each case. It is obvious that the metal trialkylsiloxides did not catalyse its condensation. By this route the derivatives (XLVII)–(LIV) were prepared.

$Ti[OSi(CH_3)_2C_2H_5]_4$ (XLVII)	$Zr[OSi(C_2H_5)_3]_4$ (LI)
$Ti[OSi(CH_3)(C_2H_5)_2]_4$ (XLVIII)	$Ta[OSi(CH_3)_2C_2H_5]_5$ (LII)
$Ti[OSi(C_2H_5)_3]_4$ (XLIX)	$Ta[OSi(CH_3)(C_2H_5)_2]_5$ (LIII)
$Zr[OSi(CH_3)_2C_2H_5]_4$ (L)	$Ta[OSi(C_2H_5)_3]_5$ (LIV)

The alkoxide-acyloxide reaction has also been successfully applied to the preparation of these siloxy-derivatives[69,74]. It was found convenient to carry out the reactions in boiling cyclohexane, removing the alkyl acetate as the binary azeotrope with the solvent.

$$4(CH_3)_3SiOCOCH_3 + Zr(OC_3H_7^i)_4 \longrightarrow [(CH_3)_3SiO]_4Zr + 4CH_3COOC_3H_7^i$$

$$4(C_2H_5)_3SiOCOCH_3 + Zr(OC_3H_7^i)_4 \longrightarrow [(C_2H_5)_3SiO]_4Zr + 4CH_3COOC_3H_7^i$$

$$5(CH_3)_3SiOCOCH_3 + Ta(OC_2H_5)_5 \longrightarrow [(CH_3)_3SiO]_5Ta + 5CH_3COOC_2H_5$$

These siloxy-derivatives of zirconium and tantalum were found to be more stable towards hydrolysis and thermal decomposition than the corresponding metal alkoxides. Tetrakis(triphenylsiloxy)-zirconium, germanium, tin (in somewhat impure state), and hafnium have all been prepared from sodium triphenylsilanolate and the tetrachlorides of the metals[125]; some properties are summarised in Table 11.

$$4(C_6H_5)_3SiONa + MCl_4 \longrightarrow [(C_6H_5)_3SiO]_4M + 4NaCl \quad M = Zr, Ge, Hf, Sn.$$

References, p. 195–199

TABLE 11

PROPERTIES OF TETRAKIS(TRIPHENYLSILOXY)-COMPOUNDS OF GROUP IV ELEMENTS

Compound	*M.p.*	*Sublimation point*	*Solubility in benzene*	*Hydrolysability with acids and bases*
$[(C_6H_5)_3SiO]_4Si$	235°	249° (1 atm.)	Very soluble	No
$[(C_6H_5)_3SiO]_4Ge$	472° (a)	400° (c)	Very slight	No
$[(C_6H_5)_3SiO]_4Sn$	322° (a)	Decomp.	Very slight	Yes
$[(C_6H_5)_3SiO]_4Ti$	502°	360° (c)	Very slight	No
$[(C_6H_5)_3SiO]_4Zr$	410° (b)	360° (c)	Soluble	Yes
$[(C_6H_5)_3SiO]_4Hf$	383° (b)	360° (d)	Soluble	Yes

(a) Partial decomposition.
(b) Decomposition with liberation of hydrocarbon.
(c) Molecular sublimation at 10^{-4} atm.
(d) Molecular sublimation at 10^{-4} atm with partial decomposition.

Trimethylsilanol esters of chromic and orthovanadic acids have been prepared. Chromic acid, refluxed in hexamethyldisiloxane at 100°, furnished trimethylsilyl chromate, $[(CH_3)_3SiO]_2CrO_2$, b.p. 75°/1 mm, which was soluble in benzene and carbon tetrachloride and hydrolysed by water to regenerate the reactants[126]. Vanadyl(V) chloride, $VOCl_3$, similarly, gave yellow $(CH_3)_3SiOVOCl_2$, b.p. 35–36°/1 mm, and trimethylchlorosilane[127]. With additional hexamethyldisiloxane (at 100°, 24 hours), the bright yellow $[(CH_3)_3SiO]_2$-VOCl, b.p. 53°/1.1 mm, was formed, but was difficult to isolate because of its tendency to decompose. Both esters were hydrolysed by water, giving hexamethyldisiloxane, hydrochloric acid, and polyvanadic acids. The colourless tris(trimethylsilyl) vanadate, $[(CH_3)_3SiO]_3VO$, b.p. 100°/9.5 mm, was obtained from silver vanadate and trimethylchlorosilane, in benzene or methylene dichloride at 8–10°, or alternatively, in poor yield, by boiling vanadium pentoxide with hexamethyldisiloxane for 60 hours. All three esters were easily soluble in organic solvents and became coloured intensely red by traces of moisture. Alcohols decomposed them to alkoxysilanes and red polyvanadic acids.

Silyl vanadates have also been prepared in 50–80% yields by

reaction of vanadium pentoxide with silanols, with azeotropic removal of the water formed, by means of benzene or another suitable solvent[128].

$$6R_3SiOH + V_2O_5 \rightleftharpoons 2(R_3SiO)_3VO + 3H_2O$$

Other methods which proved successful were: (a) reaction of silanols with $VOCl_3$ in presence of acid acceptors, such as pyridine or ammonia (yields 60–80%); (b) transesterification of trialkyl vanadates with silanols with catalytic amounts of the sodium silanolate (yields up to 90%); and (c) reaction of sodium silanolate with $VOCl_3$[130]. One siloxy-derivative of vanadium(IV), tetrakis(triphenylsiloxy)vanadium, m.p. 260°, has been reported[124]. This was prepared as follows:

$$4(C_6H_5)_3SiONa + VCl_4 \longrightarrow [(C_6H_5)_3SiO]_4V + 4NaCl$$

This ester was hydrolytically-stable and soluble in benzene. Attempts to form siloxy-derivatives of vanadium in lower oxidation state failed.

Mercury(II) chloride reacted with sodium trimethylsilanolate in dioxan to form a soluble siloxy-derivative[30], but it was so sensitive to traces of moisture that the final product was always contaminated with yellow mercuric oxide resulting from its hydrolysis.

$$2(CH_3)_3SiONa + HgCl_2 \longrightarrow [(CH_3)_3SiO]_2Hg + 2NaCl$$

Patnode and Schmidt[119] claim to have prepared bis(trimethylsiloxy)lead, a crystalline solid, by shaking lead oxide with trimethylsilanol for 2 days.

$$2(CH_3)_3SiOH + PbO \longrightarrow [(CH_3)_3SiO]_2Pb + H_2O$$

However, analysis of the compound so obtained showed a considerable discrepancy between the theoretical and experimental results (Found: Pb, 59.1%. Calc.: Pb, 53.7%). Andrianov[129] suggested that the reaction may have taken another course, since it was found that when triethylsilanol reacts with lead hydroxide a

References, p. 195–199

compound was formed, which comprised two moles of bis-(triethylsiloxy)lead and one mole of lead hydroxide.

$$3Pb(OH)_2 + 4(C_2H_5)_3SiOH \longrightarrow 2Pb[OSi(C_2H_5)_3]_2 \cdot Pb(OH)_2 + 2H_2O$$

A study of the reaction of this compound with titanium(IV) chloride led to a new synthesis of tetrakis(triethylsiloxy)titanium.

$$2\{2Pb[OSi(C_2H_5)_3]_2 \cdot Pb(OH)_2\} + 3TiCl_4 \longrightarrow$$

$$2Ti[OSi(C_2H_5)_3]_4 + 6PbCl_2 + 3Ti(OH)_4$$

Similarly[130], using vanadyl(V) chloride, tris(triethylsilyl) vanadate has been obtained.

$$3\{2Pb[OSi(C_2H_5)_3]_2 \cdot Pb(OH)_2\} + 4VOCl_3 \longrightarrow$$

$$4[(C_2H_5)_3SiO]_3VO + 6PbCl_2 + 3Pb(OH)_2$$

The infrared spectra of both the lead and the vanadium siloxanes have been investigated and the characteristic vibration frequencies reported.

Trimethylsilyl perrhenate, $(CH_3)_3SiReO_4$, has been obtained in good yield from rhenium heptoxide and hexamethyldisiloxane, and from silver perrhenate and trimethylchlorosilane[131].

Trimethylsilyl nitrate, $(CH_3)_3SiONO_2$[132], a somewhat unstable compound, has been isolated in low yield from the reaction of trimethylchlorosilane and silver nitrate in tetrahydrofuran at 10°. It decomposes into dinitrogen tetroxide, oxygen, and hexamethyldisiloxane at room temperature, even in the absence of water. Analogously, dimethylsilyl dinitrate, $(CH_3)_2Si(ONO_2)_2$, was obtained from dimethyldichlorosilane. It decomposed exothermally into nitrogen oxides and the siloxane even at 0°. Silicon tetranitrate is unstable, but a dipyridine complex has been isolated[136].

Trialkyl- and triaryl-silyl perchlorates have been made from the appropriate chlorides and silver perchlorate in benzene[133].

$$(C_2H_5)_3SiCl + AgClO_4 \longrightarrow (C_2H_5)_3SiClO_4 + AgCl$$

$$(C_6H_5)_3SiCl + AgClO_4 \longrightarrow (C_6H_5)_3SiClO_4 + AgCl$$

The trialkyl compounds were liquids, which fumed in air and detonated when quickly heated. The triaryl compounds were solids, which exploded when heated. All the perchlorates were readily solvolysed by water or methanol.

REFERENCES

1 H. J. EMELÉUS, *Proc. Chem. Soc.*, (1959) 202.
2 H. KREBS, *Angew. Chem.*, 70 (1958) 615.
3 A. A. BERLIN and V. P. PARINI, *Khim. Nauka i Prom.*, 1 (1956) 44.
4 V. V. KORSHAK and K. K. MOZGOVA, *Uspekhi Khim.*, 28 (1959) 783.
5 T. A. KOCH and P. E. LINDVIG, *J. Appl. Polymer Sci.*, 1 (1959) 164.
6 O. VOGL, *J. Polymer Sci.*, 46 (1960) 261.
7 G. HÄGG, *Z. physik. Chem.*, B 18 (1932) 206.
8 H. GERDING and N. F. MOERMAN, *Z. physik. Chem.*, B 35 (1937) 216.
9 H. GERDING, *Naturwiss.*, 25 (1937) 251.
10 D. B. SOWERBY and L. F. AUDRIETH, *J. Chem. Educ.*, 37 (1960) 2.
11 A. MICHEL, *Bull. soc. chim. France*, (1956) 1103.
12 L. G. SILLÉN, *Quart. Revs.* (*London*), 13 (1959) 146.
13 E. G. ROCHOW and M. P. BROWN, *J. Am. Chem. Soc.*, 82 (1960) 4166.
14 W. METLESICS and H. ZEISS, *J. Am. Chem. Soc.*, 82 (1960) 3324.
15 H. GILMAN, R. K. INGHAM and S. D. ROSENBERG, *Chem. Revs.*, 60 (1960) 459.
16 K. A. ANDRIANOV, *Uspekhi Khim.*, (a) 26 (1957) 895; (b) 27 (1958) 1257.
17 D. C. BRADLEY, *Metal-Organic Compounds, Advances in Chemistry Series*, Vol. 23, American Chemical Society, Washington, 1959, p. 10.
18 J. R. VAN WAZER, *Phosphorus and its Compounds*, Interscience Publishers, Vol. I, New York, 1958.
19 B. L. CHAMBERLAND and A. G. MACDIARMID, *J. Chem. Soc.*, (1961) 445.
20 W. B. BLUMENTHAL, *The Chemical Behaviour of Zirconium*, D. Van Nostrand, New York, 1958.
21 F. A. HENGLEIN and P. SCHMULDER, *Makromol. Chem.*, 13 (1954) 53.
22 K. A. ANDRIANOV, *Organic Silicon Compounds* (State Scientific Technical Publishing House for Chemical Literature, Moscow, 1955). [Translation Prepared by Technical Documents Liaison Office, MCLTD, Wright-Patterson Air Force Base, Ohio, U.S.A. Distributed by U.S. Department of Commerce, Office of Technical Service, Washington D.C., U.S.A.]
23 C. EABORN, *Organosilicon Compounds*, Butterworths, London, 1960.
24 L. H. SOMMER, E. W. PIETRUSZA and F. C. WHITMORE, *J. Am. Chem. Soc.*, 68 (1946) 2282.
25 J. F. HYDE, O. K. JOHANNSON, W. H. DAUDT, R. F. FLEMING, H. B. LAUDENSLAGER and M. P. ROCHE, *J. Am. Chem. Soc.*, 75 (1953) 5615.
26 R. WEST and R. H. BANEY, *J. Inorg. & Nuclear Chem.*, 7 (1958) 297.
27 L. H. SOMMER, L. Q. GREEN and F. C. WHITMORE, *J. Am. Chem. Soc.*, 71 (1949) 3253.

[28] V. S. Chugunov, *J. Am. Chem. Soc.*, 27 (1957) 494.
[29] K. A. Andrianov, A. A. Zhdanov, N. A. Kurasheva and V. G. Dulova, *Doklady Akad. Nauk S.S.S.R.*, 112 (1957) 1050.
[30] W. S. Tatlock and E. G. Rochow, *J. Org. Chem.*, 17 (1952) 1555.
[31] W. S. Tatlock and E. G. Rochow, *J. Am. Chem. Soc.*, 72 (1950) 528.
[32] F. S. Kipping and L. L. Lloyd, *J. Chem. Soc.*, 79 (1901) 449.
[33] H. Gilman, H. N. Bendict and H. Hartzfeld, *J. Org. Chem.*, 19 (1954) 419.
[34] L. J. Tyler, *J. Am. Chem. Soc.*, 77 (1955) 770.
[35] S. W. Kantor, *J. Am. Chem. Soc.*, 75 (1953) 2712.
[36] J. A. Meads and F. S. Kipping, *J. Chem. Soc.*, 105 (1914) 679; 107 (1915) 459.
[37] R. Robinson and F. S. Kipping, *J. Chem. Soc.*, 101 (1912) 2156; 105 (1914) 40.
[38] J. F. Hyde, *U.S.P.* 2,567,110 (1951); *U.S.P.* 2,574,265 (1951).
[39] J. F. Hyde, *J. Am. Chem. Soc.*, 75 (1953) 2166.
[40] J. F. Hyde and O. K. Johannson, *U.S. P.* 2,438,055 (1948).
[41] K. A. Andrianov and A. A. Zhdanov, *Doklady Akad. Nauk S.S.S.R.*, 114 (1957) 1005.
[42] V. S. Chugunov, *Zhur. Obshcheĭ Khim.*, 28 (1958) 336.
[43] N. S. Nametkin, A. V. Topchiev and F. F. Machus, *Doklady Akad. Nauk S.S.S.R.*, 87 (1952) 233, 705.
[44] K. A. Andrianov, *U.S.S.R. Patent* 71,115 (1947); *Byull. izobr.* (*Bulletin of Inventions*), 1948, No. 5.
[45] F. S. Kipping and J. Hackford, *J. Chem. Soc.*, 99 (1911) 138.
[46] R. O. Sauer, *J. Am. Chem. Soc.*, 66 (1944) 1707.
[47] W. C. Schumb and C. M. Saffer, *J. Am. Chem. Soc.*, 61 (1939) 363.
[48] M. C. Harvey, W. H. Nebergall and J. S. Peake, *J. Am. Chem. Soc.*, 79 (1957) 1437.
[49] H. Kautsky and B. Bartocha, *Z. Naturforsch.*, 10b (1955) 422.
[50] E. D. Hornbaker and F. Conrad, *J. Org. Chem.*, 24 (1959) 1858.
[51] K. A. Andrianov and T. N. Ganina, *Izvest. Akad. Nauk S.S.S.R., Otdel. Khim. Nauk*, (1956) 74.
[52] K. A. Andrianov, A. A. Zhdanov, N. A. Kurasheva and V. G. Dulova, *Doklady Akad. Nauk S.S.S.R.*, 112 (1957) 1050.
[53] E. Wiberg and K. Kanzler, *German Patent* 937,557 (1956).
[54] C. F. Gibbs, H. Tucker, G. Shkapenko and J. C. Park, *W.A.D.C. Technical Report* 55–453, ASTIA Document No. 131036, Sept. 1957.
[55] K. A. Andrianov, *International Symposium on High Molecular Compounds*, Prague, Sept. 1957. (See Ref. 134).
[56] W. G. Woods and M. L. Iverson, *136th Meeting American Chemical Society*, New Jersey, Sept. 1959, p. 2N.
[57] W. G. Woods and M.L. Iverson, *Conference on High Temperature Polymer and Fluid Research*, Dayton, Ohio, May 1959.
[58] S. M. Atlas and H. F. Mark, *Angew. Chem.*, 72 (1960) 249.
[59] M. G. Voronkov, B. N. Dolgov and N. A. Dmitrieva, *Doklady Akad. Nauk S.S.S.R.*, 84 (1952) 959.
[60] N. F. Orlov, *Doklady Akad. Nauk S.S.S.R.*, 114 (1957) 1033.
[61] A. H. Cowley, F. Fairbrother and N. Scott, *J. Chem. Soc.*, (1959) 717.
[62] J. F. Hyde, *U.S.P.*, 2,645,654 (1953).
[63] J. F. Hyde, *British Patent*, 685,183 (1952).

[64] H. E. PETREE, *136th Meeting American Chemical Society*, New Jersey, Sept. 1959, p. 51N.
[65] W. D. ENGLISH and L. H. SOMMER, *J. Am. Chem. Soc.*, 77 (1955) 170.
[66] V. A. ZEITLER and C. A. BROWN, *J. Am. Chem. Soc.*, 79 (1957) 4616.
[67] B. N. DOLGOV and N. F. ORLOV, *Izvest. Akad. Nauk S.S.S.R., Otdel. Khim. Nauk*, (1957) 1395.
[68] D. C. BRADLEY and I. M. THOMAS, *Chem. & Ind. (London)*, (1958) 17.
[69] D. C. BRADLEY and I. M. THOMAS, *J. Chem. Soc.*, (1959) 3404.
[70] B. N. DOLGOV and N. F. ORLOV, *Doklady Akad. Nauk S.S.S.R.*, 117 (1957) 617.
[71] J. D. DANFORTH, *J. Am. Chem. Soc.*, 80 (1958) 2585.
[72] K. A. ANDRIANOV and V. V. ASTAKHIN, *Doklady Akad. Nauk S.S.S.R.*, 127 (1959) 1014.
[73] A. N. NESMEYANOV and O. V. NOGINA, *Doklady Akad. Nauk S.S.S.R.*, 117 (1957) 249.
[74] D. C. BRADLEY and I. M. THOMAS, *Chem. & Ind. (London)*, (1958) 1231.
[75] K. A. ANDRIANOV and T. N. GANINA, *Zhur. Obshcheĭ Khim., S.S.S.R.*, 29 (1959) 605.
[76] J. B. RUST, H. H. TAKIMOTO and G. C. DENAULT, *J. Org. Chem.*, 25 (1960) 2040.
[77] B. N. DOLGOV, N. F. ORLOV and M. G. VORONKOV, *Izvest. Akad. Nauk S.S.S.R., Otdel. Khim. Nauk*, (1959) 1408.
[78] A. L. SUVOROV and S. S. SPASSKII, *Uspekhi Khim.*, 28 (1959) 1291.
[79] K. A. ANDRIANOV and V. G. DULOVA, *Izvest. Akad. Nauk S.S.S.R., Otdel. Khim. Nauk*, (1958) 644.
[80] Midland Silicones, Ltd., *British Patent*, 771,167 (1957).
[81] B. N. DOLGOV, YU. I. KHUDOBIN and N. P. KHARITONOV, *Doklady Akad. Nauk S.S.S.R.*, 122 (1958) 607.
[82] M. G. VORONKOV and V. N. ZGONNIK, *Zhur. Obshcheĭ Khim.*, 27 (1957) 1476.
[83] H. G. SCHAFER and A. LISNER, *Chem. Tech. (Berlin)*, 2 (1950) 181.
[84] E. WIBERG and U. KRÜERKE, *Z. Naturforsch.*, 8b (1953) 609.
[85] R. H. KRIEBLE, *U.S.P.*, 2,440,101 (1948).
[86] P. A. MCCUSKER and T. OSTDICK, *J. Am. Chem. Soc.*, 80 (1958) 1103.
[87] W. GERRARD and J. A. STRICKSON, *Chem. & Ind. (London)*, (1958) 860.
[88] M. J. FRAZER, W. GERRARD and J. A. STRICKSON, *J. Chem. Soc.*, (1960) 4701.
[89] K. A. ANDRIANOV and L. M. VOLKOVA, *Izvest. Akad. Nauk S.S.S.R., Otdel. Khim. Nauk*, (1957) 303.
[90] F. A. HENGLEIN, R. LANG and K. SCHEINOST, *Makromol. Chem.*, 15 (1955) 177.
[91] R. P. ANDERSON and M. M. SPRUNG, *W.A.D.C. Technical Report*, 59–61, March 1959.
[92] P. E. KOENIG and J. H. HUTCHINSON, *W.A.D.C. Technical Report*, 58–44, ASTIA Document No. AD151197, May 1958.
[93] F. A. HENGLEIN, R. LANG and L. SCHMACK, *Makromol. Chem.*, 22 (1957) 103.
[94] J. F. O'BRIEN, *W.A.D.C. Technical Report*, 75–502, ASTIA Document No. 142100, Oct. 1957.
[95] C. L. SEGAL, H. H. TAKIMOTO and J. B. RUST, *137th Meeting American Chemical Society*, Cleveland, April, 1960, p. 3S.
[96] R. M. KARY and K. C. FRISCH, *J. Am. Chem. Soc.*, 79 (1957) 2140; *U.S.P.*, 2,863,893 (1958).

97 B. L. CHAMBERLAND and A. G. MACDIARMID, *J. Am. Chem. Soc.*, 82 (1960) 4542.
98 B. L. CHAMBERLAND and A. G. MACDIARMID, *138th Meeting American Chemical Society*, New York, Sept. 1960, p. 20N; *J. Am. Chem. Soc.*, 83 (1961) 549.
99 M. SCHMIDT and H. SCHMIDBAUR, *Angew. Chem.*, 71 (1959) 553.
100 R. O. SAUER, *J. Am. Chem. Soc.*, 66 (1944) 1707.
101 M. G. VORONKOV, *Zhur. Obshcheĭ Khim.*, 25 (1955) 469.
102 M. G. VORONKOV and V. N. ZGONNIK, *Zhur. Obshcheĭ Khim.*, 27 (1957) 1483.
103 M. G. VORONKOV, V. A. KOLESOVA and V. N. ZGONNIK, *Izvest. Akad. Nauk S.S.S.R., Otdel Khim. Nauk*, (1957) 1363.
104 M. G. VORONKOV and YU. L. SKORIK, *Izvest. Akad. Nauk S.S.S.R., Otdel. Khim. Nauk*, (1958) 119.
105 F. FEHÉR, G. KUHLBÖRSCH, A. BLUMCKE, H. KELLER and K. LIPPERT, *Chem. Ber.*, 90 (1957) 134.
106 F. FEHÉR and A. BLUMCKE, *Chem. Ber.*, 90 (1957) 1934.
107 F. FEHÉR and K. LIPPERT, *Chem. Ber.*, 92 (1959) 2998.
108 A. P. KRESHKOV and D. A. KARATEEV, *Zhur. priklad. Khim.*, 32 (1959) 369.
109 R. SCHWARZ and K. SCHOELLER, *Chem. Ber.*, 91 (1958) 2103.
110 K. A. ANDRIANOV, B. N. RUTOVSKY and A. A. KAZAKOVA, *Zhur. Obshcheĭ Khim.*, 26 (1956) 267.
111 L. MALATESTA, *Gazz. chim. ital.*, 80 (1950) 527.
112 B. A. ARBUZOV and A. N. PUDOVIK, *Doklady Akad. Nauk S.S.S.R.*, 59 (1948) 1433.
113 J. FERTIG, W. GERRARD and H. HERBST, *J. Chem. Soc.*, (1957) 1488.
114 M. SCHMIDT, H. SCHMIDBAUR and A. BINGER, *Chem. Ber.*, 93 (1960) 872.
115 F. P. PRICE, *J. Am. Chem. Soc.*, 70 (1948) 871.
116 M. S. NEWMAN, R. A. CRAIG and A. B. GARRETT, *J. Am. Chem. Soc.*, 71 (1949) 869.
117 L. H. SOMMER, E. W. PIETRUSZA, G. T. KERR and F. C. WHITMORE, *J. Am. Chem. Soc.*, 68 (1946) 156.
118 L. H. SOMMER, G. T. KERR and F. C. WHITMORE, *J. Am. Chem. Soc.*, 70 (1948) 445.
119 W. PATNODE and F. C. SCHMIDT, *J. Am. Chem. Soc.*, 67 (1945) 2272.
120 M. KANAZASHI, *Bull. Chem. Soc. Japan*, 28 (1955) 44.
121 M. SCHMIDT and H. SCHMIDBAUR, *Chem. Ber.*, 93 (1960) 878.
122 N. F. ORLOV and M. G. VORONKOV, *Izvest. Akad. Nauk S.S.S.R., Otdel. Khim. Nauk*, (1959) 1506.
123 F. A. HENGLEIN, R. LANG and K. SCHEINOST, *Makromol. Chem.*, 18–19 (1956) 102.
124 H. J. COHEN and R. E. DESSY, *138th Meeting American Chemical Society*, New York, Sept. 1960, p. 20N.
125 V. GUTMANN and A. MELLER, *Monatsh. Chem.*, 91 (1960) 519.
126 M. SCHMIDT and H. SCHMIDBAUR, *Angew. Chem.*, 70 (1958) 704.
127 M. SCHMIDT and H. SCHMIDBAUR, *Angew. Chem.*, 71 (1959) 220.
128 N. F. ORLOV, B. N. DOLGOV and M. G. VORONKOV, *Doklady Akad. Nauk S.S.S.R.*, 122 (1958) 246.
129 K. A. ANDRIANOV, A. A. ZHDANOV and E. A. KASHUTINA, *Zhur. priklad. Khim.*, 32 (1959) 463.
130 K. A. ANDRIANOV, A. A. ZHDANOV and E. A. KASHUTINA, *Doklady Akad. Nauk S.S.S.R.*, 126 (1959) 1261.

[131] M. Schmidt and H. Schmidbaur, *Chem. Ber.*, 92 (1959) 2667.
[132] M. Schmidt and H. Schmidbaur, *Angew. Chem.*, 71 (1959) 220.
[133] U. Wannagat and W. Liehr, *Angew. Chem.*, 69 (1957) 783.
[134] K. A. Andrianov and A. A. Zhdanov, *J. Polymer Sci.*, 30 (1958) 513.
[135] E. W. Abel and A. Singh, *J. Chem. Soc.*, (1959) 690.
[136] I. R. Beattie and G. J. Leigh, *J. Chem. Soc.*, (1961) 4249.
[137] G. Fritz and J. Grobe, *Z. anorg. Chem.*, 311 (1961) 325.

Chapter 8

Polymetallosiloxanes. Part II. Polyorganometallosiloxanes and Polyorganosiloxymetalloxanes

by

J. IDRIS JONES

1. Introduction

Interest in polymetallosiloxanes has been stimulated partly by the desire to enlist new elements into polymer formation and partly by the hope that incorporation of heteroatoms in the polysiloxane structure might bring about certain desirable changes in properties. Of the polymeric materials presently known, the polysiloxanes are amongst the most thermally stable, and their electrical properties are of considerable interest. However, these polymers have their serious limitations. Their use at very high temperatures is restricted because of their tendency to undergo extensive rearrangement to form cyclic structures of lower molecular weight. The stability of the Si—O—Si linkage largely determines the resistance of silicone polymers to thermal degradation. Thermal stability might be improved by modifying the electronic character of the bond. It is generally recognised that as bonds become more ionic, or as covalent bonds become more polar, greater thermal stability ensues. Replacement of some (or all) of the Si—O units in the polymer chain with M—O, where M represents a metal, would, in those cases where M is more electropositive than silicon, provide a more polar bond and consequently a more ionic polymer, which might be expected to have higher thermal stability. Again, it is well known that intermolecular forces are particularly weak in organopolysiloxanes. A higher co-ordination tendency produced by the introduction of a suitable metal atom into the chain, would result in greater intermolecular interaction and this also might reduce the propensity to degrade by cyclic-compound formation. These modifications are likely to lead to higher second order transition temperatures in the polymers but, at the same time, some loss of mechanical properties is inevitable owing to the increased stiffness of the chains. Current interest in the polymetallosiloxanes stems largely from their potentialities as thermally-stable materials.

Andrianov's expedient[1] of "framing" the inorganic molecular frameworks in these polymer systems with organic groups has enabled their properties to be varied within wide limits. Thus, the inorganic polymers acquire solubility in organic solvents and they can be cast as films and lacquers. In those cases where the elements in the chain do not form metal-carbon bonds, the use of organosiloxy-groups R_3SiO— for the same purpose has considerably widened the scope of this procedure and provided a further range of interesting new polymers.

2. Silicon–oxygen–aluminium polymers

In the silanols, the reactivity of the hydroxyl group towards metals is much greater than that of the hydroxyl group in alcohols. Thus, triethylsilanol reacts with sodium much more readily than does its organic analogue, *t*-heptyl alcohol[2]. It was the observation[1,3] in 1947 that silanols react not only with the elements of the 1st Group but also with those of the 2nd and 3rd Group of the Periodic Table that led to the first synthesis of a polyorganometallosiloxane. Thus, the reaction of aluminium with silanediols proceeds with evolution of hydrogen, giving complex polymers containing the Si—O—Al linkage. Analysis of the reaction products showed that the aluminium which enters into the reaction is present in an amount equivalent to that of the evolved hydrogen. The basic reaction in the case of 1,3-dihydroxytetraethyldisiloxane may be illustrated as follows:

References, p. 252–255

$$6HOSi(C_2H_5)_2OSi(C_2H_5)_2OH + 2Al \longrightarrow 2[HOSi(C_2H_5)_2OSi(C_2H_5)_2O]_3Al + 3H_2$$

The formation of tris(triethylsiloxy)aluminium in good yield from triethylsilanol and aluminium was taken as evidence of the formation of Si—O—Al links in polyorganoaluminosiloxanes. Investigations of the reactivity of various silanols, including 1,2-dihydroxytetraethyldisiloxane, diethyldihydroxysilane, triethylhydroxysilane, and also polyphenylsiloxane, with aluminium showed that only in the cases of the siloxanediol and the monofunctional silanol did appreciable substitution of the hydrogen take place. Competition from self-condensation, with polysiloxane formation, was extensive with diethyldihydroxysilane and no reaction was observed with polyphenylsiloxane.

While investigating the properties of tris(triethylsiloxy)aluminium[4–6], Andrianov found that, under the action of water and in presence of hydrochloric acid, this compound hydrolysed just like silicones, the reaction proceeding as follows:

$$[(C_2H_5)_3SiO]_3Al + 3H_2O \xrightarrow{HCl} Al(OH)_3 + 3(C_2H_5)_3SiOH$$

However, when the hydrolysis was carried out with a small quantity of water, a polymer was formed, with its molecular chains built up of alternate atoms of oxygen and aluminium with the latter atoms carrying triethylsiloxy-groups. This constituted the first synthesis of a polyorganosiloxymetalloxane. The stepwise reaction scheme, resulting in polytriethylsiloxyaluminoxane, is as follows:

$$[(C_2H_5)_3SiO]_3Al + H_2O \longrightarrow [(C_2H_5)_3SiO]_2AlOH + (C_2H_5)_3SiOH$$

$$2[(C_2H_5)_3SiO]_2AlOH \longrightarrow [(C_2H_5)_3SiO]_2Al{-}O{-}Al[OSi(C_2H_5)_3]_2 + H_2O$$

$$\downarrow$$

$$(C_2H_5)_3SiO{-}\underset{\substack{|\\ OSi(C_2H_5)_3}}{Al}{-}O{-}\left[\underset{\substack{|\\ OSi(C_2H_5)_3}}{Al}{-}O{-}\right]_n\underset{\substack{|\\ OSi(C_2H_5)_3}}{Al}{-}OSi(C_2H_5)_3$$

When the hydrolysis was carried out in aqueous acetone solution at 20°, it was established that the viscosity of the solution continually increased with time and with an increase in the quantity of water taken for the reaction. In the initial stages, the reaction gave mostly cyclic or linear polymeric molecules without any noticeable branching. This was confirmed by the solubility of the resulting polymers in organic solvents. Only when the reaction had reached a certain stage of polymerisation did the formation of branched and cross-linked structures begin; at that point, the polymer became insoluble and the solution gelled.

No. moles water/mole $[(C_2H_5)_3SiO]_3Al$	Time prior to gelation of solution in min.
2.32	12,960
2.80	320
3.27	100
3.74	6

The polymer was also conveniently prepared by aspirating moist air through the monomeric aluminosiloxane maintained at an elevated temperature (170°). Hydrolysis proceeded slowly and its rate was determined by the amount of water introduced. The triethylsilanol produced by the reaction was swept out of the system as it was formed. A polymer formed under these conditions had a molecular weight of 4100, corresponding to a degree of polymerisation of ~ 23. It contained 13.15% Al and 18.56% Si. When tris(triethylsiloxy)aluminium was heated at 220° in a dry atmosphere, no perceptible condensation or viscosity increase occurred. The polyorganosiloxyaluminoxanes are transparent, colourless or brownish, vitreous substances, soluble in benzene, toluene, alcohol, and acetone. When the solutions are applied to solid surfaces and the solvent is allowed to evaporate, heat-resistant films are formed.

In the reaction of dimethyldiethoxysilane with sodium aluminate substances (I) and (II) were obtained[1b].

$$\mathrm{Na}\!-\!\left[\begin{array}{c}-\mathrm{OSi(CH_3)_2}\!-\!\mathrm{O}\!-\!\underset{\displaystyle\mathrm{ONa}}{\underset{|}{\mathrm{Al}}}\!-\end{array}\right]_2\!-\!\mathrm{OSi(CH_3)_2}\cdot\mathrm{ONa}\cdot 8\mathrm{H\ O}$$

(I)

References, p. 252–255

$$\mathrm{NaO}{-}\left[{-}\mathrm{Si(CH_3)_2{-}O{-}\underset{\displaystyle \mathrm{ONa}}{\overset{|}{Al}}{-}O}{-}\right]_2{-}\mathrm{Na\cdot 7H_2O}$$

(II)

Various polydimethylaluminosiloxanes have also been prepared by hydrolysis of dimethyldichlorosilane by strongly alkaline sodium aluminate solutions[7]. The composition of the final polymers depends upon the initial ratio of Si to Al in the reaction mixture.

It has been shown that tris(trialkylsiloxy)- and tris(triarylsiloxy)-aluminium compounds are formed from aluminium chloride and the alkali metal silanolates.

$$3R_3SiONa + AlCl_3 \longrightarrow (R_3SiO)_3Al + 3NaCl$$

Sodium salts of alkylsilanetriols have been prepared[8] by reacting equimolar amounts of sodium hydroxide and the polyorganosiloxane in accordance with the scheme:

$$2(RSiO_{1.5})_n + 2nNaOH + nH_2O \longrightarrow 2nRSi(OH)_2ONa$$

$$(R_2SiO)_4 + 4NaOH \longrightarrow 2NaOSiR_2OSiR_2ONa + 2H_2O$$

The sodium salts are hard, crystalline substances, containing water of crystallisation. Some of these substances, depending on the amount of water of crystallisation, are soluble in alcohol and acetone. With aluminium chloride, double decomposition should result if the reaction is carried out in an anhydrous medium.

$$3RSi(OH)_2ONa + AlCl_3 \longrightarrow [RSi(OH)_2O]_3Al + 3NaCl$$

Investigations showed that the reaction of aluminium chloride with the sodium salts of phenylsilane- and ethylsilane-triol and with the disodium salt of 1,3,5-triphenyl-1,3,5-trimethyltrisiloxane in ethanol proceeded substantially as indicated, with formation of polyorganoaluminosiloxanes.

$$3C_6H_5Si(OH)_2ONa + AlCl_3 \longrightarrow [C_6H_5Si(OH)_2O]_3Al + 3NaCl$$

$$n[C_6H_5Si(OH)_2O]_3Al \longrightarrow \{[C_6H_5Si(\overset{|}{O})O]_3Al\}_n + nH_2O$$

The polymers obtained were hard, brittle, glassy, film-forming materials, soluble in benzene, alcohol, and acetone. The product from phenylsilanetriol was found to contain Si, 18.35; Al, 7.27%, in reasonable agreement with the calculated values for a polymer with the elementary structural unit $[C_6H_5Si(\overset{|}{O})O]_3Al$.

Another general method of synthesis of polyorganometallo-siloxanes is the co-hydrolysis in an alkaline medium of the salts or alkoxy-derivatives of the metals aluminium, titanium or tin and the alkyl- or aryl-halosilanes[9–12]. Thus, polyphenylpolyalumino-siloxane was obtained by co-hydrolysis of trichlorophenylsilane with aluminium sulphate in an alkaline medium.

$$3C_6H_5SiCl_3 + 12NaOH + 0.5Al_2(SO_4)_3 \xrightarrow{H_2O}$$

$$[C_6H_5Si(OH)_2O]_3Al + 1.5Na_2SO_4 + 9NaCl.$$

In essence, this is the same as the double-decomposition of the monosodium derivative of phenylsilanetriol with aluminium sulphate, which constitutes an alternative method of synthesis.

$$3C_6H_5Si(OH)_2ONa + 0{\cdot}5Al_2(SO_4)_3 \xrightarrow{H_2O} [C_6H_5Si(OH)_2O]_3Al + 1{\cdot}5Na_2SO_4$$

Since water is present in both systems, further reactions can develop between the aluminosiloxane and phenylsilanetriol, which is formed by hydrolysis of the sodium silanolate.

$$C_6H_5Si(OH)_2ONa + H_2O \rightleftharpoons C_6H_5Si(OH)_3 + NaOH$$

$$[C_6H_5Si(OH)_2O]_3Al + C_6H_5Si(OH)_3 \longrightarrow$$

$$[C_6H_5{\cdot}Si(OH)_2O]_2Al{-}O{-}\underset{OH}{\overset{C_6H_5}{\overset{|}{\underset{|}{Si}}}}{-}O{-}\underset{OH}{\overset{C_6H_5}{\overset{|}{\underset{|}{Si}}}}{-}OH + H_2O \xrightarrow{etc.}$$

The products of these reactions may simultaneously condense through their hydroxyl groups to give polymers. The cumulative result of these reactions was to afford a polyorganoaluminosiloxane in which the relative amounts of silicon and aluminium varied in

References, p. 252–255

accordance with the amounts of reactants taken. A polyethylaluminosiloxane was also prepared by the exchange method starting from ethyltrichlorosilane. Both the co-hydrolysis and the double-decomposition reactions were carried out in a two phase system, an aromatic hydrocarbon normally being used. The polymer was extracted into the organic layer as it was formed. In the exchange reaction, the alkali metal silanolate was formed *in situ*.

The properties of a polyphenylaluminosiloxane, obtained by the exchange reaction, and containing a ratio of 4 silicon atoms to 1 aluminium atom, have been investigated. It was a colourless, transparent, brittle resin, readily soluble in benzene, ethanol, acetone, chlorobenzene, and carbon tetrachloride, but insoluble in petroleum ether and white spirit. It formed clear, brittle films, which retained high solubility in toluene even after 10 hours' heating at 150°. Some loss in weight was incurred, due to condensation involving the free hydroxyl groups in the polymer, the content of which fell from 5.53% to 2.7%. At higher temperatures (200–500°), the polymer gradually lost its solubility in organic solvents. A short heat treatment at 400° sufficed to render the material completely insoluble. This phenomenon is undoubtedly associated with cross-linking, rearrangements occurring in the chains with cleavage of siloxane and aluminosiloxane linkages of the cyclic products, and their conversion into three-dimensional structures. Polyphenylaluminosiloxane was a polydisperse copolymer. On fractionation into four fractions, covering a fourfold range of molecular weights, the individual fractions were found to

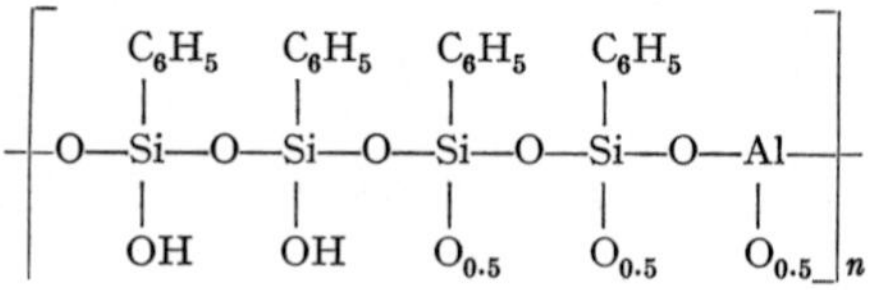

$$\left[\begin{array}{ccccccccc} & C_6H_5 & & C_6H_5 & & C_6H_5 & & C_6H_5 & \\ & | & & | & & | & & | & \\ -O- & Si & -O- & Si & -O- & Si & -O- & Si & -O-Al- \\ & | & & | & & | & & | & | \\ & OH & & OH & & O_{0.5} & & O_{0.5} & O_{0.5} \end{array}\right]_n$$

(III)

have virtually the same composition as the original polymer. The molecular weight of the parent polymer, determined ebullioscopically in benzene, was 5990. By the cryoscopic method (in benzene) it was 2415. X-ray analysis showed an amorphous structure. On the basis of chemical analysis the polymer was said to have a structure made up of (III), as the repeating unit. The mean degree of polymerisation, *n*, is thus equal to 10. From the first to the last fraction, *n* varied from 5 to 20.

The outstanding characteristic of polyphenylaluminosiloxane and the related polyethylaluminosiloxane is their complete infusibility. Neither shows any tendency to melt or sinter at temperatures up to 500°. These polymers are readily soluble in organic solvents but their melting points lie above their decomposition temperatures, as in the case of infusible cross-linked polymers. Unlike the latter, plastic properties can be conferred on these polymers by the addition of suitable plasticisers. This phenomenon, and the likely structure of the polymers, will be discussed in more detail later. Suffice it to say here, that these polyorganoaluminosiloxanes constitute a unique class of polymeric materials, soluble but infusible, and therefore intermediate between the familiar soluble and fusible thermoplastics, and the insoluble-infusible cross-linked polymers.

A range of polydimethylaluminosiloxanes, with a Si/Al ratio from 0.8 to 23.3, has also been made by the double-decomposition reaction according to the scheme[13]:

$$[(CH_3)_2SiO]_n + 2NaOH \longrightarrow NaO[Si(CH_3)_2O]_nNa + H_2O.$$

$$3NaO[Si(CH_3)_2O]_nNa + 2AlCl_3 \longrightarrow [OAl_{0.5}(Si(CH_3)_2O)_{1.5n}]_x$$

The polymers, obtained as solutions, were stable, but after removal of the solvent, their solubility was found to be dependent upon the chemical composition of the polymer chain. The polymers with a Si/Al ratio of 0.8 and 1.3 formed, on evaporation of the solvent, hard, brittle materials, insoluble in organic solvents. A polymer with a Si/Al ratio of 3.2 gave a film which retained partial solubility in polar solvents but was insoluble in weakly polar solvents. Polymers with Si/Al ratios of 6.8 and 23.3 were soluble in polar and weakly polar solvents, even after heating for 6 hours at 150°. The solubility of these polymers and the results of infrared absorption studies indicated that, structurally, these polydimethylaluminosiloxanes were branched molecules containing considerably

References, p. 252–255

less polyalumino-organosiloxane cyclic units than polyphenyl- and polyethyl-aluminosiloxanes.

Andrianov's attempts to apply the exchange reaction to the synthesis of polymers containing other metals, in particular, cobalt and nickel, were unsuccessful[14]. The reaction of the sodium salt of phenyl- or ethyl-silanetriol with nickel or cobalt chloride, in an aqueous alcohol medium, invariably proceeded with precipitation of these metals as oxides or hydroxides. Evidently, hydrolytic processes intervene, due to the presence of water in the reaction medium, both in the solvent and in the salt used. Thus, apart from the expected reaction:

$$2RSi(OH)_2ONa + MCl_2 \longrightarrow [RSi(OH)_2O]_2M + 2NaCl$$

the following processes also occur:

$$RSi(OH)_2ONa + H_2O \rightleftharpoons RSi(OH)_3 + NaOH$$

$$MCl_2 + 2\,NaOH \longrightarrow \underset{\substack{\downarrow \\ MO + H_2O}}{M(OH)_2} + 2NaCl$$

The alkali, formed by hydrolysis of the silanolate, thus may react with the cobalt or nickel chloride with precipitation of the hydroxide. This is a termination process and removes the metal from the sphere of reaction. The introduction of a component capable of lowering the concentration of alkali should favour the formation of metallosiloxane. It was found that addition of aluminium chloride served this purpose by virtue of the reaction:

$$AlCl_3 + 3NaOH \longrightarrow Al(OH)_3 + 3NaCl$$

but, since aluminium salts are known to undergo the exchange reaction, the resulting condensation product was found to be a mixed polymer (polyorganoaluminocobalto- or polyorganoalumino-nickelo-siloxane). Experiments showed that in the double-decomposition of a mixture of cobalt and aluminium chlorides with the sodium salt of ethylsilanetriol the amount of cobalt entering the reaction increased as the molar ratio of $CoCl_2:AlCl_3$ increased from 0 to 1. As soon as the molar ratio became greater than 1, the amount of cobalt chloride reacting fell sharply. The aluminium reacted almost quantitatively, as did the cobalt at molar ratios $CoCl_2:AlCl_3$ equal to or less than unity. A dark-violet polymer derived from ethylsilanetriol, aluminium chloride, and cobalt chloride was found to be soluble in organic solvents and contained Si, 23.27; Al, 7.50; Co, 5.55%. The corresponding polymer from phenylsilanetriol was fractionated from its solution in benzene by precipitation with petroleum ether. Analysis of fractions showed that the aluminium was fairly uniformly distributed among the fractions, whereas cobalt was concentrated mainly in the less-soluble fractions. A dark-green, soluble polymer, containing Al, 6.12; Ni, 1.93%, was similarly obtained from the sodium salt of ethylsilanetriol, aluminium chloride, and nickel chloride.

Various polymeric compounds, containing aluminium, oxygen, and phosphorus in the molecular chain and triorganosiloxy-groups as the framing groups, have been prepared by Andrianov and his co-workers[4–6,15]. These polyorganosiloxyphosphoroaluminoxanes were synthesised by the following two routes:

$$n(R_3SiO)_3Al + nR_3SiOPO(OH)_2 \longrightarrow$$

$$R_3SiO-\left[\begin{array}{c} -Al-O-\overset{\overset{\displaystyle O}{\|}}{P}-O- \\ \quad | \qquad\qquad | \\ OSiR_3 \quad OSiR_3 \end{array}\right]_n-H + (n-0.5)R_3SiOSiR_3 + (n-0.5)\,H_2O$$

$$n(R_3SiO)_3Al + n(R_3SiO)_3P{=}O \xrightarrow{H_2O}$$

$$R_3SiO-\left[\begin{array}{c} -Al-O-\overset{\overset{\displaystyle O}{\|}}{P}-O- \\ \quad | \qquad\qquad | \\ OSiR_3 \quad OSiR_3 \end{array}\right]_n-SiR_3 + (2n-1)R_3SiOSiR_3$$

In the reaction of tris(triethylsiloxy)aluminium with triethylsilyldihydrogen phosphate at 170–230°, hexaethyldisiloxane and a glass-like polymer were formed. When the reaction was complete,

References, p. 252–255

the polymer had an average molecular weight of 2336, corresponding to an average degree of polymerisation of 6, and it was soluble in toluene. Similarly, when tris(triethylsiloxy)aluminium was heated with tris(triethylsilyl) phosphate at 160–180°, with simultaneous passage of moist air, hexaethyldisiloxane and a glass-like polymer were formed. The course of the reaction was followed by measuring the viscosity of the polymer formed. The final polymer had a molecular weight of 3566, which corresponds to a degree of polymerisation of 9. Generally, the character of the polymers formed and their properties depended on the nature of the organic radical in the framing trialkylsiloxy-groups. The condensation of tris(triethylsiloxy)aluminium with triethylsilyl dihydrogen phosphate or tris(triethylsilyl) phosphate at 200–220° furnished polymers, which were soluble in organic solvents and which were converted into an insoluble, infusible state by further heating. Under the same conditions, condensation of the analogous methyl compounds proceeded very rapidly, yielding solid, infusible, insoluble polymers, probably of a three-dimensional structure. Confirmation of the reaction scheme presented above was obtained[15] by a study of the condensation of 2 moles of tris(triethylsiloxy)aluminium with 1 mole of triethylsilyl dihydrogen phosphate. Under these conditions, a low-molecular-weight intermediate was formed, together with hexaethyldisiloxane and water in amounts corresponding to the equation:

$$2[(C_2H_5)_3SiO]_3Al + (C_2H_5)_3SiOPO(OH)_2 \longrightarrow$$

$$\begin{array}{ccccc} & & O & & \\ & & \| & & \\ (C_2H_5)_3SiO{-}Al & {-}O{-} & P & {-}O{-} & Al{-}OSi(C_2H_5)_3 \\ | & & | & & | \\ OSi(C_2H_5)_3 & & OSi(C_2H_5)_3 & & OSi(C_2H_5)_3 \end{array}$$

$$+ (C_2H_5)_3SiOSi(C_2H_5)_3 + H_2O$$

The intermediate was a clear, viscous liquid, which was readily soluble in alcohol, benzene, and toluene.

In contrast to the Russian work, American studies on polymetallosiloxanes have been directed largely towards the synthesis of linear polymers of known structure, wherein the metal atoms are incorporated in the molecular chain in a regular repeating order. The favoured experimental approach has been by heterofunctional condensation with appropriately substituted intermediates. Thus, the reaction between acetoxysilanes and aluminium alkoxides leads to the formation of aluminosiloxanes, $(R_3SiO)_nAl(OR)_{3-n}$, where $n = 1, 2$, or 3[16–18]. An extension of this reaction to diacetoxy-silicon compounds led to the synthesis of polyorganoalumino-siloxanes[19].

$$CH_3COO-\underset{R}{\overset{R}{\underset{|}{\overset{|}{Si}}}}-OCOCH_3 + Al(OR')_3 \longrightarrow \left[-\underset{R}{\overset{R}{\underset{|}{\overset{|}{Si}}}}-O-\underset{OR'}{\underset{|}{Al}}-O- \right]_n$$

The aluminium compounds, $Al(OR')_3$, $RAl(OR')_2$, and $R_2Al(OR')$, suffer from hydrolytic instability. A factor contributing to the susceptibility to hydrolysis of aluminium compounds of this type is their electron-deficiency, which makes them liable to attack by nucleophilic reagents. Efforts to prepare high-molecular-weight polyphenoxyaluminoxanes, by the partial hydrolysis of di-iso-propoxyphenoxyaluminium, have led to insoluble and infusible products[16]. Partial hydrolysis of $(C_6H_5)_3SiOAl(OC_3H_7^i)_2$ gave a toluene-soluble product of low molecular weight. Replacement of two of the chloro- or alkoxy-groups of aluminium trichloride or trialkoxide by trialkylsiloxy-groups stabilises the remaining group. When dimethyldiacetoxysilane was condensed with trimethyl-siloxyaluminium di-isopropoxide, a linear poly(trimethylsiloxy)-aluminosiloxane, with a weight average molecular weight of 42,500, was obtained[19,93].

$$nCH_3COO-\underset{CH_3}{\overset{CH_3}{\underset{|}{\overset{|}{Si}}}}-OCOCH_3 + n(CH_3)_3SiOAl(OC_3H_7^i)_2 \longrightarrow$$

$$\left[-\underset{CH_3}{\overset{CH_3}{\underset{|}{\overset{|}{Si}}}}-O-\overset{OSi(CH_3)_3}{\overset{|}{Al}}-O- \right]_n + 2nCH_3COOC_3H_7^i$$

References, p. 252–255

Treatment of trimethylsiloxyaluminium di-isopropoxide with acetic anhydride gave a poly(trimethylsiloxy)aluminoxane.

$$C_3H_7^iO{-}\underset{}{\overset{\displaystyle OSi(CH_3)_3 \atop |}{Al}}{-}OC_3H_7^i + (CH_3CO)_2O \longrightarrow$$

$$C_3H_7^iO{-}\left[\overset{\displaystyle OSi(CH_3)_3 \atop |}{Al}{-}O{-}\right]_n{-}COCH_3 + CH_3COOC_3H_7^i$$

Attempts to satisfy the electron-deficiency of aluminium compounds by chelation have led to the preparation of compounds of the type:

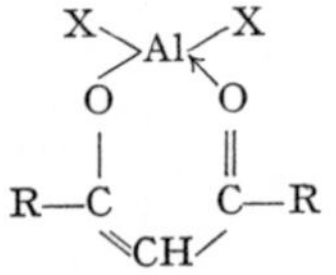

$$\begin{array}{ccccc} & X & & X & \\ & & \!\!\!>Al\!\!\swarrow\!\!\!< & & \\ & O & & O & \\ & | & & \| & \\ R{-}C & & & & C{-}R \\ & \searrow\!\! & CH & \!\!\swarrow & \end{array}$$

where $R = CH_3, C_6H_5$

and $X = R, OR, Cl.$

Because of their increased stability and difunctionality, compounds of this type have been used as a source of linear co-ordination polymers[20]. They have also been examined as starting materials for the synthesis of linear polyorganoaluminosiloxanes. Attempts to prepare polymers by the reaction of aluminium chelates of this type, by condensation with difunctional silicon compounds containing either alkoxide or chloride groups, resulted in an exchange of functional groups[21].

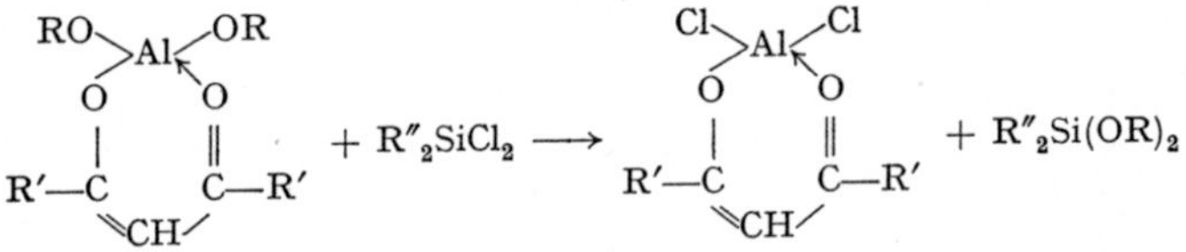

$$\begin{array}{ccc} RO & & OR \\ & >Al\swarrow< & \\ O & & O \\ | & & \| \\ R'{-}C & & C{-}R' \\ & \searrow CH \swarrow & \end{array} + R''_2SiCl_2 \longrightarrow \begin{array}{ccc} Cl & & Cl \\ & >Al\swarrow< & \\ O & & O \\ | & & \| \\ R'{-}C & & C{-}R' \\ & \searrow CH \swarrow & \end{array} + R''_2Si(OR)_2$$

However, reaction of equimolar quantities of dichloroaluminium acetylacetonate and disodium diphenylsilanediolate in benzene afforded a yellow, resinous product, soluble in benzene, and having a molecular weight of 600.

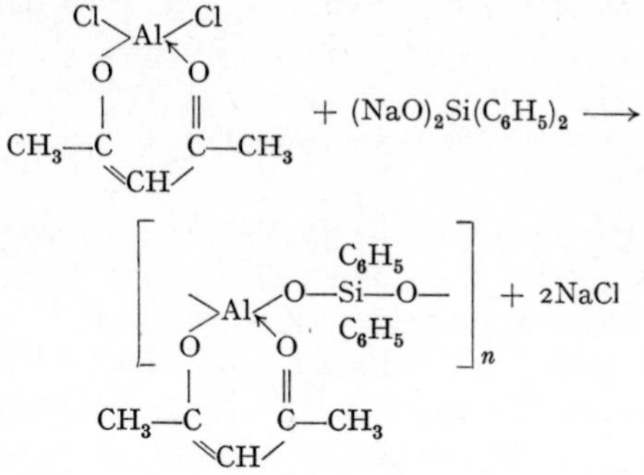

$$\begin{array}{c} Cl\diagdown\quad\diagup Cl \\ Al \\ O \quad\quad O \\ | \quad\quad \| \\ CH_3{-}C \quad\quad C{-}CH_3 \\ \diagdown CH \diagup \end{array} + (NaO)_2Si(C_6H_5)_2 \longrightarrow$$

$$\left[\begin{array}{c} \quad\quad\quad C_6H_5 \\ >Al\diagup O{-}Si{-}O{-} \\ O \quad\quad O \quad C_6H_5 \\ | \quad\quad \| \\ CH_3{-}C \quad\quad C{-}CH_3 \\ \diagdown CH \diagup \end{array}\right]_n + 2NaCl$$

The alkoxide-acyloxide reaction proved to be a more successful approach. From di-isopropoxyaluminium acetylacetonate and diethyldiacetoxysilane in boiling toluene, two products were formed, one soluble in benzene, the other insoluble. The molecular weight of the soluble product was 1200. Other products obtained by a similar reaction were soft resins, waxes, or powders, with molecular weights ranging from 30,000–40,000.

3. Silicon–oxygen–titanium polymers

A survey of the recent literature reveals that there is considerable interest in titanium alkoxides and a rapid increase in their industrial applications[22]. Most of these applications are based on the tendency of titanium alkoxides to hydrolyse or react with hydroxyl groups. Detailed hydrolytic studies have been carried out by Boyd[23], Minami and Ishino[24], and Bradley, Gaze, and Wardlaw[25]. Boyd reported that when the molar ratio of water to alkoxide is $\geqslant 1$, essentially linear polymers were formed, with some chain branching, but no cross-linking, in accordance with the following mechanism[23]:

$$n\text{Ti(OR)}_4 + (n-1)\text{H}_2\text{O} \longrightarrow (\text{RO})_3\text{Ti}{-}\text{O}{-}\left[\begin{array}{c}\text{OR}\\ | \\ {-}\text{Ti}{-}\text{O}{-}\\ | \\ \text{OR}\end{array}\right]_{n-2}{-}\text{Ti(OR)}_3 + 2(n-1)\text{ROH}$$

References, p. 252–255

Depending on the water content, within this range, the products vary in nature from viscous liquids to waxy solids. When a larger quantity of water is used, solid, insoluble, cross-linked polymers result. Despite the fact that the rate of hydrolysis of titanium alkoxides becomes smaller as the degree of hydrolysis increases, the usefulness of polyalkoxytitanoxanes is limited by their hydrolytic instability.

Titanium does not normally form stable compounds having Ti—C bonds; consequently it is impossible to synthesise polyorganotitanoxanes analogous to polyorganosiloxanes. However, as already shown (see Chapter 7), titanium forms a series of stable, organosiloxy-compounds. Furthermore, the hydrolytic stability of the siloxy-groups in these compounds is greater by several orders of magnitude than that of alkoxy-groups in analogous[4–6] derivatives. Thus, tetrakis(trimethylsiloxy)titanium was recovered unchanged even after heating at 50° for 3 hours with 0.5 mole of water in acetone. Use of acidic catalysts, however, promotes hydrolysis, and if not more than 1 mole of water per mole of tetrakis(trimethylsiloxy)titanium is used, polymers are formed. Trimethylsilanol and hexamethyldisiloxane are formed as by-products. The polytrimethylsiloxytitanoxanes are formed in accordance with the following reaction scheme:

$$[(CH_3)_3SiO]_4Ti + H_2O \longrightarrow [(CH_3)_3SiO]_3TiOH + (CH_3)_3SiOH$$

$$2[(CH_3)_3SiO]_3TiOH \longrightarrow [(CH_3)_3SiO]_3Ti{-}O{-}Ti[OSi(CH_3)_3]_3 + H_2O \longrightarrow$$

$$(CH_3)_3SiO{-}\left[\begin{array}{c} OSi(CH_3)_3 \\ | \\ {-}Ti{-}O{-} \\ | \\ OSi(CH_3)_3 \end{array}\right]_n{-}Si(CH_3)_3$$

During the initial stages of the reaction, polymers soluble in organic solvents are formed, but further heating with an excess of water results in the formation of insoluble polymers. Hard lacquer films are obtained from the soluble polymers.

Polyorganotitanosiloxanes were first prepared by Andrianov[1,26] by the cohydrolysis of alkyl- or aryl-chlorosilanes with butyl titanate:

$$R_2SiCl_2 + Ti(OC_4H_9)_4 \xrightarrow[NaOH]{H_2O} \left[-O-\overset{R}{\underset{R}{Si}}- \right]_n -O- \left[-\overset{OC_4H_9}{\underset{OC_4H_9}{Ti}}-O- \right]_m$$

Another method involved the condensation of butyl titanate at 200° with the products of hydrolysis of alkyl- or aryl-chlorosilanes. The polymers obtained were vitreous, soluble in alcohol, acetone and mixtures of alcohol and toluene. The ratio of silicon to titanium in the polymers varied within the limits 5:1 to 30:1 according to the proportions of reactants used. Various claims have been made in the patent literature relating to the use of titanium alkoxides and their partial hydrolysis products for the modification of polyorganosiloxanes[1,22]. Recently, the synthesis of polymethyl- and polyethyl-titanosiloxanes was described[27]; they were soluble, infusible polymers analogous to the polyalkyl- and polyaryl-aluminosiloxanes. They were prepared by the exchange reaction between titanium tetrachloride and the alkali metal silanolates derived from the hydrolysis of alkyltrichlorosilanes.

$$RSiCl_3 + 3H_2O \longrightarrow RSi(OH)_3 + 3HCl$$

$$RSi(OH)_3 \xrightarrow[-1.5\ H_2O]{} RSiO_{1.5}$$

$$4RSiO_{1.5} + 4NaOH + TiCl_4 \xrightarrow[2\ H_2O]{} [RSi(OH)_2O]_4Ti + 4NaCl$$

$$n[RSi(OH)_2O]_4Ti \longrightarrow [(RSi(\overset{|}{O})O)_4Ti(H_2O)]_n + 3nH_2O$$

$$R = CH_3,\ C_2H_5$$

$$\left[-O-\overset{C_2H_5}{\underset{OH}{Si}}-O-\overset{C_2H_5}{\underset{OH}{Si}}-O-\overset{C_2H_5}{\underset{O_{0.5}}{Si}}-O-\overset{C_2H_5}{\underset{O_{0.5}}{Si}}-O-\overset{O_{0.5}}{\underset{O_{0.5}}{Ti}}- \right]_n$$

$$n = 22$$

$(C_8H_{22}Si_4TiO_9)_n$; Found: Si = 26.55%
HO = 8.05%
Ti = 11.33%.

References, p. 252–255

The infrared spectra of the polymers have been obtained and a linear, polycyclic structure for the macromolecules has been proposed.

Polyorganotitanosiloxanes have been obtained from the reaction between ethyl titanate and methyl-, ethyl- or phenyl-silanolates[28]. The main disadvantage of this ester-interchange reaction is the competition from the reaction of self-condensation of the silanols. The alkoxide-acyloxide reaction again offers considerable advantages and it has been successfully applied by Segal, Takimoto, and Rust[19,29] to the synthesis of linear titanosiloxane polymers of unequivocal structure. In a detailed study of the reaction of trimethylacetoxysilane with tetraisopropyl titanate, using highly pure materials, it was possible[30] to isolate and characterise four products, depending upon the stoicheiometry of the reaction:

$$n(CH_3)_3SiOCOCH_3 + Ti(OC_3H_7^i)_4 \longrightarrow$$

$$[(CH_3)_3SiO]_nTi(OC_3H_7^i)_{4-n} + nCH_3COOC_3H_7$$

where $n = 1, 2, 3$ and 4.

The bis(trimethylsiloxy)di-isopropoxytitanium was used as an intermediate in polymer synthesis, utilising the alkoxide-acyloxide reaction. With dimethyldiacetoxysilane (and sodium ethoxide as a catalyst) a linear polymer with a regular sequence of —Si—O—Ti—O— linkages was obtained.

$$CH_3COO\text{—}\underset{\underset{CH_3}{|}}{\overset{\overset{CH_3}{|}}{Si}}\text{—}OCOCH_3 + C_3H_7^iO\text{—}\underset{\underset{OSi(CH_3)_3}{|}}{\overset{\overset{OSi(CH_3)_3}{|}}{Ti}}\text{—}OC_3H_7^i \xrightarrow{NaOC_2H_5}$$

$$\left[\text{—}\underset{\underset{CH_3}{|}}{\overset{\overset{CH_3}{|}}{Si}}\text{—}O\text{—}\underset{\underset{OSi(CH_3)_3}{|}}{\overset{\overset{OSi(CH_3)_3}{|}}{Ti}}\text{—}O\text{—}\right]_n$$

The molecular weight of the polymer was 42,300. It was soluble in benzene and toluene. When methyltriacetoxysilane was substituted for dimethyldiacetoxysilane, an insoluble, cross-linked polymer resulted.

By combining diphenyldiacetoxysilane with bis(triphenylsiloxy)-di-isopropoxytitanium, the following polymer was obtained:

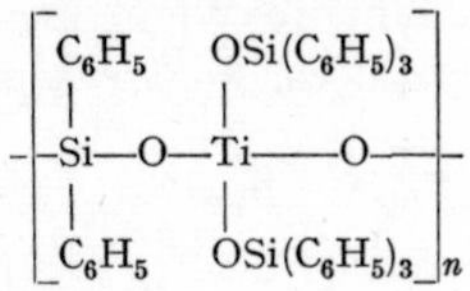

$$\left[-\underset{C_6H_5}{\overset{C_6H_5}{\underset{|}{\overset{|}{Si}}}}-O-\underset{OSi(C_6H_5)_3}{\overset{OSi(C_6H_5)_3}{\underset{|}{\overset{|}{Ti}}}}-O- \right]_n$$

Segal and his co-workers have also devised an interesting new synthesis of linear polyorganosiloxymetalloxanes of known and regular structure[29]. Thus, when bis(trimethylsiloxy)di-isopropoxy-titanium is treated with acetic anhydride, alkoxide-acyloxide exchange occurs and polymer formation ensues. The polymer was

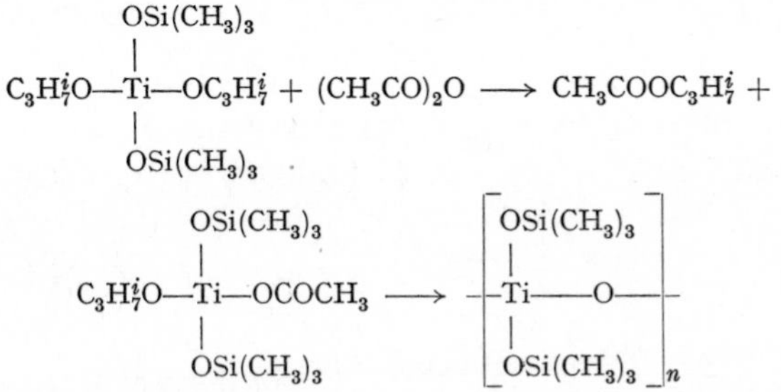

$$C_3H_7^iO-\underset{OSi(CH_3)_3}{\overset{OSi(CH_3)_3}{\underset{|}{\overset{|}{Ti}}}}-OC_3H_7^i + (CH_3CO)_2O \longrightarrow CH_3COOC_3H_7^i +$$

$$C_3H_7^iO-\underset{OSi(CH_3)_3}{\overset{OSi(CH_3)_3}{\underset{|}{\overset{|}{Ti}}}}-OCOCH_3 \longrightarrow \left[-\underset{OSi(CH_3)_3}{\overset{OSi(CH_3)_3}{\underset{|}{\overset{|}{Ti}}}}-O- \right]_n$$

a whitish solid which melted above 300° without signs of discoloration, had a molecular weight of 26,000, and could be formed into films and fibres.

By an extension of these reactions, both polyorganoalumino-siloxanes and polyorganosiloxyaluminoxanes have been prepared (see Section 2) and also representatives of a new class of siloxane polymer:

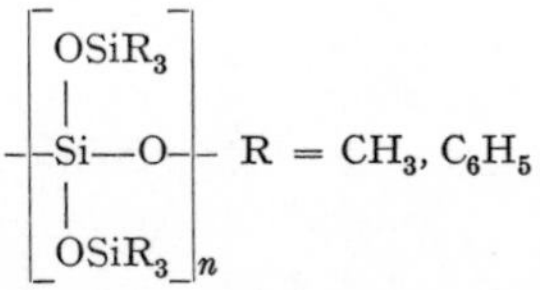

$$\left[-\underset{OSiR_3}{\overset{OSiR_3}{\underset{|}{\overset{|}{Si}}}}-O- \right]_n \quad R = CH_3, C_6H_5$$

Thus, poly(triphenylsiloxy)- and poly(trimethylsiloxy)-siloxane polymers resulted from the combination of acetic anhydride or water with the appropriate bis-derivative of ethyl orthosilicate. Polymers containing tin in the linear chain, or in the side group, were also synthesised by the same route.

Titanium esters form chelate complexes with acetylacetone, benzoyl-acetophenone, 8-hydroxyquinoline, etc. The structure of di-isopropoxytitanium acetylacetonate is illustrated below.

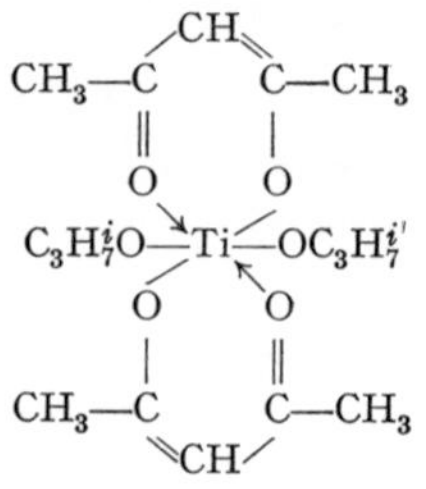

$$\begin{array}{ccc} & CH & \\ CH_3-C & & C-CH_3 \\ \| & & | \\ O & & O \\ C_3H_7^iO- & Ti & -OC_3H_7^i \\ O & & O \\ | & & \| \\ CH_3-C & & C-CH_3 \\ & CH & \end{array}$$

Segal, Takimoto, and Rust[29] have taken advantage of the difunctionality of these complexes in the synthesis of polychelated metalloxane and metallosiloxane polymers of the following idealised structure:

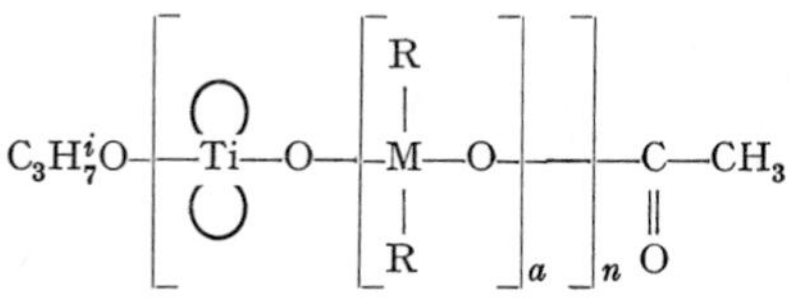

$$C_3H_7^iO-\left[-Ti-O-\left[-\overset{R}{\underset{R}{M}}-O- \right]_a - \right]_n -\underset{\underset{O}{\|}}{C}-CH_3$$

where the loops appended to titanium represent the chelate groups, M is either silicon or tin, R is either methyl or butyl, and *a* is either zero or one. It was found that similar polymers could be prepared by two routes: (a) the alkoxide–acyloxide reaction, involving a diacetoxydialkylmetallane (or acetic anhydride) and the appropriate bischelatedialkoxy-titanium; (b) the acyloxide-trimethylsiloxy reaction involving a diacetoxydialkylmetallane (or acetic anhydride) and the appropriate bischelatebis(trimethylsiloxy)-titanium. The resulting polymers ranged from viscous fluids to rigid solids which were partially soluble in polar and non-polar solvents and could be formed into fibres and films.

4. Silicon–oxygen–tin polymers

The synthesis of polymers, the primary chains of which are made up of atoms of silicon, oxygen, and tin, "framed" with organic groups, also originated with Andrianov and his school[26]. The Si—O—Sn linkage is highly polar and the polymers would therefore be expected to display a high degree of thermal stability. The first synthesis of polyorganostannosiloxanes was based on the co-hydrolysis of diethyldichlorostannane with dimethyl- or diethyl-dichlorosilane and also with mixtures of diethyldichlorosilane and phenyltrichlorosilane, with subsequent condensation of the products of co-hydrolysis[26]. The reaction probably proceeds according to the following scheme:

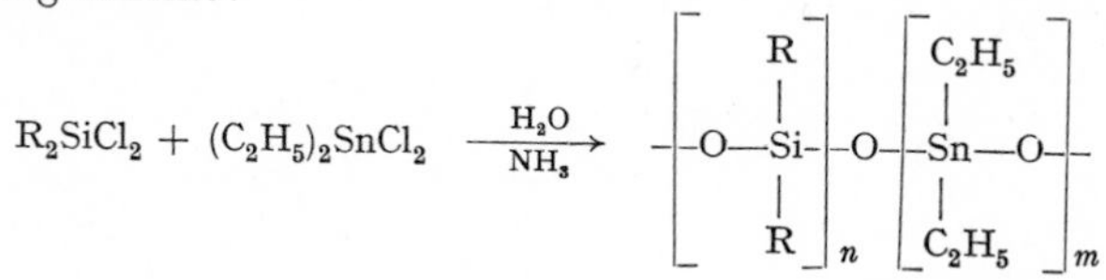

$$R_2SiCl_2 + (C_2H_5)_2SnCl_2 \xrightarrow[NH_3]{H_2O} -\left[-O-\underset{R}{\overset{R}{|}}\!\!\!\!Si-\right]_n\!\!-O-\left[-\underset{C_2H_5}{\overset{C_2H_5}{|}}\!\!\!\!Sn-O-\right]_m\!\!-$$

This results in the random integration of tin into the polymeric siloxane chain. The composition of the polystannosiloxanes depends upon the ratio of the monomers taking part in the reaction. By fractionation of the polymers it was established that in one and the same polymer there were fractions in which the ratio Si:Sn varied from 4 to 14. The composition of the polymers is governed partly by the relative rates of hydrolysis of the two components and partly by the ease with which the two hydrolysed materials undergo self-condensation or inter-condensation.

Another approach to the preparation of polyorganostannosiloxanes is by condensation of organotin oxides with silanols[1,31,18,32].

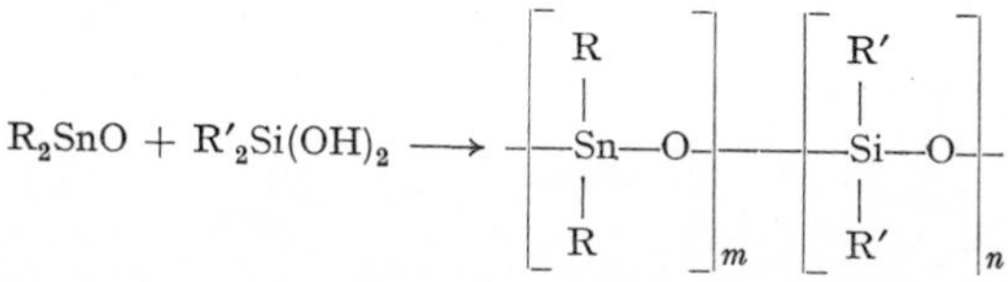

$$R_2SnO + R'_2Si(OH)_2 \longrightarrow -\left[-\underset{R}{\overset{R}{|}}\!\!\!\!Sn-O-\right]_m\!\!-\left[-\underset{R'}{\overset{R'}{|}}\!\!\!\!Si-O-\right]_n\!\!-$$

The reaction was carried out in a solvent such as dioxane or xylene and as the reaction proceeded the insoluble organotin oxide

References, p. 252–255

gradually went into solution and the polymeric product was recovered by evaporating the solvent. Alternatively, the reaction may take place in the absence of a solvent, merely by heating the mixed solid reagents in a vacuum. The polymers were obtained as transparent brittle resin with low melting points (50–70°) and were partly soluble in organic solvents. The molecular weights, determined cryoscopically in benzene, varied within the limits 1000–5,000. The polymers reacted with difficulty with water, but dilute inorganic acids caused rapid hydrolysis. The properties of these polymers as a function of the Si/Sn ratio and the nature of the organic substituents on the metal atoms have been discussed[32]. Those stannosiloxanes having phenylsilicon moieties were more stable than their methylsilicon counterparts and an increase in tin content was reflected in increased stability.

The reaction of organotin chlorides with alkali metal silanolates has also been applied to the synthesis of simple and polymeric stannosiloxanes[31, 33].

$$R_2SnCl_2 + R'_2Si(ONa)_2 \longrightarrow \left[-\overset{\displaystyle R}{\underset{\displaystyle R}{\overset{|}{\underset{|}{Sn}}}}-O-\overset{\displaystyle R'}{\underset{\displaystyle R'}{\overset{|}{\underset{|}{Si}}}}-O- \right]_n$$

Under appropriate conditions, this reaction leads to polymers with a regular structure, but undoubtedly the most versatile reaction for the synthesis of polystannosiloxanes of unequivocal structure is the alkoxide-acyloxide reaction; this was first investigated by Henglein and co-workers[34]. On heating dimethyldiethoxysilane with diacetoxytin[35] at 120°, ethyl acetate and a polymer containing 56.8% Sn and 13.4% Si were produced.

$$(CH_3)_2Si(OC_2H_5)_2 + Sn(OCOCH_3)_2 \longrightarrow \left[-\overset{\displaystyle CH_3}{\underset{\displaystyle CH_3}{\overset{|}{\underset{|}{Si}}}}-O-Sn-O- \right]_n + 2CH_3COOC_2H_5$$

Similarly, from dimethyldiethoxysilane and di-isobutyldiacetoxystannane, a polymer incorporating tin(IV) was obtained.

$$(CH_3)_2Si(OC_2H_5)_2 + (C_4H_9^i)_2Sn(OCOCH_3)_2 \longrightarrow \left[-\underset{CH_3}{\overset{CH_3}{\underset{|}{\overset{|}{Si}}}}-O-\underset{C_4H_9^i}{\overset{C_4H_9^i}{\underset{|}{\overset{|}{Sn}}}}-O- \right]_n + 2CH_3COOC_2H_5$$

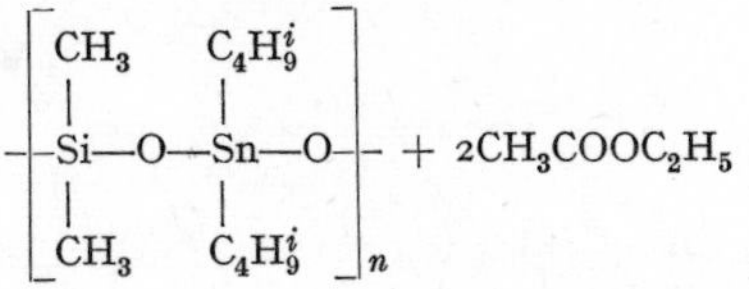

As a by-product in this latter reaction, a stannoxane of the following structure was obtained:

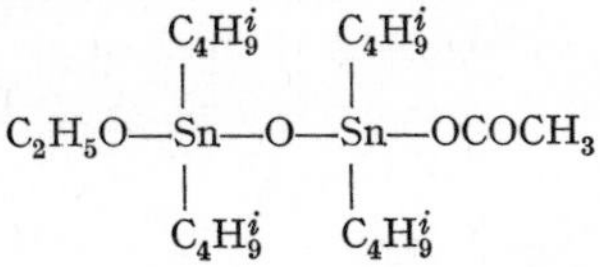

$$C_2H_5O-\underset{C_4H_9^i}{\overset{C_4H_9^i}{\underset{|}{\overset{|}{Sn}}}}-O-\underset{C_4H_9^i}{\overset{C_4H_9^i}{\underset{|}{\overset{|}{Sn}}}}-OCOCH_3$$

Recent American[36] work has shown that in the synthesis of poly-organostannosiloxanes by the alkoxide-acyloxide reaction, it is possible to use either acetoxytin derivatives and alkoxysilanes, or acetoxysilanes and alkoxytin compounds.

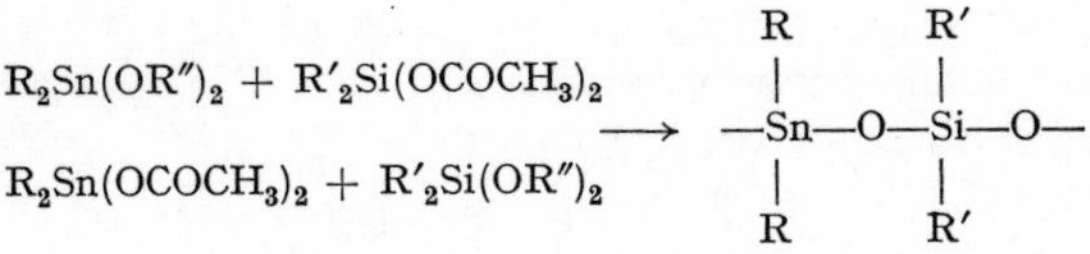

$$\begin{array}{l} R_2Sn(OR'')_2 + R'_2Si(OCOCH_3)_2 \\ R_2Sn(OCOCH_3)_2 + R'_2Si(OR'')_2 \end{array} \longrightarrow -\underset{R}{\overset{R}{\underset{|}{\overset{|}{Sn}}}}-O-\underset{R'}{\overset{R'}{\underset{|}{\overset{|}{Si}}}}-O-$$

Not only polymers containing tin in the linear polymer chain, but also polymers with tin in the side group as R_3SnO–, have been prepared by the alkoxide-acyloxide reaction[29]. Polymers containing Ti—O—Sn—O[29] and As—O—Sn—O[37,38] linkages in the basic chain have also been described. Koton and Kiseleva[39] have recently applied the alkoxide-acyloxide reaction to the synthesis of the polyorganostannoxane:

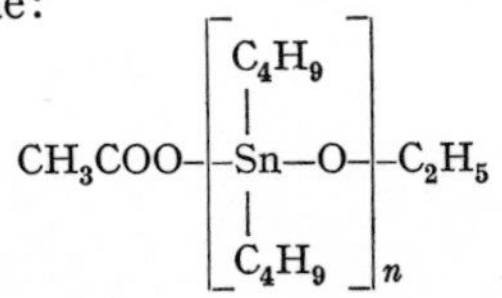

$$CH_3COO-\left[-\underset{C_4H_9}{\overset{C_4H_9}{\underset{|}{\overset{|}{Sn}}}}-O- \right]_n-C_2H_5$$

This, on hydrolysis with boiling water, gave an insoluble, infusible product of the composition:

References, p. 252–255

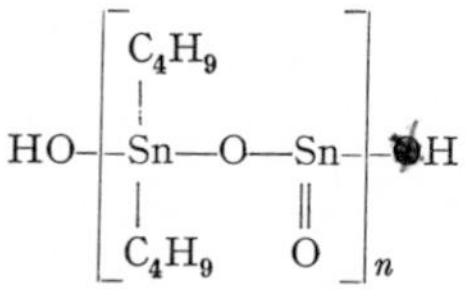

$$\text{HO}-\left[\begin{array}{c}\text{C}_4\text{H}_9\\ |\\ -\text{Sn}-\text{O}-\text{Sn}-\\ |\qquad\quad \|\\ \text{C}_4\text{H}_9\qquad \text{O}\end{array}\right]_n-\text{OH}$$

Organic compounds of tin, in particular dibutyltin, have been recommended as cold hardening agents for polydimethylsiloxane rubbers. Dibutyltin diacetate and di-2-ethylhexanoate are extensively used as curing catalysts in the application of silicones to textiles and paper. It is likely that these applications depend upon the formation of stannosiloxane linkages[40].

5. Silicon–oxygen–arsenic polymers

Kary and Frisch[41] have studied the hydrolysis of compounds of arsenic(V) containing Si—O—As linkages. The compounds included bis(dimethylchlorosilyl)methyl-, bis(methyldichlorosilyl)methyl-, and bis(phenyldichlorosilyl)phenyl-arsonates. The polymeric hydrolysis products, which contained both arsenic and silicon, ranged from transparent, rubbery materials to fine, white powders. From the elementary analysis of the products, it was clear that some cleavage of the Si—O—As linkage had taken place, as the arsenic to silicon ratio was only 1 to 12.

Chamberland and MacDiarmid[42] found that both tris(triphenylsilyl) arsenite and tris(triphenylsilyl) arsenate were hydrolysed only very slightly when dissolved in acetone-water solutions. In an attempt to prepare polymers containing a regular sequence of Si—O—As—O linkages, the reaction of diphenyldichlorosilane with excess potassium dihydrogen arsenate, in ether at room temperature, was investigated. The overall reaction may be expressed by the equation:

$$4n\text{KH}_2\text{AsO}_4 + 2n(\text{C}_6\text{H}_5)_2\text{SiCl}_2 \longrightarrow (2n-1)\text{H}_3\text{AsO}_4 +$$

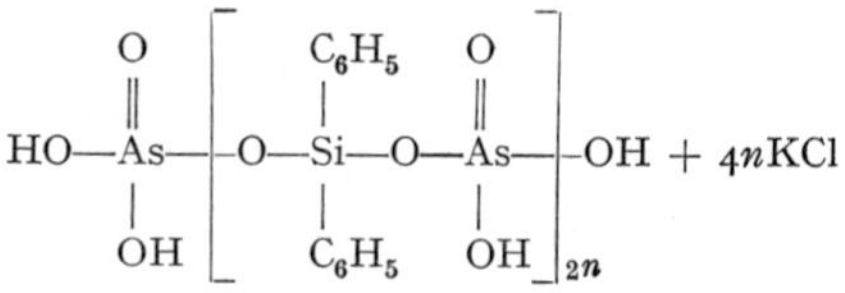

$$\text{HO}-\overset{\overset{\text{O}}{\|}}{\underset{\underset{\text{OH}}{|}}{\text{As}}}-\left[-\text{O}-\overset{\overset{\text{C}_6\text{H}_5}{|}}{\underset{\underset{\text{C}_6\text{H}_5}{|}}{\text{Si}}}-\text{O}-\overset{\overset{\text{O}}{\|}}{\underset{\underset{\text{OH}}{|}}{\text{As}}}-\right]_{2n}-\text{OH} + 4n\text{KCl}$$

The initial product, obtained after removal of the solvent, corresponded to the above species where n equals one. The product decomposed slowly on standing giving arsenic acid and a material whose composition approached the formula:

$$\left[-O-\overset{C_6H_5}{\underset{C_6H_5}{\overset{|}{\underset{|}{Si}}}}-O-\overset{O}{\underset{OH}{\overset{\|}{\underset{|}{As}}}}- \right]_n$$

The isolation of some hexaphenylcyclotrisiloxane, $[(C_6H_5)_2SiO]_3$, as a by-product suggests that a small number of Si—O—As linkages may have undergone a reaction of the following type:

$$3\left[-\overset{O}{\underset{OH}{\overset{\|}{\underset{|}{As}}}}-O-\overset{C_6H_5}{\underset{C_6H_5}{\overset{|}{\underset{|}{Si}}}}-O-\overset{O}{\underset{HO}{\overset{\|}{\underset{|}{As}}}}- \right] \longrightarrow [(C_6H_5)_2SiO]_3 + 3\left[-\overset{O}{\underset{OH}{\overset{\|}{\underset{|}{As}}}}-O-\overset{O}{\underset{HO}{\overset{\|}{\underset{|}{As}}}}- \right]$$

Co-hydrolysis of arsenic(III) chloride and diphenyldichlorosilane gave, as the principal product, the cyclic arsenosiloxane.

$$As\begin{cases} O-Si(C_6H_5)_2-O \\ O-Si(C_6H_5)_2-O \\ O-Si(C_6H_5)_2-O \end{cases}As$$

This, although relatively stable to hydrolysis, showed a tendency to form polymeric species (see p. 184). In addition to the above, another substance, of composition corresponding to the formula:

$$As\begin{cases} O-Si(C_6H_5)_2-O-Si(C_6H_5)_2-O \\ O-Si(C_6H_5)_2-O-Si(C_6H_5)_2-O \\ O-Si(C_6H_5)_2-O-Si(C_6H_5)_2-O \end{cases}As$$

was isolated. This material, which softened and melted at 35–50°, was not fully characterised. Its wide melting point range and the

References, p. 252–255

somewhat viscous nature of its solution suggests that it might contain linear as well as cyclic products.

By condensation of diphenylsilanediol with di-iodophenylarsine, in the presence of ammonia[37], a cyclic dimeric species was obtained.

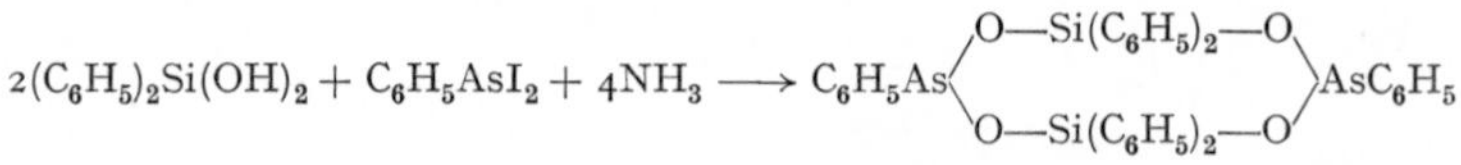

$$2(C_6H_5)_2Si(OH)_2 + C_6H_5AsI_2 + 4NH_3 \longrightarrow C_6H_5As\begin{matrix} \diagup O—Si(C_6H_5)_2—O \diagdown \\ \diagdown O—Si(C_6H_5)_2—O \diagup \end{matrix}AsC_6H_5$$

This crystalline cyclic product may be regarded as a dimer of the series $[—OSi(C_6H_5)_2—O—As(C_6H_5)—]_n$. A resinous, polymeric species ($n > 2$) was also formed in the same reaction. Its empirical formula and infrared spectrum were identical with those of the dimer, but attempts to obtain the polymer free of dimer were unsuccessful. On distilling the dimer at 350° *in vacuo*, a glassy material of identical composition but higher molecular weight was obtained. This product is believed to consist predominantly of the trimer ($n = 3$).

Co-hydrolysis of arsenic(III) chloride and phenyltrichlorosilane produced a polymeric material of approximate composition $[(C_6H_5SiO_{1.5})_8.\ AsO_{1.5}.H]_n$, which, although soluble in a variety of organic solvents, neither softened nor melted on heating. The polymer was assigned the structure:

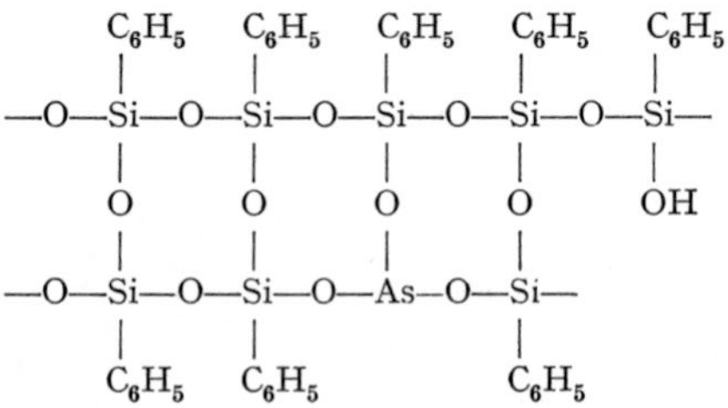

$$\begin{array}{ccccccccc} & C_6H_5 & & C_6H_5 & & C_6H_5 & & C_6H_5 & & C_6H_5 \\ & | & & | & & | & & | & & | \\ —O— & Si & —O— & Si & —O— & Si & —O— & Si & —O— & Si— \\ & | & & | & & | & & | & & | \\ & O & & O & & O & & O & & OH \\ & | & & | & & | & & | & & \\ —O— & Si & —O— & Si & —O— & As & —O— & Si— & & \\ & | & & | & & & & | & & \\ & C_6H_5 & & C_6H_5 & & & & C_6H_5 & & \end{array}$$

on the basis of elemental analysis and infrared data. This material is analogous to the polyphenylaluminosiloxane[12].

In the preparation of tris(trimethylsilyl) orthoarsenate, from silver arsenate and trimethylchlorosilane, Schmidt and Schmidbaur[43] found that waxy trimethylsilyl meta-arsenate, $[(CH_3)_3SiOAsO_2]_n$, was produced as a by-product. Polyarsenosiloxanes were also formed on refluxing arsenic pentoxide with hexamethyldisiloxane.

6. Silicon–oxygen–boron polymers

Several methods have been described for the synthesis of polymers containing —Si—O—B—O— linkages from di- and tri-functional silicon compounds[1]. These include the following condensation reactions:

(a) organosilicon acetates and alkoxyboron compounds[44];
(b) organosilicon alkoxides and acetoxyboron compounds[45];
(c) organosilicon alkoxides and boric acid[46];
(d) organosilicon halides and boric acid[46];
(e) organosilicon hydroxides and boric acid[47].

In the alkoxide-acyloxide reactions (a) and (b), polyorganoborosiloxanes are obtained and an acetic ester liberated.

$$B(OR)_3 + R'_2Si(OCOCH_3)_2 \longrightarrow$$

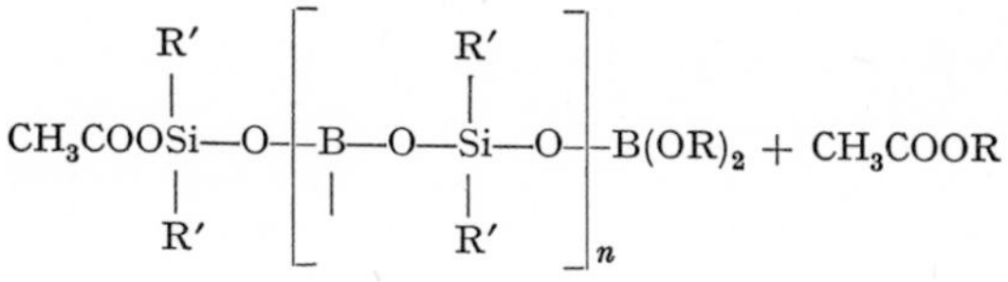

$$CH_3COOSi(R')_2—O—\left[—\overset{|}{B}—O—Si(R')_2—O—\right]_n—B(OR)_2 + CH_3COOR$$

$$B(OCOCH_3)_3 + R'_2Si(OR)_2 \longrightarrow$$

$$RO—Si(R')_2—O—\left[—\overset{|}{B}—O—Si(R')_2—O—\right]_n—B(OCOCH_3)_2$$

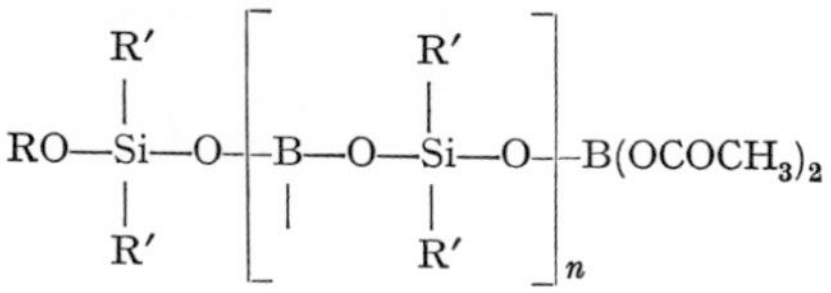

$$+ CH_3COOR$$

The reactions proceed step-wise. The direction of rupture of the bonds in these condensations has been the subject of a recent investigation by Andrianov, Kudryavtsev, and Kursanov[48], using the heavy isotope ^{18}O. Thus, trimethyl borate and tetramethoxy-

References, p. 252–255

silane with a relatively high concentration of ^{18}O (0.4 at.% excess of ^{18}O) were prepared. In the interaction of tetramethoxysilane with triacetoxyboron, methyl acetate containing all the excess ^{18}O from the tetramethoxysilane, was obtained.

$$3Si(\vdots\!-\!\overset{18}{O}\!-\!CH_3)_4 + 4B(-O\vdots\!-\!CO\!-\!CH_3)_3 \longrightarrow 12CH_3CO^{18}OCH_3$$

It was concluded, therefore, that during the reaction, cleavage occurred at the Si—O and C—O bonds as indicated by the dotted lines. In the condensation of trimethyl borate and diethyldiacetoxysilane:

$$2B(\vdots\!-\!\overset{18}{O}\!-\!CH_3)_3 + 3(C_2H_5)_2Si(-O\vdots\!-\!CO\!-\!CH_3)_2 \longrightarrow 6CH_3CO^{18}OCH_3$$

the methyl acetate again contained the whole of the excess ^{18}O from the trimethyl borate and hence it follows that, in this case, rupture of the B—O and C—O bonds occurred as indicated.

The synthesis of polyorganoborosiloxanes by reaction of boric acid with alkoxysilanes has been investigated[46]. Thus, by heating dimethyldiethoxysilane (3 moles) with boric acid (1 mole), a viscous, soluble polymer, having a boron content of 4.2%, was obtained. The reaction proceeded readily, with formation of ethyl alcohol and also triethyl borate. The composition and properties of the polyborosiloxanes depended largely upon the relative proportions of the reactants used in the condensation, and upon the structure of the alkoxysilanes. During the reaction of boric acid with an equimolecular amount of methyltriethoxysilane, ethyl alcohol separated in approximately theoretical amount, and a solid, infusible, insoluble polymer was formed. Taking advantage of the sensitivity of the Si—O—B bonds to hydrolysis, the reaction of diethyldiethoxysilane with boric acid has been utilised in order to prepare polydiethylsiloxane free from traces of polymers containing ethoxy-groups in their molecules[59]. Another convenient method of synthesising polyorganoborosiloxanes is the reaction of boric acid with various chlorosilanes[46]. For example, by reacting dimethyldichlorosilane with boric acid in a molar ratio of 3:2, a polymer approximating in composition to $[B_2O_3 \cdot 3(CH_3)_2SiO]_n$ was obtained.

Polyorganoborosiloxanes have acquired prominence by virtue of the extraordinary physical properties of "bouncing putty". In the patent literature, it is claimed that the treatment of polydimethylsiloxane with boric acid, its esters, or anhydride, confers upon the polymer a number of distinctive and interesting properties[47, 49, 50, 51]. This so-called "bouncing putty" possesses what appear to be mutually contradictory properties, flow and bounce. Thus, the putty may be drawn into threads and will flow to fill a container, but when moulded into a ball and dropped, it can rebound to 90% of the original height. The more rapidly the force is applied, the greater the resistance, and under the sudden impact of a hammer it behaves like brittle glass and shatters. It has been established[47] that, structurally, "bouncing putty" is a polydimethylborosiloxane, within the composition range of one boron atom to every 3–100 silicon atoms in the chain, in which linear polydimethylsiloxane units are linked through Si—O—B—O bonds. The high elasticity of these polymers is the more remarkable since their molecular weight is relatively low. The usual method of preparation is by condensation of boric acid with hydroxyl end-blocked polysiloxanes of low molecular weight. Wick[47] has prepared a product with a molecular weight of only 600 by careful hydrolysis of $B[OSi(CH_3)_2OC_2H_5]_3$. This had the typical properties of "bouncing putty". Some of the polymers prepared by the methods outlined above also displayed the same characteristics. Beyond their use as a novelty for children (and adults!), these bouncing putties had, until recently, found little application. One reason for this is their sensitivity to hydrolysis. On long contact with moisture (even from the atmosphere) they gradually lose their rubbery, elastic properties and their bounce. Hydrolysis causes rupture of the B—O—Si linkages with formation of polyorganosiloxanes of lower molecular weight, and boric acid. Attempts to vulcanise bouncing silicone putty with the usual cross-linking agents, *e.g.*, peroxides or silicic acid–metal soap systems, used in silicone technology, have proved unsuccessful.

Recently, a group of novel, hydrolytically-stable borosiloxane elastomers with interesting and commercially-valuable properties

References, p. 252–255

has been developed. Wick[47] has given some details about these elastomers, which are structurally related to "bouncing putty". The significant observation was made that borosiloxane polymeɪs containing less than one boron atom to 100 silicon atoms, and with molecular weights over 70,000, and prefeɪably within the range 350,000—500,000, can be vulcanised to completely non-viscous, elastic materials, which have the property of self-welding. The vulcanisates, on standing, weld together into a solid, homogeneous mass. If the boron content is increased beyond this limit, even by an almost insignificant amount, then it is no longer possible to vulcanise the siloxane, and only a product resembling "bouncing putty" is obtained. The best vulcanisates, with the best welding properties, were obtained in the composition range 1 boron atom to 300–400 silicon atoms. For the preparation of such borosiloxane elastomers, the following methods may be used:

(a) condensation with boric acid at 120° of polydialkylsiloxanes, end-blocked with hydroxyl groups, and with molecular weights between 1,000 and 10,000,

(b) condensation with boron triacetate of polydiorganosiloxanes, end-blocked wuth ethoxy-groups.

In these reactions, the boron compound serves not only to incorporate boron atoms into the siloxane chain but, at the same time, functions as a catalyst for the condensation. Optionally, ferric chloride, a common condensation catalyst in silicone chemistry, may be used as well, but this is not necessary. Control of the molecular weight is achieved by addition of hexamethyldisiloxane as chain-stopper. The compounded borosiloxane polymer, with filler and vulcanising agent, is extruded in bands 0.35 mm thick, which, directly after leaving the extruder, are vulcanised at 300°. An alternative, and commercially attractive, method of preparing the elastomers is to introduce the boric acid, in appropriate quantities, with the filler and vulcaniser in the silicone–rubber mixture and then to vulcanise. Silicic acid is used as the filler and 2,4-dichlorobenzoyl peroxide as vulcanising agent. On heating, the boric acid cleaves the siloxane linkages, the borosiloxane is formed *in situ*, an equilibrium with the polyorganosiloxanes being established. Concerning the mechanism of the self-welding reaction, certain pertinent observations have been made. If the extruded bands or tapes are stored with exclusion of moisture, the welding power is retained. Prolonged contact with atmospheric moisture renders the bands incapable of welding in the cold and only feebly do they exhibit this property at temperatures above 100°. A condition of self-welding at room temperature is that the Si—O—B linkages in the polymer should remain intact. Once welding has occurred, the material becomes hydrolytically stable. Presumably, therefore, the Si—O—B linkages contribute only to the initial stages of the process. The welding reaction is accelerated by addition of condensation catalysts for organosilicon compounds, *e.g.*, ferric oxide, ferric chloride, aerosil containing hydrogen chloride. This suggests a condensation of silanol groups. The mechanism envisaged involves a two-stage process; in the first stage rupture of Si—O—B bonds occurs under the influence of moisture:

$$\text{—}\underset{|}{\overset{|}{\text{Si}}}\text{—O—}\overset{|}{\text{B}}\text{—O—}\underset{|}{\overset{|}{\text{Si}}}\text{—} \xrightarrow{H_2O} \text{—}\underset{|}{\overset{|}{\text{Si}}}\text{—OH} + B(OH)_3 + \text{HO—}\underset{|}{\overset{|}{\text{Si}}}\text{—}$$

and in the second, cold vulcanisation follows, through condensation of the silanol groups, thus effecting the actual welding. If this mechanism is correct, then the self-welding phenomenon constitutes a special case of cold vulcanisation of silicone rubber[52]. The electrical properties of the self-welding borosiloxane rubber are excellent and already the material is finding extensive uses in the electrical industry.

7. Silicon–oxygen–phosphorus polymers

Monomeric phosphorosiloxanes have been extensively studied. In contrast, polyorganophosphorosiloxanes have received scant attention. The methods which have been developed for the synthesis of the simple compounds, if applied to polyfunctional organosilicon compounds, lead to polymer formation. In many cases, these polymers are complex, three-dimensional structures, which makes characterisation difficult. The susceptibility of the Si—O—P linkage

References, p. 252–255

to hydrolysis may account for the lack of commercial interest in these materials.

When diethyldichlorosilane is hydrolysed by water, liquid polymers are obtained, which on heating with phosphorus pentoxide at 200° are converted into solid gels[53]. If the gels are warmed with an excess of water, the solids quickly revert to oils, similar in viscosity to the original materials. This suggests that the formation reaction is predominantly one of condensation, involving the silanol end-groups and phosphorus pentoxide in phosphorosiloxane formation, rather than an acceleration of siloxane formation by the dehydrating action of the phosphorus pentoxide.

$$
\begin{array}{c}
\begin{array}{ccc}
\begin{array}{c} C_2H_5 \\ | \\ \text{—O—Si—OH} \\ | \\ C_2H_5 \end{array} & + & \begin{array}{c} C_2H_5 \\ | \\ \text{HO—Si—O—} \\ | \\ C_2H_5 \end{array}
\end{array} \\
+ \; P_2O_5 \\
\begin{array}{ccc}
\begin{array}{c} C_2H_5 \\ | \\ \text{—O—Si—OH} \\ | \\ C_2H_5 \end{array} & + & \begin{array}{c} C_2H_5 \\ | \\ \text{HO—Si—O—} \\ | \\ C_2H_5 \end{array}
\end{array}
\end{array}
\longrightarrow
\begin{array}{ccccc}
C_2H_5 & & O & & C_2H_5 \\
| & & \| & & | \\
\text{—O—Si} & \text{—O—} & \text{P} & \text{—O—} & \text{Si—O—} \\
| & & | & & | \\
C_2H_5 & & | & & C_2H_5 \\
 & & O & & \\
C_2H_5 & & | & & C_2H_5 \\
| & & | & & | \\
\text{—O—Si} & \text{—O—} & \text{P} & \text{—O—} & \text{Si—O—} \\
| & & \| & & | \\
C_2H_5 & & O & & C_2H_5
\end{array}
$$

Polyfunctional alkoxysilanes react with phosphorus pentoxide, phosphoric acid, or phosphoryl chloride to give polyorganophosphorosiloxanes[54–58]. A similar polymeric product is obtained when dimethyldiethoxysilane is heated either with phosphoryl

$$
\begin{array}{ccccc}
CH_3 & & O & & CH_3 \\
| & & \| & & | \\
\text{—O—Si} & \text{—O—} & \text{P} & \text{—O—} & \text{Si—O—} \\
| & & | & & | \\
CH_3 & & O & & CH_3 \\
 & & | & & \\
 & & CH_3\text{—Si—}CH_3 & & \\
 & & | & & \\
 & & O & & \\
 & & | & & \\
 & & \text{—O—P—O—} & & \\
 & & \| & & \\
 & & O & &
\end{array}
$$

chloride or with phosphorus pentoxide[54]. Its presumed structural formula contains alternating Si—O—P bonds.

The same product (polydimethylphosphorosiloxane) has also been obtained both from dimethyldichlorosilane and dimethyldimethoxysilane with orthophosphoric acid[58]. Trifunctional alkylalkoxysilanes react with phosphorus pentoxide according to the following scheme[57]:

$$2n\mathrm{RSi(OR')_3} + n\mathrm{P_2O_5} \longrightarrow [\mathrm{RSi(OR')_2OP_2O_4OSi(OR')_2R}]_n + n\mathrm{R'_2O}$$

$$\text{where } \mathrm{R} = \mathrm{CH_3},\ \mathrm{C_2H_5}$$
$$\mathrm{R'} = \mathrm{C_2H_5}$$

Polymers have also been formed from tetra-alkoxysilanes and phosphoryl chloride[55,56].

Leznov, Sabun, and Andrianov[59] have studied in some detail the reaction of phosphoric acid on diethyldiethoxysilane (and mixtures of it with triethylethoxysilane) at molar ratios of alkoxysilane to acid of from 3:2 to 1:2. The object of the study was to see whether, by subsequent hydrolysis, polydiethylsiloxane, free from traces of polymers containing ethoxyl groups in their molecules, could be obtained. They claim that two species of polydiethylphosphorosiloxanes, (IV) and (V), are formed in the reaction with diethyldiethoxysilane and that these are stable in the reaction medium.

$$\mathrm{(C_2H_5)_2Si(OC_2H_5)_2} + \mathrm{H_3PO_4} \xrightarrow[-\mathrm{H_2O}]{-\mathrm{C_2H_5OH}}$$

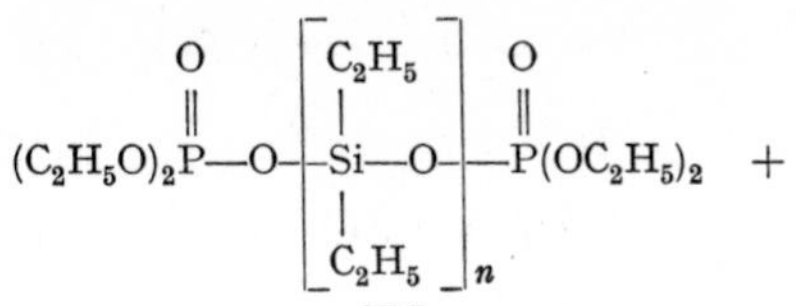

$$\mathrm{(C_2H_5O)_2\overset{\overset{\displaystyle O}{\|}}{P}}\!-\!\mathrm{O}\!-\!\left[\begin{array}{c}\mathrm{C_2H_5}\\ | \\ -\mathrm{Si}-\mathrm{O}- \\ | \\ \mathrm{C_2H_5}\end{array}\right]_n\!-\!\mathrm{\overset{\overset{\displaystyle O}{\|}}{P}(OC_2H_5)_2} \quad +$$

(IV)

$$\left[\begin{array}{ccc}\mathrm{O} & & \mathrm{C_2H_5}\\ \| & & | \\ -\mathrm{P}-\mathrm{O} & - & \mathrm{Si}-\mathrm{O}- \\ | & & | \\ \mathrm{OC_2H_5} & & \mathrm{C_2H_5}\end{array}\right]_n$$

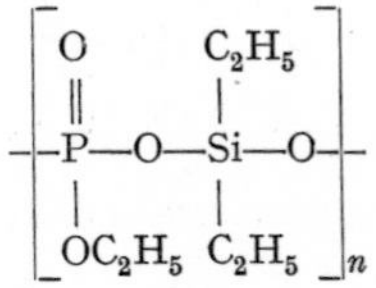

(V)

References, p. 252–255

Hydrolysis of the reaction products proceeds with liberation of polydiethylsiloxanes and acid ethyl esters of phosphoric acid.

$$(IV) \xrightarrow{H_2O} [(C_2H_5)_2SiO]_n + (C_2H_5O)_2PO(OH)$$

$$(V) \xrightarrow{H_2O} [(C_2H_5)_2SiO]_{n'} + (C_2H_5O)PO(OH)_2$$

The polyphosphorosiloxanes could not be isolated. Decomposition set in during an attempt to distil the reaction mixture in high vacuum, after removal of the alcohol. Fractionation of the polydiethylsiloxanes, formed on hydrolysis, furnished evidence in support of the above reaction scheme. The final polymers were found to be free from ethoxyl groups. The action of phosphoric acid on a mixture of diethyldiethoxysilane and triethylethoxysilane, followed by hydrolysis, led to the formation of polydiethylsiloxanes, which largely contained linear polymers with triethylsilyl end-groups.

$$(C_2H_5)_2Si(OC_2H_5)_2 + (C_2H_5)_3Si(OC_2H_5) \xrightarrow[-H_2O \atop -C_2H_5OPO(OH)_2]{H_3PO_4}$$

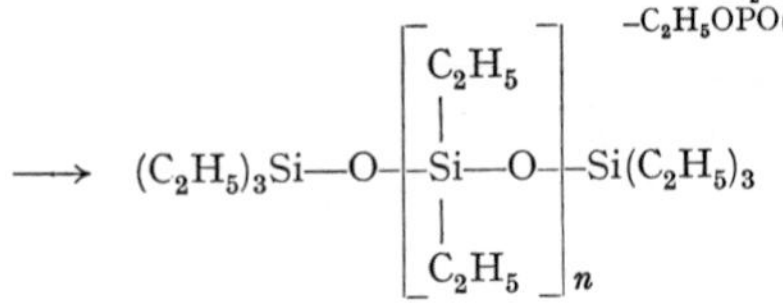

$$\longrightarrow (C_2H_5)_3Si{-}O{-}\left[\begin{array}{c} C_2H_5 \\ | \\ {-}Si{-}O{-} \\ | \\ C_2H_5 \end{array}\right]_n{-}Si(C_2H_5)_3$$

Fehér and Lippert[60] have described a step-wise synthesis of a low molecular weight polyorganophosphorosiloxane of known structure.

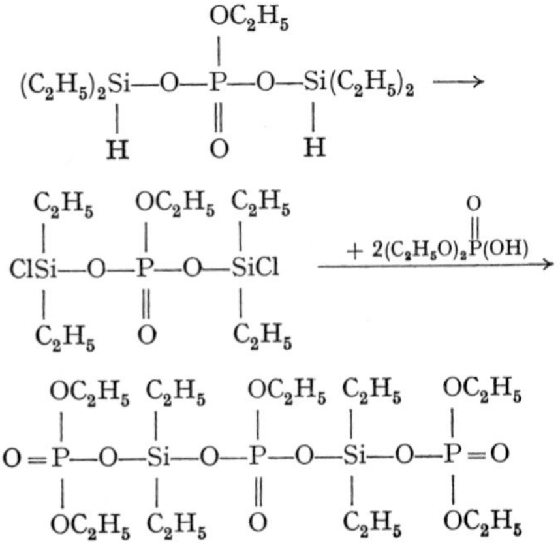

$$\begin{array}{ccccc} & & OC_2H_5 & & \\ & & | & & \\ (C_2H_5)_2Si & {-}O{-} & P & {-}O{-} & Si(C_2H_5)_2 \\ | & & \| & & | \\ H & & O & & H \end{array} \longrightarrow$$

$$\begin{array}{ccccc} C_2H_5 & & OC_2H_5 & & C_2H_5 \\ | & & | & & | \\ ClSi & {-}O{-} & P & {-}O{-} & SiCl \\ | & & \| & & | \\ C_2H_5 & & O & & C_2H_5 \end{array} \xrightarrow{+\,2(C_2H_5O)_2\overset{O}{\overset{\|}{P}}(OH)}$$

$$\begin{array}{ccccccccc} OC_2H_5 & & C_2H_5 & & OC_2H_5 & & C_2H_5 & & OC_2H_5 \\ | & & | & & | & & | & & | \\ O{=}P & {-}O{-} & Si & {-}O{-} & P & {-}O{-} & Si & {-}O{-} & P{=}O \\ | & & | & & \| & & | & & | \\ OC_2H_5 & & C_2H_5 & & O & & C_2H_5 & & OC_2H_5 \end{array}$$

Possible practical applications for some of the polyorganophosphorosiloxanes are hinted at in the Russian literature[54,57,61]. It is claimed[61] that addition of polymers, such as polydimethylphosphorosiloxane to cement pastes, in amounts of 0.5–1% of the weight of dry cement, has a favourable effect on the water absorption, compressive strength, and frost resistance of the cements.

8. Silicon–oxygen–sulphur polymers

Dimeric dimethylsilyl sulphate, a polyfunctional silanol ester of sulphuric acid, has recently been prepared and characterised[62].

```
            SO2
           /   \
          O     O
         /       \
(CH3)2Si          Si(CH3)2
         \       /
          O     O
           \   /
            SO2
```

It is obtained in high yield by the reaction of dimethyldichlorosilane and sulphuric acid, or by treating dimethylpolysiloxane with sulphur trioxide (see p. 188). Methyltrichlorosilane reacts slowly with sulphuric acid, yielding resinous high polymers of the composition $[(CH_3Si)_2(SO_4)_3]_n$, while mixtures of trimethylchlorosilane and dimethyldichlorosilane with sulphuric acid give, in addition to the silyl sulphates $[(CH_3)_3Si]_2SO_4$ and $[(CH_3)_2SiSO_4]_2$, compounds of composition $(CH_3)_3SiSO_4[(CH_3)_2SiSO_4]_nSi(CH_3)_3$. These sulphate esters readily hydrolyse.

Polydiethylsiloxanes, free from admixtures of polymers containing ethoxyl groups in the molecule, have been prepared by treating diethyldiethoxysilane with concentrated sulphuric acid[63]. Polydiethylsiloxane sulphates are formed as intermediates in the reaction, which proceeds as follows:

$$(C_2H_5)_2Si(OC_2H_5)_2 + 2H_2SO_4 \longrightarrow (C_2H_5)_2Si(OH)_2 + 2C_2H_5OSO_3H$$

$$(C_2H_5)_2Si(OH)_2 \longrightarrow [(C_2H_5)_2SiO]_x + H_2O$$

References, p. 252–255

$$[(C_2H_5)_2SiO]_x \underset{}{\overset{H_2SO_4}{\rightleftharpoons}} (C_2H_5)_2\underset{\displaystyle OH}{Si}—O—\left[\underset{\displaystyle C_2H_5}{\overset{\displaystyle C_2H_5}{Si}}—O—\right]_y—\underset{\displaystyle OSO_3H}{Si}(C_2H_5)_2$$

$$\downarrow H_2O \mid -H_2SO_4$$

$$[(C_2H_5)_2SiO]_{x'} \xleftarrow{-H_2SO_4} (C_2H_5)_2\underset{\displaystyle OH}{Si}—O—\left[\underset{\displaystyle C_2H_5}{\overset{\displaystyle C_2H_5}{Si}}—O—\right]_y—\underset{\displaystyle OH}{Si}(C_2H_5)_2$$

where $y \leqslant x - 2;\ x' > x$.

9. Silicon–oxygen–antimony polymers

Although it has been claimed that polyorganoantimonysiloxanes can be prepared by the alkoxide-acyloxide reaction, the products have not been well-characterised[64]. In the reaction of dimethyldiacetoxysilane with antimony triethoxide, it was found that, at temperatures below 100°, a simple exchange reaction occurred.

$$C_2H_5O—\overset{\displaystyle OC_2H_5}{Sb}—OC_2H_5 + CH_3COO—\underset{\displaystyle CH_3}{\overset{\displaystyle CH_3}{Si}}—OCOCH_3 \longrightarrow$$

$$Sb(OCOCH_3)_3 + C_2H_5O—\underset{\displaystyle CH_3}{\overset{\displaystyle CH_3}{Si}}—OC_2H_5 + CH_3COOC_2H_5 \text{ (trace)}$$

Only a small amount of ethyl acetate was formed. On raising the temperature to above 100°, a vigorous polycondensation reaction set in with evolution of ethyl acetate. The end product was found to contain 55.3% Sb, 8.4% Si, and 15.5% residual acetate groups. This corresponds to a polymer with a ratio of antimony: silicon atoms of 2:3. The polymer readily hydrolyses with water and on standing in hydrochloric acid solution it is converted into a silicone rubber, the antimony trioxide remaining in solution in the acid. The possibility that cyclic structures such as:

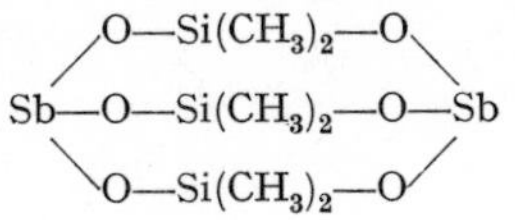

$$\begin{array}{ccc} & O\text{—}Si(CH_3)_2\text{—}O & \\ \diagup & & \diagdown \\ Sb\text{—} & O\text{—}Si(CH_3)_2\text{—}O & \text{—}Sb \\ \diagdown & & \diagup \\ & O\text{—}Si(CH_3)_2\text{—}O & \end{array}$$

might be formed in the exchange reaction was considered, but such a compound was not isolated.

10. Silicon–oxygen–germanium polymers

A certain analogy exists between the behaviour on hydrolysis of organosilicon dihalides and organogermanium dihalides. Just as the former yield silanediols, which condense to polysiloxanes, $(R_2SiO)_n$, germanium dihalides, likewise, yield cyclic trimers and tetramers, and what are presumed to be high-polymeric forms of diorganogermanium oxide, $(R_2GeO)_n$. Thus, tetrameric dimethylgermanium oxide, m.p. 92°, was obtained in 67% yield by hydrolysis of dimethyldichlorogermane with aqueous sodium hydroxide, followed by solvent extraction[65]. By analogy with octamethylcyclotetrasiloxane, an eight-membered ring structure is assumed for this tetramer. Unlike its silicon analogue, the tetramer is very soluble in water, although the rate of dissolution is somewhat slow. Hydration to the monomeric diol, $(CH_3)_2Ge(OH)_2$, takes place, but this reaction is reversible, since, on allowing the aqueous solution to evaporate, a white fibrous polymeric material, m.p. 132–133°, is obtained.

$$[(CH_3)_2GeO]_4 + 4H_2O \longrightarrow 4(CH_3)_2Ge(OH)_2$$

$$n(CH_3)_2Ge(OH)_2 \rightleftharpoons [(CH_3)_2GeO]_n + nH_2O.$$

Its general behaviour suggests a high-polymeric structure which breaks down on melting. At temperatures of 160–250°, and in the

References, p. 252–255

vapour phase at pressures of about 100 mm, dimethylgermanium oxide exists as the trimer $[(CH_3)_2GeO]_3$. By rapidly cooling the vapour at 210°, the trimer was isolated in the form of unstable, fern-like crystals. On standing it slowly reverted to the high polymeric form.

The following inter-relationships hold in the case of diphenylgermanium oxide[66]:

$(C_6H_5)_2GeBr_2$
b.p. 140–143°/0.2 mm

HBr ↑↓ $H_3\overset{+}{O}$ or OH′

HBr (from $[(C_6H_5)_2GeO]_4$ to $(C_6H_5)_2GeBr_2$)

$[(C_6H_5)_2GeO]_n$ m.p. 298° ⇌ (EtOH, H_2O / HOAc) $[(C_6H_5)_2GeO]_4$ m.p. 218° ⇌ (Distn. / HOAc) $[(C_6H_5)_2GeO]_3$ m.p. 149°

Polydimethylgermanosiloxanes have been prepared by co-hydrolysis of dimethyldichlorosilane and dimethyldibromogermane in the molar ratio 95:5[67]. Hydrolysis was effected in aqueous alcohol at 5–10°. The product of this co-hydrolysis was a colourless, oily polymer of low molecular weight. By analysis it was shown to be a cyclic product with a 98:2 ratio of $(CH_3)_2SiO$ to $(CH_3)_2GeO$. These low-molecular-weight germanosiloxanes, on polymerisation by concentrated sulphuric acid, produced soft, rubber-like products comparable to $[(CH_3)_2SiO]_n$ rubber, but containing germanium atoms in a siloxane structure. Examination of the properties of these polymers disclosed that, with increase of germanium content, the relative length of the chain decreased. It was also found that the thermal stability of the polymer was not affected by the presence of germanium in the siloxane structure.

11. Silicon–oxygen–chromium systems

Organosilicon–chromium co-ordination complexes, prepared by reaction of chromyl chloride and hydroxysiloxane compounds, have been described in the patent literature[68]. Again, when a solution of chromic oxide in polydimethylsiloxane was heated at 150°, polydimethylsilyl chromates, $[(CH_3)_2SiCrO_4]_n$, were said to be formed, but were not isolated[68a].

Certain water-soluble, co-ordination chromium complexes of carboxylic acids have found extensive applications by virtue of their ability to modify the surface characteristics of many substrates[69]. Typical of these is "Volan" (methacrylatochromic chloride).

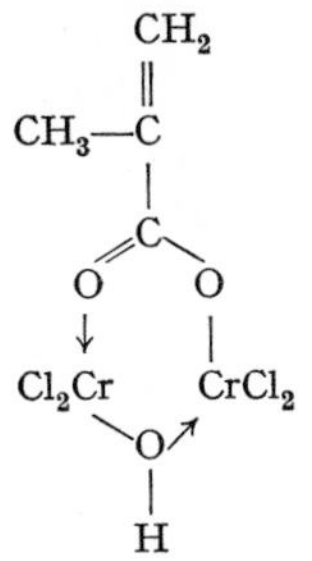

```
            CH2
            ||
      CH3—C
            |
           C
        //    \
      O         O
      ↓         |
   Cl2Cr        CrCl2
        \     ↗
           O
           |
           H
```

When the pH of a dilute chromium complex solution is raised from about 3–4 to 6, polymerisation occurs with formation of bridges,

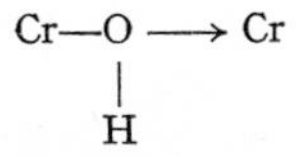

```
Cr—O ——→ Cr
   |
   H
```

following the elimination of hydrogen ions from the water molecules co-ordinated to the chromium atoms. When this diluted complex is applied to a substrate and the treated surface is heated, further polymerisation occurs to give an insoluble coating which will attach firmly to negatively charged surfaces containing polar groups. The complex is held to the surface by both covalent bonds and polar forces. Surfaces which contain OH groups are particularly susceptible to strong bond formation. The presence of silanol groups on the surface of silica and glass makes it possible to modify their surface properties by this treatment. Indeed one important industrial application has been the treatment of glass

References, p. 252–255

fibres. The bonding between "Volan" and the surface of a glass fibre is through Si—O—Cr linkages as represented by:

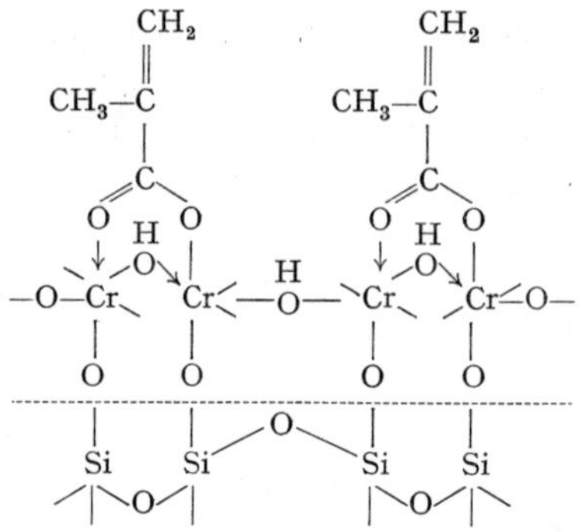

```
          CH2                        CH2
          ||                         ||
     CH3—C                      CH3—C
          |                          |
          C                          C
        //  \                      //  \
       O  H   O                   O  H   O
       ↓  O   |         H         ↓  O   |
 —O—Cr         Cr  —O—  Cr          Cr—O—
       |        |                 |      |
       O        O                 O      O
 ..........................................
       |        |      O          |      |
       Si       Si               Si      Si
         \  O  /                   \  O  /
```

Iler[70] calculated that a finely-divided, amorphous silica, surface area of 100 square metres per gram, treated with approximately an equivalent weight of stearatochromic chloride ("Quilon") is essentially completely covered with stearate groups[70].

12. Miscellaneous polyorganometallosiloxanes

When liquid polymethylsiloxanes are heated in the presence of lead oxide, the liquid gradually becomes turbid and a precipitate settles out. Patnode and Schmidt[71] suggested that the course of the reaction is as follows:

$$(CH_3)_3Si[OSi(CH_3)_2]_nOSi(CH_3)_3 + PbO \longrightarrow$$

$$\begin{matrix} (CH_3)_3Si[OSi(CH_3)_2]_x\text{—}O \\ (CH_3)_3Si[OSi(CH_3)_2]_y\text{—}O \end{matrix}\Big\rangle Pb$$

In support of this mechanism, the formation of bis(trimethylsiloxy) lead from trimethylsilanol and lead oxide was cited. However, this claim has been questioned by Andrianov[72] (see p. 193). Formation of organoplumbosiloxanes from alkoxysilanes and lead acetate and alkoxysilanes and sodium plumbate has been claimed by Andrianov[1], but no details have been given. Polyorganozirconium siloxanes have also been claimed to be produced by treating silanols both with metallic zirconium and its hydroxy derivatives[1].

In most of the polymetallosiloxanes already discussed, the heteroelements bear organic substituents. Few studies have been made of metallosiloxanes in which the metal atoms are unsubstituted. By the reactions of disodium diphenylsilanediolate with metal chlorides and diphenylsilanediol with metal alkyls, Hornbaker and Conrad[73] have attempted to synthesise such polymers, incorporating the divalent metals tin, lead, magnesium, copper, zinc, and mercury.

$$-\left[\begin{array}{c} C_6H_5 \\ | \\ -Si-O- \\ | \\ C_6H_5 \end{array}\right]_x - \left[-M-O-\right]_y -$$

The results suggest that the reaction of the disodium silanediolate with metal chlorides proceeds through a polymeric intermediate in which the expected metallosiloxane bonds are formed; in most cases, however, the polymers decomposed to form a siloxane derivative and, except in the case of mercury, the corresponding metal oxide. The same behaviour was observed in the reactions of diethylmagnesium and diethylzinc with the silanediol. Metallosiloxane polymers were formed which decomposed rather easily upon heating to give siloxane derivatives and metallic oxide.

13. Structure and general properties of polymetallosiloxanes

It will be clear from the foregoing that two different approaches to the synthesis and study of polyorganometallosiloxanes have been and are currently being pursued. One approach has as its objective the synthesis of linear polymers of unequivocal structure, wherein the inorganic chain consists of a regular sequence of metallosiloxane structural units —Si—O—M—O—. The alkoxide-acyloxide reaction affords a convenient route to such polymers. As yet, few details of the properties of these polymers have been published, but one recent report[93] deserves mention. The obvious advantages of using

References, p. 252–255

linear polymers of known structure commend this approach for a systematic study of the effect on the properties of introducing a heteroatom into the polysiloxane chain. The other approach, based on the reactions of hydrolysis or co-hydrolysis and double decomposition, leads to more complex structures, of variable composition, which have, however, been found to exhibit some unique properties. The elucidation of the structures of these polymers, and the intimate mechanism of the reactions by which they are formed, presents considerable problems. Indeed, the structures of conventional organosilicon polymers, particularly those derived from trifunctional monomers, are very complex. However, recent structural studies[74–83] have added substantially to our knowledge of their molecular architecture and this knowledge has been profitably applied to the polyorganometallosiloxanes.

In the hydrolysis of difunctional organosilicon compounds, the overall reaction takes place as follows, giving cyclic polysiloxanes.

$$nR_2SiX_2 + nH_2O \longrightarrow (R_2SiO)_n + 2nHX$$

A number of such products has been isolated and characterised, with values of *n* ranging from 3 to 9[84]. In the co-hydrolysis of various bifunctional monomers, mixed cyclic structures are obtained, and again several individual compounds have been characterised[84]. In the case of trifunctional systems, the picture is more complicated. Attempts have been made to demarcate the initial stages of the sequence of hydrolysis and condensation reactions and various intermediates have been postulated but these are largely conjectural. However, some low polymeric end-products of the hydrolysis of trifunctional silanes have been defined. Thus, Barry and Gilkey[80] reported cyclic products of empirical composition $(C_2H_5SiO_{1.5})_8$, $(C_3H_7^nSiO_{1.5})_8$, and $(C_4H_9^nSiO_{1.5})_8$, (VII). These products have been described more fully by Barry and his co-workers[81], as were hexaphenylhexasilsesquioxane, (VI), and dodecamethyldodecasilsesquioxane, (VIII). It is reasonable to suppose that higher polymers of this type exist in the complex, intractable products resulting from the casual hydrolysis of trifunctional silanes. Sprung and Guenther[82,83] have also carried out extensive studies of the partial hydrolysis of trialkoxysilanes. It was found that bulky substituents permit relatively large amounts of low-molecular-weight partial-hydrolysis products to be isolated, since these substituents stabilise the silanol functions against further condensation. Cyclic poly-ethoxysiloxanols, in the molecular weight range 500–1000, are the

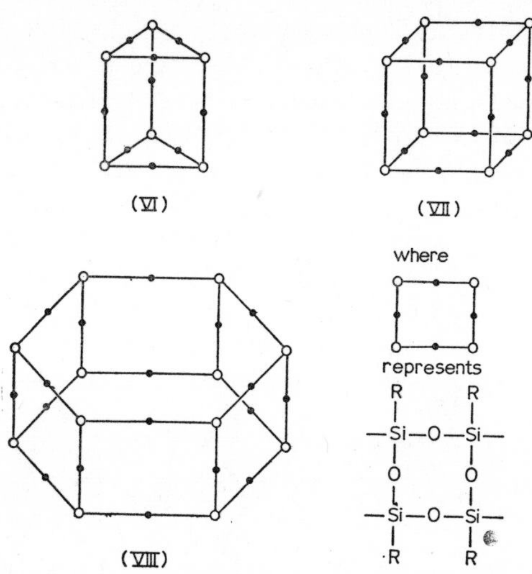

principal products of acid catalysed hydrolysis. More extensive condensation occurs under alkaline conditions, yielding low-polymeric silsesquioxanes, mainly the octamers. The well-known redistribution reaction[85], whereby Si—O linkages of a siloxane or mixture of siloxanes are continuously broken and reformed until the system reaches an equilibrium condition at the thermodynamically most stable state, is undoubtedly of importance in this connection. Heating alone will bring about this equilibration by redistribution of siloxane linkages, but the process is markedly catalysed by acids and bases. Thus, it is known that higher yields of characterisable materials, such as the cubic octamers and hexagonal prismatic dodecamers, are obtained by heating a soluble hydrolysis product of an alkyltrichlorosilane in contact with powdered sodium or potassium hydroxide[81]. The alkali forms polysiloxanol salts, which

References, p. 252–255

catalyse both siloxanol condensation and siloxane rearrangement. Under conditions of extensive hydrolysis and condensation, involving cross-linking, the structural possibilities become very numerous indeed. However, stereochemical considerations favour certain structural types. Sprung and Guenther[82] suggested the possible formation of "ladder-like", linear, network structures, consisting of two parallel polysiloxane chains linked through oxygen at every successive pair of silicon atoms, and terminated by four functional groups. This structure is one of three general types suggested earlier by Wiberg and Simmler[78] to be the most likely. The second is a plate-like structure, which is essentially a two-dimensional array of cyclohexasiloxanes. The third is the three-dimensional, adamantane-like, polysilsesquioxane type. It is easy to see that the last type could be derived from the first by intramolecular condensation of the reactive end-groups. A very significant development bearing on this problem, has recently been reported[86]. High-molecular-weight, soluble, double chain or "ladder-like" polymers

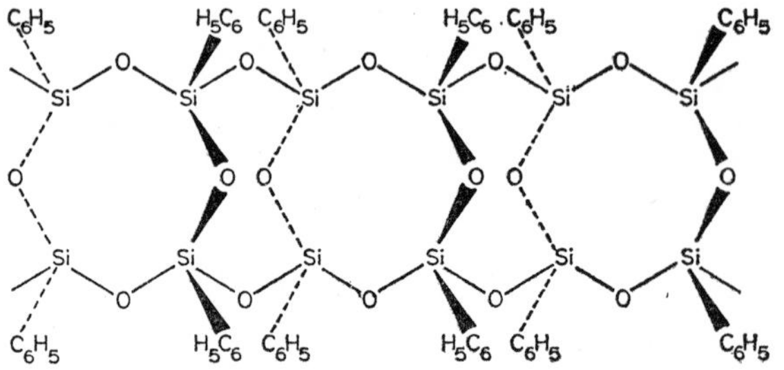

(IX)

Reproduced, with permission, from J. F. Brown, L. F. Vogt, A. Katchman, J. W. Eustace, K. M. Kiser and K. W. Krantz, *J. Am. Chem. Soc.*, 82 (1960) 6194.

of phenylsilsesquioxane have been synthesised by equilibrating the hydrolysate of phenyltrichlorosilane with 0.1% potassium hydroxide in boiling toluene, with removal of water. These polymers possess a stereoregular configuration, the phenylsilsesquioxane units ($C_6H_5SiO_{1.5}$) being joined together to form syndiotactic chains which, in turn, are linked together through *cis*-fusion to give a linear "ladder-like" network structure, (IX).

Small amounts of crystalline octaphenyloctasilsesquioxane and dodecaphenyldodecasilsesquioxane are also formed. The polymer, with a weight average molecular weight of 26,000, analysed correctly for $(C_6H_5SiO_{1.5})_n$. On fractionation, it gave a series of fractions which showed the steep, linear log $[\eta]$ *vs.*log $\overline{MW}$ relation ($\alpha = 0.92$), characteristic of linear, nearly rigid, rod-like polymers. Infrared and X-ray diffraction data showed that the soluble phenylsilsesquioxane polymers, obtained by Sprung and Guenther[83] from phenyltriethoxysilane by base-catalysed hydrolysis, were essentially similar in structure, but of somewhat higher molecular weight. When a smaller proportion of solvent is used in the equilibration reaction, high-molecular-weight polymers are obtained. Polymers with $\overline{MW} = 200{,}000$ showed no discernible branching. Higher polymers ($\overline{MW} = 4 \times 10^6$), however, did show some evidence of branching. High-molecular-weight polymers can be made similarly from low polymers, and even from the dodecamer, $(C_6H_5SiO_{1.5})_{12}$. All the phenylsilsesquioxane polymers were infusible; on heating to above 400°, they neither melted not charred. They were readily soluble in benzene, tetrahydrofuran, and methylene chloride. Transparent films, made from the higher polymers, could be oriented by stretching in benzene vapour. Detailed X-ray and infrared studies, coupled with end-group determinations, indicated that 95–98% of the phenylsilsesquioxane units in the higher polymers were in the *cis*-syndiotactic configuration.

Barry and his co-workers[81] found that when the hydrolysis-products of alkyltrichlorosilanes were heated above 400° at low pressure, thermal depolymerisation occurred and low-polymer alkylsilsesquioxanes distilled. This uncatalysed depolymerisation afforded low yields of distillate and was attended by considerable pyrolysis. Silsesquioxanes formed less readily than the cyclic and polycyclic siloxanes. Alkali-catalysed siloxane-cracking proceeded much more readily and at lower temperatures. In fact, this method served for the preparation of low-polymer silsesquioxanes. The major product of hydrolysis of phenyltriethoxysilane, in a ketonic solvent with tetraethylammonium hydroxide as

References, p. 252–255

catalyst, was an amorphous high polymer virtually free of functional groups[83]. However, in inert solvents, in the presence of some residual catalyst, an extremely facile rearrangement occurred at relatively low temperature, giving the octamer (and possibly some hexamer) in very high yield. Sprung and Guenther interpret this re-arrangement in terms of the "ladder-like", but flexible, structure of the polymer. The depolymerisation is initiated by a silanolate ion, situated at an end-group position, which attacks a sterically adjacent siloxane bond. With the postulated polymer structure, such attack could travel through a chain segment, splitting off a molecule of a low-polymeric silsesquioxane at each step. In schematic form, with the symbol

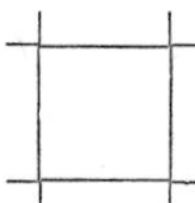

representing a tetraphenylcyclotetrasiloxane unit, (X),

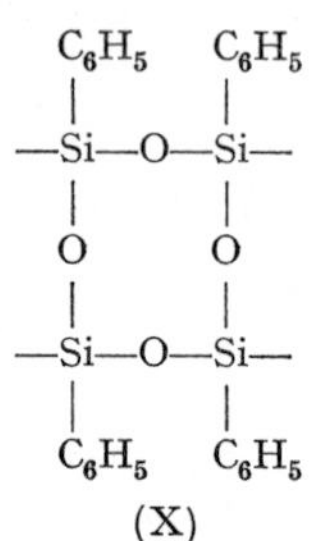

(X)

the hypothetical fragmentation process is illustrated by (XI) and (XII).

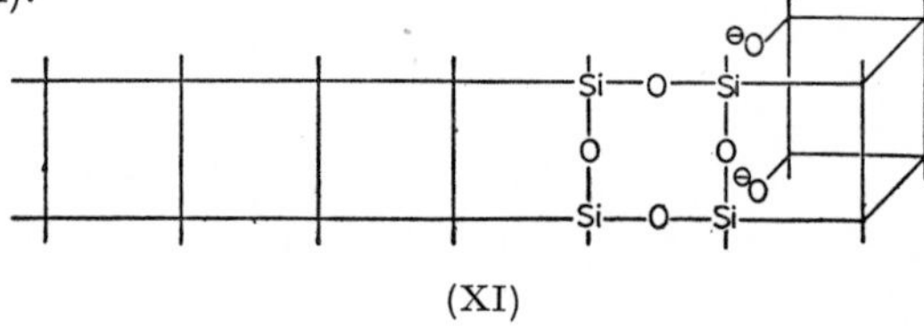

(XI)

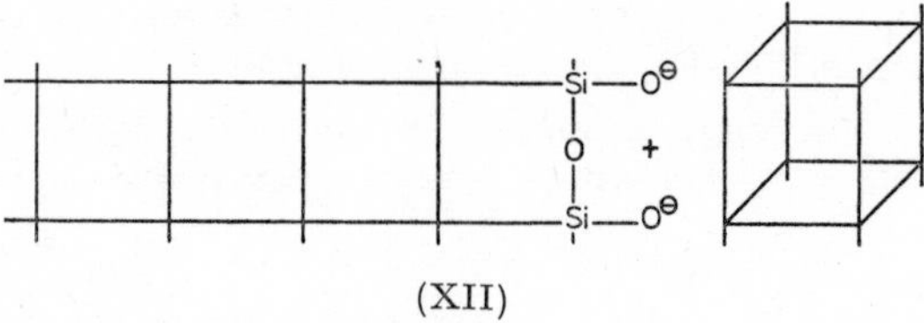

(XII)

This process is repeated, the polymer "ladder"-chain doubling back on itself and causing further octameric units to be cleaved off. It is likely that the process is more random than is suggested in the above scheme; indeed, appropriately situated hexasilsesquioxanes could be eliminated similarly.

Andrianov[84] claims that, in the synthesis of polyorganometallosiloxanes by co-hydrolysis and condensation or double decomposition and condensation, predominantly "cyclolinear" or "ladder-like", double-chain macromolecules are formed when using organosilicon monomers with functionality greater than two. This is true of polyphenylaluminosiloxane and polymethyltitanosiloxane. Typical elementary compositions for the polymers are given as:

Polyphenylaluminosiloxane:	C,	49.18,	49.09%;
	H,	4.42,	4,16%;
	Si,	18.91,	18.48%;
	Al,	4.24,	4.36%;
Polymethyltitanosiloxane:	C,	12.97,	13.24%;
	H,	4.97,	4.91%;
	Si,	29.91,	29.84%;
	Ti,	12.92,	13.18%.

Both polymers have a low content of hydroxyl groups. A precise representation of their structures is not possible, but evidence points to the existence of a sequence of cyclic unit structures (XIII) and (XIV), constituting cyclolinear chains (XV) and (XVI).
The small loss in weight observed on heating the polymers at 150° may be due to the elimination of water between hydroxyl groups, resulting in the formation of a siloxane bond. No loss of solubility is incurred on heating to this temperature, but at higher temperatures more deep-seated structural changes occur, with loss

References, p. 252–255

of solubility. Investigation of the infrared absorption spectra of these polymers showed an intense absorption in the region 1080–1100 cm^{-1} and weak absorption in the region 1020–1030 cm^{-1}, characteristic of SiO groups in 8-membered rings.

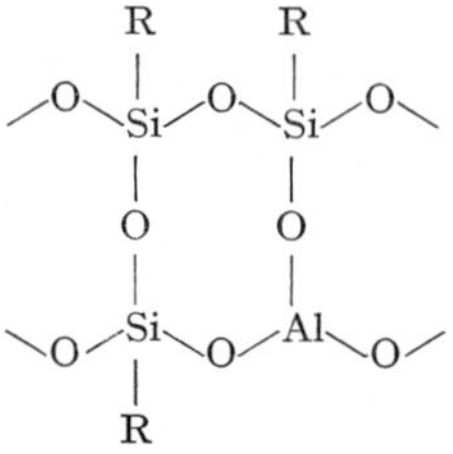

(XIII)

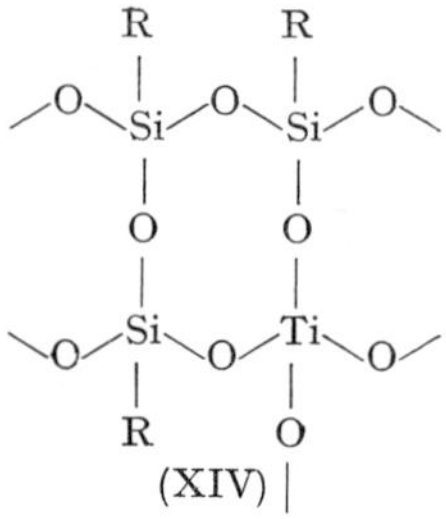

(XIV)

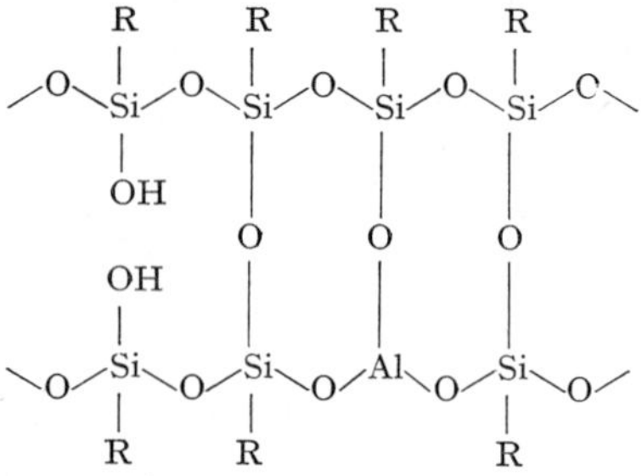

(XV)

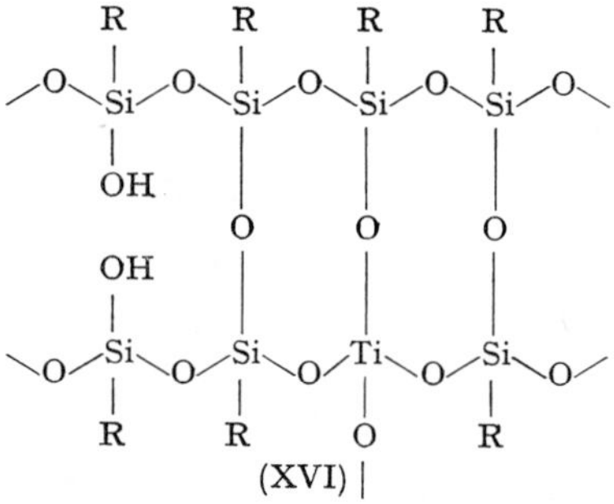

(XVI)

The possibility of the existence of a small number of 6-membered rings in the polymeric structures is not, however, ruled out. The specific cyclolinear structure of the primary chain in these macromolecules is held to be responsible for the characteristic properties of the polymers, in particular, the solubility in organic solvents and the infusibility up to 600°. The capacity of polyphenylaluminosiloxanes and polymethyltitanosiloxanes to be polymerised under the action of catalysts capable of opening up siloxane bonds in cyclic molecules is considered to support the cyclolinear structure. Andrianov[84] has reported some data on the change in viscosity of solutions of these two polymers under the action of 0.3% caustic soda at 80°. Further evidence in support of the double-chain structure was derived from the study of the thermomechanical properties of the polymers[84,86,87]. On heating, they exhibit no plastic properties up to 700°. However, after the introduction of plasticisers, they behave in a manner typical of non-structurised polymers. This property has been demonstrated by reference to a series of "thermomechanical" curves, illustrating the relationship between percentage deformation and temperature, in the case of unplasticised and plasticised polymers[84]. The former showed no appreciable deformation up to 600° but deformation increased with increasing content of plasticiser. However, if the original polymers are first heated to 300° and then plasticised, no deformation is observed. Clearly, some structural changes are incurred during the heat treatment, probably involving loss of water and a rearrangement of the rings.

The hope that incorporation of metal atoms into polysiloxane structures would enhance their thermal stability has been a major stimulus to the study of polyorganometallosiloxanes. Certain claims have been made, some of them somewhat exaggerated, regarding the exceptional thermal stability of polyorganometallosiloxanes. In assessing thermal stability, it is necessary to distinguish between inherent thermodynamic stability and apparent or kinetic stability. Oxidation phenomena intervene when the materials are heated in air and these changes profoundly modify the subsequent behaviour at high temperature. Andrianov[89] has compared the oxidative stabilities of organic polymers and polymers with inorganic molecular chains by estimating the change in weight on heating in an oxidising atmosphere. Degradation of organic po-

References, p. 252–255

lymers proceeds continuously with evolution of volatile products. Polymers with inorganic molecular chains undergo considerable loss in weight only in the initial stages of heating; thereafter, the process is considerably slowed down. Oxidative degradation reactions in this latter system probably take place initially in the organic part of the molecule, *i.e.*, in the organic groups fringing the main chain. Cleavage of the organic groups occurs with cross-linking of molecular chains through siloxane bonds and the nett result of these structural changes is to retard further oxidation.

$$\begin{array}{ccc} \begin{array}{ccc} | & & | \\ -\mathrm{Si} & -\mathrm{O}- & \mathrm{Si}- \\ | & & | \\ \mathrm{R} & & \mathrm{R} \\ & & \\ \mathrm{R} & & \mathrm{R} \\ | & & | \\ -\mathrm{Si} & -\mathrm{O}- & \mathrm{Si}- \\ | & & | \end{array} & + \; \mathrm{O_2} \longrightarrow & \begin{array}{ccc} | & & | \\ -\mathrm{Si} & -\mathrm{O}- & \mathrm{Si}- \\ | & & | \\ \mathrm{O} & & \mathrm{O} \\ | & & | \\ -\mathrm{Si} & -\mathrm{O}- & \mathrm{Si}- \\ | & & | \end{array} \; + \; \mathrm{CO_2} \end{array}$$

The susceptibility to oxidation is governed partly by the nature of the fringing groups. Thus, phenyl groups are readily split off only at temperatures above 400°, whilst ethyl groups undergo ready oxidation at 250°, and methyl groups at 300°. A considerable reduction in the weight loss on heating is observed with polyorgano-alumino- and polyorganotitano-siloxanes.

The thermal stabilities of polyorganometallosiloxanes have been discussed with reference to the results of differential thermochemical analysis[84,89]. Structural changes involving ring opening reactions take place at temperatures above those at which the

$$\begin{array}{c} | \\ \diagup\mathrm{O}\diagdown\mathrm{Si}\diagup\mathrm{O}\diagdown \\ | \longleftarrow \\ \mathrm{O} \\ | \\ \diagdown\mathrm{O}\diagup\mathrm{X}\diagdown\mathrm{O}\diagup \end{array}$$

organic fringing groups are cleaved from the inorganic chain. The thermal breakdown occurs at the point indicated.

The temperature of breakdown is dependent on the nature of X

(500° for Si, and 600° for Al and Ti). It is thus claimed that the introduction of metals such as aluminium and titanium into polysiloxanes increases by fully 100° the temperature at which ring opening occurs. Transannular interactions of the type[90]:

```
  |      |
—Si—O—Si—
  |   ↓  |
—O—Al—O—
```

are claimed to be responsible for this enhanced stability, such interaction restricting the degradation of the siloxane chain by hindering the formation of cyclic structures. An interesting observation is that polyethylaluminosiloxane catalyses the polymerisation of polyorganosiloxanes, and it has been established that, in the process, co-ordinate bonds are formed between the oxygen atoms of the polyorganosiloxane and the aluminium atoms of the aluminosiloxane[90].

Zeitler and Brown[92] have calculated the bond strength of the Ti—O bond to be about 112 kcal./mole and that of the Si—O bond to be approximately 103 kcal./mole. On this basis, the thermal stability of Si—O—Ti and Ti—O—Ti compounds should be of the same order or somewhat higher than that of Si—O—Si compounds. However, on heating the tetrakis(triphenylsiloxy)-derivatives of titanium and silicon it was observed that the former discoloured and showed signs of decomposition at 460–470°, whereas the latter showed little change even at 605°. Replacement of the Si—O bond by Ti—O in this system had a weakening effect on neighbouring Si—C bonds. Clearly, there is need for more systematic information on the thermal behaviour of organometallosiloxanes, both simple and polymeric.

Another aspect of the chemistry of metallosiloxanes, as yet virtually unexplored, is the stereochemistry of the metal atom in the siloxane environment. There have been numerous studies of the stereochemistry of metal alkoxides and certain structural principles have emerged[22]. One of these, which relates to covalent metal alkoxides, is that an alkoxide undergoes the minimum degree of polymerisation consistent with the attainment of the maximum covalency of the metal. This is well illustrated by the behaviour of

References, p. 252–255

titanium and aluminium alkoxides. Thus, in the limiting trimeric form of titanium tetraethoxide, each titanium atom is said to exhibit its maximum covalency of 6 in approximately the octahedral configuration. Aluminium is a tervalent metal which has a pronounced tendency towards the covalency of 4 and can exhibit a maximum covalency of 6. Several primary alkoxides of aluminium have been shown to be tetrameric. This is in agreement with the structural model (XVII).

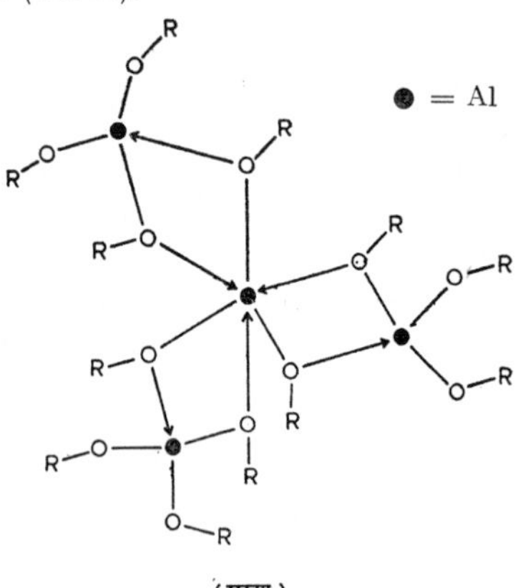

(XVII)

Reproduced, with permission, from D. C. BRADLEY, *Metal-Organic Compounds, Advances in Chemistry Series*, Vol. 23, American Chemical Society, Washington, 1959, p. 24.

In (XVII), the central aluminium atom is octahedrally 6-co-ordinate and the remaining three aluminium atoms are tetrahedrally 4-co-ordinate. An octahedral structure has also been proposed for the chelates of titanium esters with acetylacetone and ethyl acetoacetate. It is not easy to see how such octahedral structures for titanium and aluminium could be formed in the polyorganometallosiloxanes. However, it is conceivable that by intermolecular association of oxygen with the metal atoms the tendency of the metals to attain a higher co-ordination number may partially be satisfied[90]. It is highly probable that the unique properties of bouncing putty may be attributed to interchain interaction between boron atoms and oxygen in the borosiloxane system[47].

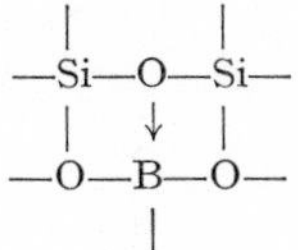

Available information on the hydrolytic stability of metallosiloxanes is largely qualitative, but there are[89,91] some quantitative data on the triethylsiloxy-derivatives of aluminium, titanium, and tin (Table 12), and on three polymeric systems, polyphenylaluminosiloxane, (XVIII), polyethylaluminosiloxane, and polyphenyltitanosiloxane, (XIX).

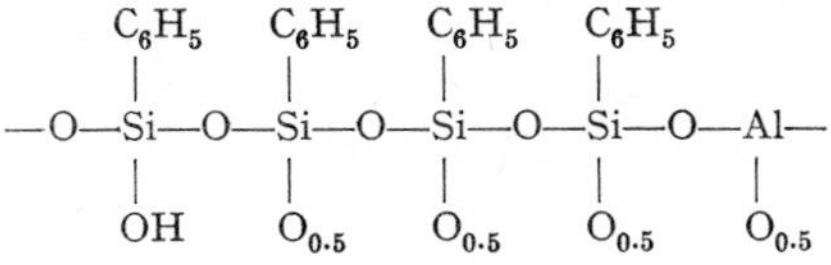

```
      C6H5     C6H5     C6H5     C6H5
       |        |        |        |
  —O—Si—O—Si—O—Si—O—Si—O—Al—
       |        |        |        |       |
      OH      O0.5     O0.5     O0.5    O0.5
                    (XVIII)

                                          |
      C6H5     C6H5     C6H5     C6H5     O
       |        |        |        |       |
  —O—Si—O—Si—O—Si—O—Si—O—Ti—
       |        |        |        |       |
      OH      O0.5     O0.5     O0.5    O0.5
                     (XIX)
```

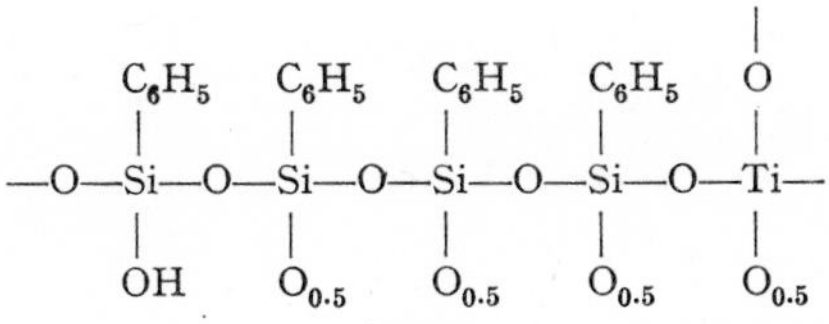

The relative rates of hydrolysis have been found to depend on the particular metal forming part of the molecule.

TABLE 12

Compound	*Constants for rate of hydrolysis*	*Relative rates of hydrolysis*
$Sn[OSi(C_2H_5)_3]_4$	200×10^{-3}	2220
$Al[OSi(C_2H_5)_3]_3$	2.45×10^{-3}	27.2
$Ti[OSi(C_2H_5)_3]_4$	0.09×10^{-3}	1

Experiments showed that, under the action of 10% hydrochloric acid at 95°, the Si—O—Ti linkage in polyphenyltitanosiloxane suf-

References, p. 252–255

fered only a small degree of hydrolysis, only 1.5% of titanium entering the solution in 10 hours. Under the same conditions the Si—O—Al linkage in polyphenylaluminosiloxane and polyethylaluminosiloxane underwent 87 and 68.7% degradation, respectively. With 30% hydrochloric acid, the Si—O—Ti linkage in polyphenyltitanosiloxane was cleaved to the extent of 25% in 1 hour, while the Si—O—Al linkages in the polyphenyl- and polyethylaluminosiloxanes suffered to the extent of 95.2 and 87.5%, respectively. These results suggest that the hydrolytic stability of the Si—O—Ti linkage in polyphenyltitanosiloxane is considerably higher than that of Si—O—Al in polyorganoaluminosiloxanes[88].

Without disclosing any details, Russian workers claim that the polyorganometallosiloxanes are being applied industrially on an increasing scale and further developments may confidently be anticipated with increasing knowledge of their chemistry and properties.

REFERENCES

1 K. A. Andrianov, *Uspekhi Khim.*, (a) 26 (1957) 895; (b) 27 (1958) 1257.

2 L. H. Sommer, E. W. Pietrusza and F. C. Whitmore, *J. Am. Chem. Soc.*, 68 (1946) 2282.

3 K. A. Andrianov, *U.S.S.R. Patent* 71,115 (1947); *Byull. izobr.* (*Bulletin of Inventions*) 1948, No. 5.

4 K. A. Andrianov, A. A. Zhdanov, N. A. Kurasheva and V. G. Dulova, *Doklady Akad. Nauk S.S.S.R.*, 112 (1957) 1050.

5 K. A. Andrianov, A. A. Zhdanov and A. A. Kazakova, *Izvest. Akad. Nauk S.S.S.R., Otdel. Khim. Nauk* (1959) 466.

6 K. A. Andrianov and A. A. Zhdanov, *J. Polymer Sci.*, 30 (1958) 513.

7 I. K. Stavitskii and S. N. Borisov, *Vysokomol. Soedineniya*, 1 (1959) 1496.

8 K. A. Andrianov and A. A. Zhdanov, *Doklady Akad. Nauk S.S.S.R.*, 114 (1957) 1005.

9 K. A. Andrianov, A. A. Zhdanov and S. A. Pavlov, *Doklady Akad. Nauk S.S.S.R.*, 102 (1955) 85.

10 K. A. Andrianov, A. A. Zhdanov and T. N. Ganina, *Bull. Mendeleev All-Union Chem. Soc.*, 3 (1955) 2.

11 K. A. Andrianov, A. A. Zhdanov and E. Z. Asnovich, *Doklady Akad. Nauk S.S.S.R.*, 118 (1958) 1124.

12 K. A. Andrianov, A. A. Zhdanov and E. Z. Asnovich, *Izvest. Akad. Nauk S.S.S.R., Otdel. Khim. Nauk*, (1959) 1760.

13 K. A. Andrianov and A. I. Petrashko, *Vysokomol. Soedineniya*, 1 (1959) 1514.

14 K. A. Andrianov and A. A. Zhdanov, *Izvest. Akad. Nauk S.S.S.R., Otdel. Khim. Nauk*, (1959) 1590.

[15] K. A. Andrianov, A. A. Zhdanov and A. A. Kazakova, *Zhur. Obshcheĭ Khim.*, 29 (1959) 1281.
[16] W. G. Woods and M. L. Iverson, *138th Meeting American Chemical Society* New Jersey, Sept. 1959, p. 2N.
[17] W. G. Woods and M. L. Iverson, *Conference on High Temperature Polymer and Fluid Research,* Dayton, Ohio, May 1959.
[18] S. M. Atlas and H. F. Mark, *Angew. Chem.*, 72 (1960) 249.
[19] C. L. Segal, H. H. Takimoto and J. B. Rust, *137th Meeting American Chemical Society*, Cleveland, April 1960, p. 3S.
[20] T. R. Patterson, F. J. Pavlick, A. A. Baldoni and R. L. Frank, *J. Am. Chem. Soc.*, 81 (1959) 4213.
[21] *W.A.D.C. Techn. Report* 58–160, *ASTIA Document* No. 155675.
[22] D. C. Bradley, *Metal-Organic Compounds, Advances in Chemistry Series*, Vol. 23, American Chemical Society, Washington, 1959, p. 10.
[23] T. Boyd, *J. Polymer Sci.*, 7 (1951) 591.
[24] S. Minami and T. Ishino, *Techn. Repts. Osaka Univ.*, 3 (1953) 357.
[25] D. C. Bradley, R. Gaze and W. Wardlaw, *J. Chem. Soc.*, 721 (1955) 3977; (1957) 469.
[26] K. A. Andrianov, T. N. Ganina and W. Khrustaleva, *Izvest. Akad. Nauk S.S.S.R., Otdel. Khim. Nauk,* (1956) 798.
[27] K. A. Andrianov and E. Z. Asnovich, *Vysokomol. Soedineniya,* 2 (1960) 136.
[28] H. C. Gulledge, *U.S.P.* 2,512,058 (1948).
[29] C. L. Segal, H. H. Takimoto and J. B. Rust, *137th Meeting American Chemical Society*, Cleveland, April 1960, p. 3S; *J. Org. Chem.*, 26 (1961) 2467.
[30] J. B. Rust, H. H. Takimoto and G. C. Denault, *J. Org. Chem.*, 25 (1960) 2040.
[31] P. E. Koenig and J. H. Hutchinson, *W.A.D.C. Techn. Report* 58–44. *ASTIA Document* No. AD151197, May 1958.
[32] R. D. Crain and P. E. Koenig, *Conference on High Temperature Polymer and Fluid Research,* Dayton, Ohio, May 1959.
[33] W. S. Tatlock and E. G. Rochow, *J. Org. Chem.*, 17 (1952) 1555.
[34] F. A. Henglein, R. Lang and L. Schmack, *Makromol. Chem.* 22 (1957) 103.
[35] D. T. Hurd, *U.S.P.* 2,645,628 (1951).
[36] J. F. O'Brien, *W.A.D.C. Techn. Report* 57–502, *ASTIA Document* No. 142100, Oct. 1957.
[37] B. L. Chamberland and A. G. MacDiarmid, *138th Meeting American Chemical Society*, New York, Sept. 1960, p. 20N; *J. Am. Chem. Soc.*, 83 (1961) 549.
[38] B. L. Chamberland and A. G. MacDiarmid, *J. Chem. Soc.*, (1961) 445.
[39] M. M. Koton and T. M. Kiseleva, *Doklady Akad. Nauk S.S.S.R.*, 130 (1960) 86.
[40] H. Gilman, R. K. Ingham and S. D. Rosenberg, *Chem. Revs.*, 60 (1960) 459.
[41] R. M. Kary and K. C. Frisch, *J. Am. Chem. Soc.*, 79 (1957) 2140; *U.S.P.* 2,863,893 (1958).
[42] B. L. Chamberland and A. G. MacDiarmid, *J. Am. Chem. Soc.*, 82 (1960) 4542.
[43] M. Schmidt and H. Schmidbaur, *Angew. Chem.*, 71 (1959) 553.
[44] F. A. Henglein, R. Lang and K. Scheinost, *Makromol. Chem.*, 15 (1955) 177.

[45] K. A. Andrianov and L. M. Volkova, *Izvest. Akad. Nauk. S.S.S.R., Otdel Khim. Nauk*, (1957) 303.
[46] M. G. Voronkov and V. N. Zgonnik, *Zhur. Obshcheĭ Khim.*, 27 (1957) 1476.
[47] M. Wick, *Kunststoffe*, 50 (1960) 433.
[48] K. A. Andrianov, R. V. Kudryavtsev and D. N. Kursanov, *Zhur. Obshcheĭ. Khim.*, 29 (1959) 1497.
[49] R. R. McGregor and E. L. Warrick, *U.S.P.* 2,431,878 (1947).
[50] R. R. McGregor, *Silicones and Their Uses*, McGraw Hill, New York, 1954, p. 186.
[51] F. S. Martin, *U.S.P.* 2,609,201 (1952).
[52] S. Nitzskhe and M. Wick, *Kunststoffe*, 47 (1957) 431.
[53] T. Alfrey, F. J. Hohn and H. F. Mark, *J. Polymer Sci.*, 1 (1946) 102.
[54] A. P. Kreshkov and D. A. Karateev, *Zhur. Priklad. Khim.*, 32 (1959) 369.
[55] A. P. Kreshkov and D. A. Karateev, *Zhur. Obshcheĭ Khim.*, 27 (1957) 2715.
[56] A. P. Kreshkov and D. A. Karateev, *Zhur. Priklad. Khim.*, 30 (1957) 1416.
[57] A. P. Kreshkov and D. A. Karateev, *Zhur. Obshcheĭ Khim.*, 29 (1959) 4082.
[58] M. G. Voronkov and V. N. Zgonnik, *Zhur. Obshcheĭ Khim.*, 27 (1957) 1483.
[59] N. S. Leznov, L. A. Sabun and K. A. Andrianov, *Zhur. Obshcheĭ Khim.*, 29 (1959) 1276.
[60] F. Fehér and K. Lippert, *Chem. Ber.*, 92 (1959) 2998.
[61] A. P. Kreshkov, V. I. Khromova and D. A. Karateev, *Authors' Certificate* No. 113143 (1958).
[62] M. Schmidt and H. Schmidbaur, *Chem. Ber.*, 93 (1960) 878.
[63] N. S. Leznov, L. A. Sabun and K. A. Andrianov, *Zhur. Obshcheĭ Khim.*, 29 (1959) 1270.
[64] F. A. Henglein, R. Lang and K. Scheinost, *Makromol. Chem.*, 18–19 (1956) 102.
[65] E. G. Rochow and M. P. Brown, *J. Am. Chem. Soc.*, 82 (1960) 4166.
[66] W. Metlesics and H. Zeiss, *J. Am. Chem. Soc.*, 82 (1960) 3324.
[67] S. N. Borisov, I. K. Stavitskii, V. A. Ponomarenko, N. G. Sviridova and G. Ya. Zueva, *Vysokomol. Soedineniya*, 1 (1959) 1502.
[68] Midland Silicones, Ltd., *British. Patent* 822,862 (1957).
[68a] M. Schmidt and H. Schmidbaur, *Angew. Chem.*, 70 (1958) 704.
[69] F. B. Hauserman, *Metal-Organic Compounds, Advances in Chemistry Series*, Vol. 23, American Chemical Society, Washington, 1959, p. 338.
[70] R. K. Iler, *Ind. Eng. Chem.*, 46 (1954) 766.
[71] W. Patnode and F. C. Schmidt, *J. Am. Chem. Soc.*, 67 (1945) 2272.
[72] K. A. Andrianov, A. A. Zhdanov and E. A. Kashutina, *Zhur. Priklad. Khim.*, 32 (1959) 463.
[73] E. D. Hornbaker and F. Conrad, *J. Org. Chem.*, 24 (1959) 1858.
[74] K. A. Andrianov, *Zhur. Obshcheĭ Khim.*, 8 (1938) 1255; 16 (1946) 633.
[75] H. J. Fletcher and M. J. Hunter, *J. Am. Chem. Soc.*, 71 (1949) 2918, 2922.
[76] C. Tamborski and H. W. Post, *J. Org. Chem.*, 17 (1952) 1400.
[77] K. A. Andrianov and B. M. Breitman, *Zhur. Obshcheĭ Khim.*, 17 (1947) 1522.
[78] E. Wiberg and W. Simmler, *Z. anorg. Chem.*, 283 (1956) 401.
[79] L. J. Tyler, *J. Am. Chem. Soc.*, 77 (1955) 771.
[80] A. J. Barry and J. W. Gilkey, *U.S.P.* 2,465,188 (1949).

[81] A. J. BARRY, W. H. DAUDT, J. J. DOMICONE and J. W. GILKEY, *J. Am. Chem. Soc.*, 77 (1955) 4248.
[82] M. M. SPRUNG and F. O. GUENTHER, *J. Am. Chem. Soc.*, 77 (1955) 3990, 3996, 4173, 6045.
[83] M. M. SPRUNG and F. O. GUENTHER, *J. Polymer Sci.*, 28 (1958) 17.
[84] K. A. ANDRIANOV, *I.U.P.A.C. Symposium on Macromolecular Compounds*, Moscow, June 1960. *Khimiya i Tekhnologiya Polymerov*, Moscow, 1960, 26–41.
[85] C. EABORN, *Organosilicon Compounds*, Butterworths, London, 1960.
[86] J. F. BROWN, L. H. VOGT, A. KATCHMAN, J. W. EUSTANCE, K. M. KISER and K. W. KRANTZ, *J. Am. Chem. Soc.*, 82 (1960) 6194.
[87] K. A. ANDRIANOV, G. L. SLONIMSKII, T. A. DIKAREVA and E. Z. ASNOVICH, *Vysokomol. Soedineniya*, 1 (1959) 244.
[88] K. A. ANDRIANOV and E. Z. ASNOVICH, *Vysokomol. Soedineniya*, 1 (1959) 743.
[89] K. A. ANDRIANOV, *Society of Chemical Industry, Monograph* No. 13, 1961.
[90] K. A. ANDRIANOV and A. A. ZHDANOV, *Vysokomol. Soedineniya*, 2 (1960) 1071.
[91] K. A. ANDRIANOV and A. A. ZHDANOV, *Vysokomol. Soedineniya*, 1 (1959) 894.
[92] V. A. ZEITLER and C. A. BROWN, *J. Am. Chem. Soc.*, 79 (1957) 4616.
[93] J. B. RUST, C. L. SEGAL and H. H. TAKIMOTO, *Research on High Temperature Polymers*, U.S. Department of Commerce, Office of Technical Services, PB 171522.

Chapter 9

Metal Chelate Polymers

by

C. N. KENNEY

1. Introduction

The present interest in inorganic polymers undoubtedly stems from the growing need for materials which have thermal stability or good mechanical properties under conditions in which polymers based on carbon are unsatisfactory. One group of such compounds which has only recently come under investigation, is that of the metal chelate polymers, in which metal ions are linked by di- or poly-functional organic ligands to form polymer chains. Metal chelate polymers thus occupy an intermediate position between organic and purely inorganic compounds, and their study may lead to the production of polymers which are thermally stable and can be fabricated easily to give materials of high mechanical strength. This Chapter provides a brief summary of the methods which have been employed in their preparation and of some of the factors which may be expected to affect their properties.

It will be recalled that although strong bonding between the atoms comprising a polymer chain is necessary for high thermal and chemical stability, fibre-forming and elastomeric character are conferred largely by suitable combinations of molecular shape and chain flexibility, and by the magnitude of the forces between the chains. The most usual type of inter-chain force in organic polymers is due to hydrogen bonds, which have relatively low energies of 4–10 kcal, but in many simple inorganic compounds the presence of highly electropositive metal atoms leads to forces with energies several times as large as this. In order to construct a polymer containing transition metal ions which might show some of the mechanical characteristics of organic polymers, it is probably necessary to find some way of reducing the magnitude of such forces, and chelation offers a possible method of achieving this end. Both the volatility of the metal acetylacetonates (some of which may be distilled above 200°) and their solubility in organic solvents indicate that properties usually associated with covalent compounds may be conferred by employing suitable ligands. Consequently, by ensuring that both the co-ordination number of the metal ion and its electrovalency are satisfied, it should be possible to enclose the metal ion in an uncharged organic shell and produce polymers which have properties similar, at least superficially, to those of polymers based on carbon. In addition, any discussion of metal chelate polymers will also be concerned with the factors affecting chelate formation, and in particular with the conditions governing the formation of stable co-ordinate bonds. For this reason, it is appropriate to consider metal chelate polymers as inorganic compounds in spite of the fact that a large proportion of the structural units usually consists of elements such as carbon, hydrogen, and nitrogen. It should be mentioned that linear polymers, such as gold or nickel cyanide, are also known, in which metal atoms are linked by co-ordinate bonds, but where chelate structures do not occur. However, in these polymers the shielding of the metal ion is incomplete and they will not be considered in this Chapter.

2. Synthetic methods

In view of the foregoing discussion, it is not surprising that the preparative methods used for chelate polymers are based largely on the standard methods of organic polymer synthesis. They may be classified in the following way:

(i) the linking of polydentate ligands by metal ions;

(ii) the formation of polymer with simultaneous incorporation of the metal ions;

(iii) the incorporation of metal ions into an existing polymer;

References, p. 273–274

(iv) the formation of a polymer by reactions with chelates containing functional groups.

Finally, it is convenient to consider under a separate heading:

(v) the preparation of ferrocenes.

The division into these classes is to some extent arbitrary, and some polymers may legitimately be placed in more than one category.

(i) Linking of ligands with ions

The thermal stability of the metal acetylacetonates makes them an obvious subject of investigation, and various workers[1,2] have studied the possibilities of making polymers such as (I) and (II) from different types of bis-β-diketone.

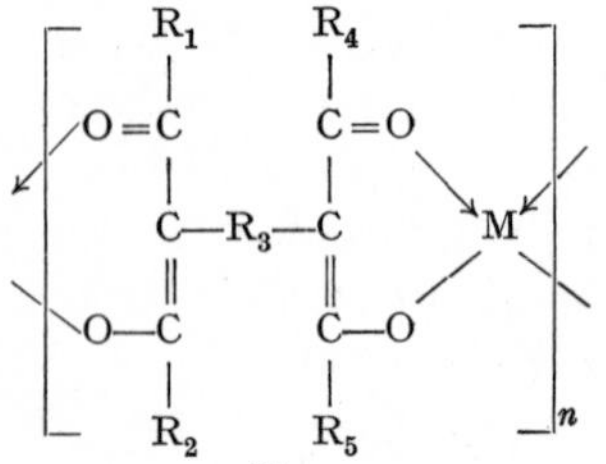

(I)

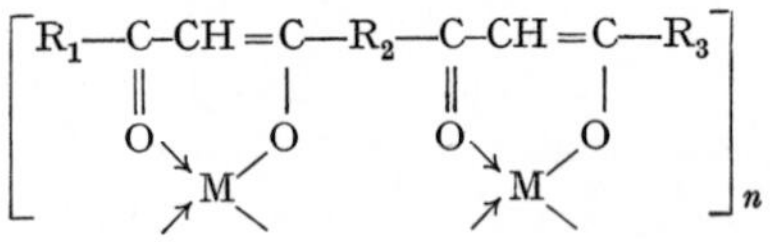

(II)

At least three different methods may be employed for the preparation of such polymers. In the first method, an alkaline solution of the bis-β-diketone is added to a solution of the metal ion. In the second method, the polymer is precipitated from a solution of the ketone, metal salt, and excess urea; on warming, ammonia is slowly liberated and the solution becomes alkaline. The third method is melt polymerisation. In this case, the metal acetylacetonate is heated under low pressure with a bis-β-diketone and as the exchange reaction takes place the lower boiling diketone, acetylacetone, distils off. The first two methods tend to give powders, while the last produces amorphous glassy materials, the colours of which vary with the metal ion. The colours, melting points, and thermal stabilities of some polymers prepared from sebacoyl-diacetophenone by melt polymerisation[3] are shown in Table 13. Films cast from these polymers are brittle and it has been estimated from viscosity measurements that molecular weights are usually below 4000[1]. However, brittle fibres have been obtained from the beryllium-containing polymers[2].

TABLE 13

SEBACOYL DIACETOPHENONE—METAL POLYMERS

Metal	*Colour*	*M.P.*	*Approximate weight loss% in 3 hr. at 300° in air*
Beryllium	Brown	~ 70°	20
Aluminium	Yellow Orange	230–250°	26
Copper	Brown	~ 100°	16
Nickel	Green	230–250° (Decomp.)	43
Cobalt	Black	~ 230°	20
Zinc	Brown	150°	16
Iron	Black	300°	30

Reproduced, with permission, from C. N. KENNEY, *Chem. & Ind.* (*London*), (1960) 880.

More recent work showed that the beryllium compounds were degraded thermally at 150° to 225° in a vacuum, to give cyclic monomers or, alternatively, dimers[4]. These cyclic products can be purified by sublimation and then thermally polymerised to high-molecular-weight polymers. This subsequent polymerisation, the addition polymerisation of a cyclic monomer, constitutes another synthetic method.

In an attempt to prepare derivatives of higher molecular weight, the technique of interfacial polymerisation has been applied to tetraketones at room temperature[5,7] and at 40–60°[6]. It has been reported[6] that the melting points of the polymers decrease with increasing atomic number of the metal ion.

It is possible to formulate many other similar polymers based on

References, p. 273–274

bis-chelating groups, of which some typical examples are given in Table 14.

TABLE 14

BIS-CHELATING GROUPS USED IN POLYMER FORMATION

Bis-(β-diketones)	$RCOCH_2CO{-}X{-}COCH_2COR$ $(RCO)_2CH{-}X{-}CH(COR)_2$
Bis-(α-amino acids)	$HOOC{-}CH(NH_2){-}X{-}CH(NH_2){-}COOH$
Bis-(salicylaldehyde-diimines)	$C_6H_4(OH){-}CH{=}N{-}X{-}N{=}CH{-}C_6H_4(OH)$
Bis-(8-hydroxyquinolines)	HO—(quinoline, N)—X—(quinoline, N)—OH
Bis-(dithiocarbamates)	$HS(S{=})C{-}N(R){-}X{-}N(R){-}C({=}S)SH$
Bis-(xanthates)	$HS(S{=})C{-}O{-}X{-}O{-}C({=}S)SH$
Bis-(o-hydroxyaldehydes)	HO, OH, OHC, CHO (benzene ring); HO—(ring, OHC)—X—(ring, CHO)—OH
Bis-(nitrosophenols)	ON, NO, HO, OH (benzene ring)
Bis-(glyoximes)	RC(:NOH)C(:NOH)—X—C(:NOH)C(:NOH)R

Reproduced, with permission, from D. B. SOWERBY and L. F. AUDRIETH, *J. Chem. Educ.*, 37 (1960) 134.

Thus, a polynuclear beryllium complex, (III)[8], of naphthazarin and metal derivatives of 2,5-dihydroxybenzoquinone[9], 1,6-dihydroxyphenazine[10], and 4-hydroxy-5-formyl-salicaldehyde have been reported.

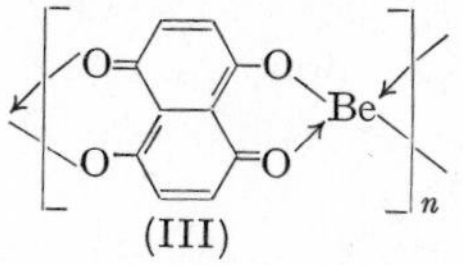

(III)

A series of compounds derived from bis-α-amino acids has been prepared[11]. It is clear that if a trivalent ion, such as Co^{3+}, with a co-ordination number of six, is used, three-dimensional cross-linked structures are possible, in addition to linear polymers. These might show greater chemical stability but would not be expected to exhibit plasticity. An attempt has been made[12] to utilise tridentate compounds, such as bis-iminodiacetic acid, in order to prepare linear polymers, but the products had poor thermal stability.

The results obtained in the above experiments all suggest that the molecular weights of the polymers were too low to show plastic behaviour, and their insolubility in all the solvents investigated indicates that the polymers were precipitated from solution during formation, before a high degree of polymerisation had been reached. However, a material, (IV), with useful properties has been prepared[13,14] from copper and nickel salts of rubeanic acid.

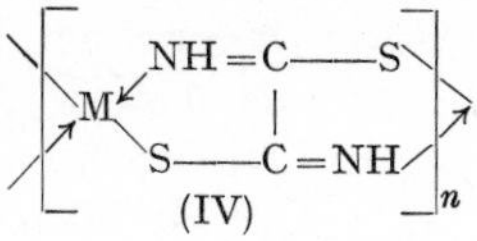

(IV)

By staining a poly(vinyl alcohol) sheet with such a compound, and subsequently stretching the sheet to orient the molecules of poly(vinyl alcohol), a dichroic substance, which may be used as a light polariser, has been obtained.

(ii) Polymer formation in the presence of metal

The high thermal stabilities of the metal phthalocyanines, some of which may be sublimed in a vacuum at 500°, have been recog-

References, p. 273–274

nised for many years, and attempts have been made[15,16] to prepare polymers (V), containing such groups. In the presence of copper salts, tetracarboxydiphenyl ether reacted with phthalic anhydride under phthalocyanine-forming conditions to give a low-molecular-weight polymer, in which oxygen atoms formed the bridging groups. The product was soluble in dimethylformamide. Tetracyanodiphenyl ether also yielded dimers or trimers with phthalonitrile.

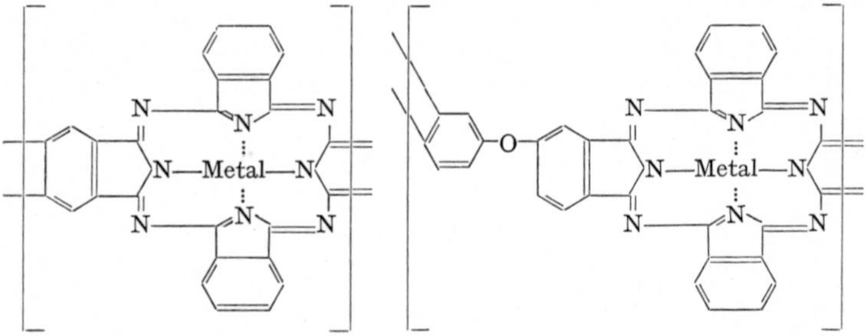

(V)

Reproduced, with permission, from C. S. MARVEL and J. H. RASSWEILLER, *J. Amer. Chem. Soc.*, 80 (1958) 1197.

The only high-molecular-weight materials obtained were cross-linked products from the fusion of tetracyanodiphenyl ether with copper bronze. These decomposed at 350°. Polymers with molecular weights of about 4000, formed from pyromellitic dianhydride, cupric chloride, and urea, in the presence of a catalyst, have been described[17]. End-group analysis showed that chains, rather than sheets, the possible alternative, had been formed. Although the molecular weights are high, they correspond to a chain of only six units.

(iii) Incorporation of metal ions in a preformed polymer

One way of avoiding the difficulties arising from the insolubility of co-ordination compounds of high molecular weight, is to synthesise an organic polymer by standard methods and then to introduce metal ions. The introduction can be used either to reinforce an existing linear polymer, or, alternatively, to effect cross-linking. This latter approach has been most widely used commercially and its potentialities have recently been surveyed[18]. It is clear, that molecules containing several chelating groups, such as pentaerythrityl tetraacetoacetate or poly(allyl acetoacetate), will form highly cross-linked structures when they combine with suitable metal ions. Some of these ion-ligand systems are soluble and stable in solution, but give tough coatings on metals when the solvent is evaporated by air-drying or heating[19,20].

Linear polymers have been prepared[21] from Schiff's bases by mixing a solution of the polymer with a soluble metal salt, the insoluble polymer, (VI), being precipitated from solution. Viscosity measurements indicated molecular weights of about 10,000.

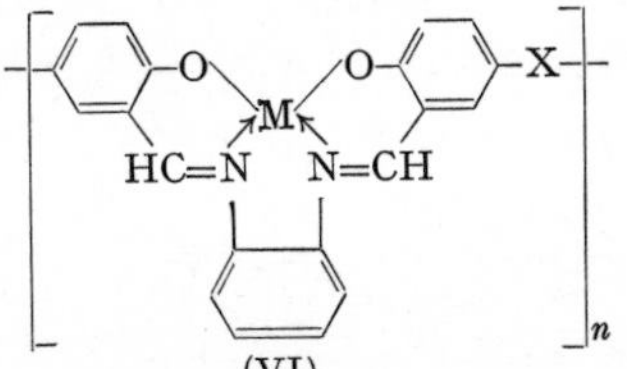

HC=N N=CH M X $X = SO_2$ or CH_2

(VI)

Some of these compounds could be heated to 250° for a few hours without appreciable decomposition, but, in general, they were less stable than the corresponding monomeric chelates. Polymers of unknown molecular weights, containing cupric and ferrous ions, have also been described[22]. These were obtained from the condensate of pyridine dialdehyde and ethylenediamine. In these compounds, however, the polyterdentate ligands are uncharged, and consequently the resultant polymer, containing metal ions, is positively charged. Such materials might have ion-exchange properties, but are unlikely to show useful mechanical properties. Schiff's base polymers, showing exchange properties, have been prepared from glyoxal and various aminophenols[23]. More recently[24], gummy products, which decompose at about 150°, have been obtained from dimercaptals, (VII). Similar polymers have been obtained from the condensation products of 1,8-diamino-3,6-dithio-octane with acetylacetone and of dialdehydes and diketones with the semicarbazones.

References, p. 273–274

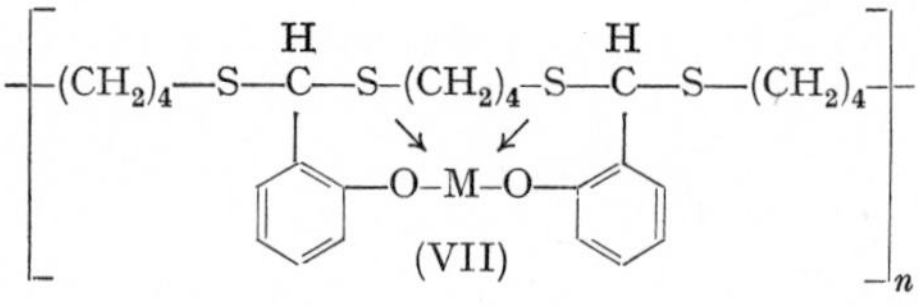

$$\left[-(CH_2)_4-S-\underset{|}{\overset{H}{C}}-S-(CH_2)_4-S-\underset{|}{\overset{H}{C}}-S-(CH_2)_4- \right]_n$$

(VII)

(iv) Reactions with chelates containing functional groups

This method is the most versatile of those described and probably provides the best way of preparing high-molecular-weight materials. Both free radical and condensation polymerisation may be employed, and both methods have been used to polymerise basic beryllium carboxylates[25]. In these unusual compounds, beryllium atoms occupy the corners of a tetrahedron, at the centre of which is an oxygen atom. The carboxylate groups lie along the tetrahedron edges, as in (VIII).

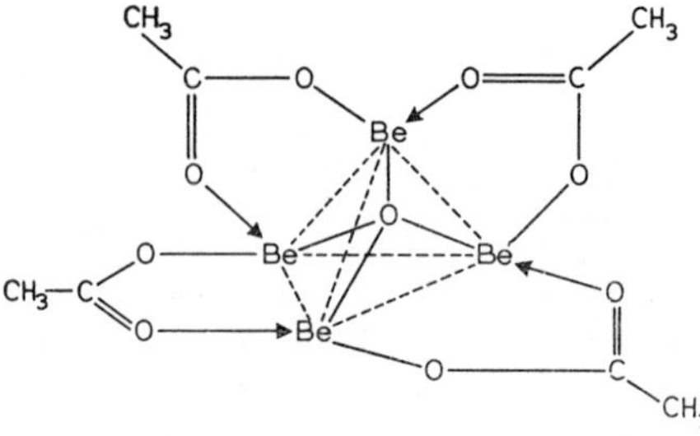

(VIII)

Reproduced, with permission, from C. S. MARVEL and M. M. MARTIN, *J. Amer. Chem. Soc.*, 80 (1958) 619.

Polymers, obtained from compounds containing difunctional unsaturated acids, do not lose volatile material at temperatures as

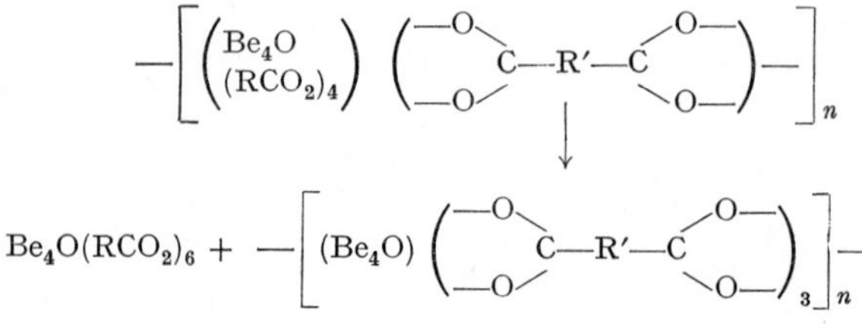

$$-\left[\begin{pmatrix}Be_4O\\(RCO_2)_4\end{pmatrix}\left(\begin{matrix}-O\\-O\end{matrix}\!\!>C-R'-C<\!\!\begin{matrix}O-\\O-\end{matrix}\right)-\right]_n$$

$$\downarrow$$

$$Be_4O(RCO_2)_6 + -\left[(Be_4O)\left(\begin{matrix}-O\\-O\end{matrix}\!\!>C-R'-C<\!\!\begin{matrix}O-\\O-\end{matrix}\right)_3\right]_n- \quad (IX)$$

high as 400°, but disproportionate even at room temperature. The disproportionation is believed to occur as shown in (IX).

The aluminium alkoxide derivatives, (X), of acetylacetone and ethyl acetoacetate, are particularly suitable for interchange reactions.

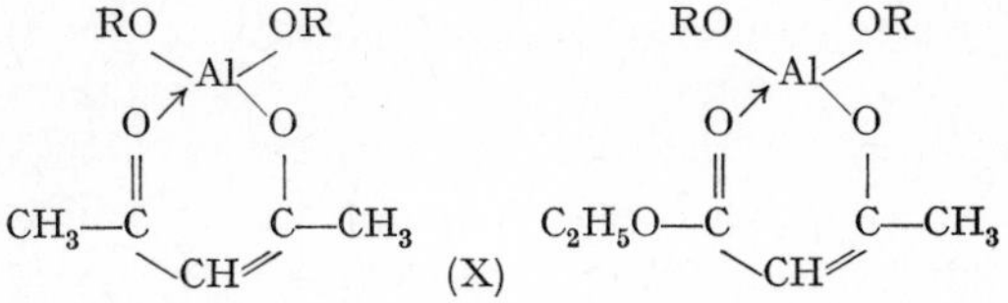

RO OR Al O O CH_3—C C—CH_3 CH (X) RO OR Al O O C_2H_5O—C C—CH_3 CH

A number of polymeric substances, so obtained, have been described[26,27]. An attempt has been made[12] to prepare the polyterephthalate and polyurethane of (XI), but the products were thermally unstable.

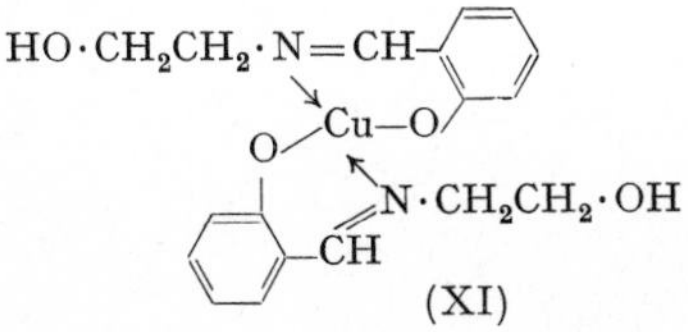

HO·CH_2CH_2·N=CH— Cu—O O N·CH_2CH_2·OH CH

(XI)

The nickel derivative of β-hydroxethylglycine is reported to be stable at 320°, but although condensation occurs with terephthalic acid, only trimers are formed. β-Hydroxyethylethylenediamine gives highly stable cobalt complexes, but attempts to carry out condensation reactions have all proved unsuccessful. A similar approach has been used[3], involving hydroxy-derivatives of the Schiff's base complex (XII).

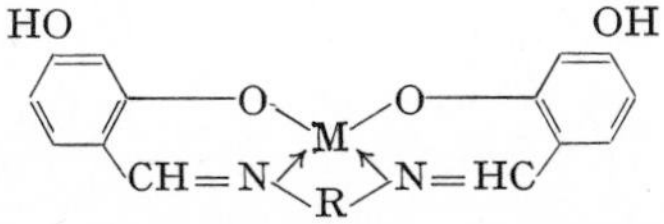

HO OH O M O CH=N R N=HC

(XII)

The complexes were heated with diphenyl carbonate and also treated with phosgene in alkaline solution, in the hope that both

References, p. 273–274

reactions would lead to the formation of polycarbonate-type polymers containing Schiff's base groups. In some experiments with phosgene, evidence was obtained of the formation of chloroformates, but no polymers were produced. The reaction with toluene di-isocyanate resulted only in the formation of cyanurates.

One advantage of this method is that it can readily be extended to melt polymerisation, provided that the complexes themselves are stable at their melting points. It may, therefore, provide a means of circumventing the difficulties arising from low solubility. Using this approach[3], metal thiopicolinamides, (XIII), containing free amino groups, were reacted with bis-acid chlorides at 200°. Some of the metal thiopicolinamides are stable at 400° and polymers from bis-thiopicolinamides, some of which are stable at 350°, have been prepared[28]. In both cases, only infusible, insoluble powders were obtained.

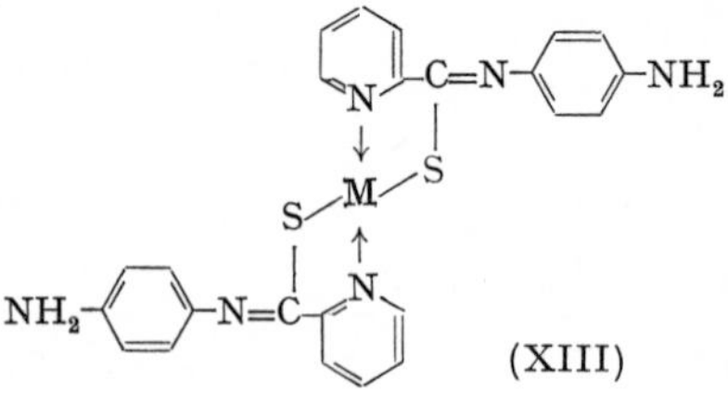

(XIII)

In all these examples, the ligand has provided the functional group for carrying out further reactions, but there is no reason why the metal ion should not do so. It has been shown[29] that manganese phthalocyanine groups may be linked by oxygen atoms bonded to tetravalent manganese atoms. The recently-reported chloro-, phenoxy-, and siloxy-germanium phthalocyanines[30] may lead to phthalocyanine polymers, in which the metal atom is hexa-co-ordinate, instead of tetraco-ordinate and planar.

(v) Ferrocenes

The ferrocenes are sufficiently different from the compounds just described to justify separate discussion. However, as their chemistry is highly specialised and some excellent reviews have been published[31,32], a few examples only will be mentioned here.

The interest in such compounds stems from the fact that biscyclopentadienyliron is stable up to 470°, but there are few reports of the preparation of stable polymers containing ferrocene groups. Vinylferrocene forms homo- and co-polymers[33]. *Trans*-cinnamoylferrocene has been shown to copolymerise readily with a number of unsaturated compounds, such styrene, acrylonitrile, and butadiene[34]. The treatment of lithio-ferrocene, and lithio-dimethylferrocene, with carbon dioxide gave polymers with molecular weights of 15,000 and 6,000 respectively[35]. Thermal stabilities were not reported, but these compounds are probably fairly susceptible to oxidative attack. Siloxanylferrocenes have been prepared but these contained only two ferrocene groups and attempts to make higher-molecular-weight compounds were unsuccessful[36]. 1,1′-Bis(chloroformyl)ferrocene condensed with a number of polymethylenediamines and diphenols to give polymers[51]. A related type of polymer, involving bonds between a metal and an unsaturated molecule, was obtained from nickel cycloctatetraene[37].

3. Chemical and physical properties

It is possible to make qualitative deductions about the behaviour of metal chelate polymers, but as relatively scant experimental data are available, it is necessary, for the most part, to use the information obtained from the examination of simple complex compounds.

The thermodynamic stability of the co-ordinate link is clearly of great importance. The dissociation energies, Q, of simple metal-ammine ions, $M(NH_3)_6^{2+}$, may be derived by considering them as large spherically symmetrical ions and applying a Born-Haber cycle (Fig. 23)[38]. The results are consistent for different halides of the same metal ion and are shown in Fig. 24, in which the difference between the upper dashed curve and the lower smooth curve is attributed to ligand field stabilisation. These results indicate that fairly strong co-ordinate bonds are formed with energies of the order of 60 kcal. This may be compared with about 98 kcal for the heat of formation of sodium and chloride ions, 100 kcal for the carbon-hydrogen bond, 83 kcal for the carbon-carbon bond,

References, p. 273–274

and 73 kcal for the carbon-nitrogen link. Such values agree quite well with calculations based upon vapour pressure data for transition metal halides which take up ammonia reversibly. The diagram

$$2X^-_{(g)} + M^{2+}_{(g)} + 6NH_{3(g)} \xleftarrow{Q} M(NH_3)^{2+}_{6(g)} + 2X^-_{(g)}$$

$2X^-_{(g)} \uparrow 2A_X$ from $2X_{(g)}$; $M^{2+}_{(g)} \uparrow (I_1 + I_2)$ from $M_{(g)}$; $6NH_{3(g)} \uparrow 6\Delta Hf°_{NH_3}$ from $3N_{2(g)} + 9H_{2(g)}$; $M(NH_3)^{2+}_{6(g)} + 2X^-_{(g)} \uparrow E_L$ from $M(NH_3)_6X_{2(s)}$

$2X_{(g)} \uparrow D_{X_2}$ from $X_{2(g)}$; $M_{(g)} \uparrow \Delta H_V^M$ from $M_{(s)}$; $M(NH_3)_6X_{2(s)} \uparrow \Delta Hf°$ from $X_{2(g)} + M_{(s)} + 3N_{2(g)} + 9H_{2(g)}$

$$X_{2(g)} + M_{(s)} + 3N_{2(g)} + 9H_{2(g)}$$

$X_{2(g)} \uparrow \Delta H_V^{X_2}$ from $X_{2(s\text{ or }L)}$

$$Q = -\Delta Hf° + 6\Delta Hf°_{NH_3} + D_{X_2} + 2A_X + \Delta H_V^{X_2} + (I_1 + I_2) + \Delta H_V^M - E_L$$

Fig. 23. Reproduced, with permission, from F. A. Cotton, *Acta. Chem. Scand.*, 10 (1956) 1520.

(Fig. 24) is very similar to that obtained[39] for the analogous hydrated metal ions in solution, although the values of Q are about 100 kcal smaller than for the hydrated ions. The principal cause

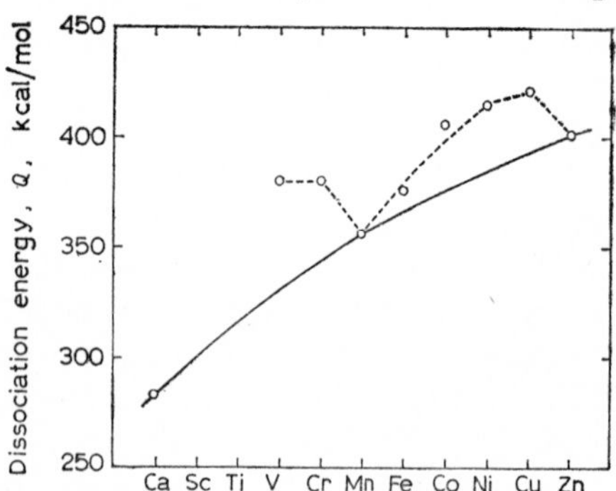

Fig. 24. Energy in kcal/mole of the gas phase dissociation of $M(NH_3)^{6+}$ ions. Calculated points, o; O---O values predicted by adding ligand field stabilization energies to points on solid curve. Reproduced, with permission, from F. A. Cotton, *Acta Chem. Scand.*, 10 (1956) 1520.

of this difference is that the values for the hydrated metal ions refer to formation in solution, whereas the results shown here apply to the formation of the ammine in the gas phase. Unfortunately, it is rather difficult at present to obtain reliable results for more complicated ligands.

In order to apply the Born–Haber cycle, an effective radius for the ion and the ionic complex have to be assumed, often in the absence of structural data. An alternative approach would be to make use of the extensive equilibrium data on complex systems in solution, from which the free energy for the following reaction may be obtained.

$$M(H_2O)_n^{2+} + nL \rightleftharpoons ML_n^{2+} + nH_2O$$

However, in order to derive results which can be related to gas phase equilibria, the value for the solvation energy of the complex ion must be introduced into the calculation, and there is no reliable way of obtaining this[31]. Nevertheless, thermodynamic stability will presumably follow the order of Irving and Williams for divalent ions[40].

$$Mg < Mn < Fe < Co < Ni < Cu > Zn$$

If other variables are unaltered, the strength of the bond increases with the electronegativity of the metal ion. The most commonly used ligands have nitrogen or oxygen as donor atoms, the coordinating strength being generally N > O. For a given donor atom, the strength of the bonding in solution varies with the availability of electrons at that atom. Thus the strong inductive effect of the trifluoromethyl group in $CF_3COCH_2COCH_3$ makes this compound a weaker chelating agent than acetylacetone.

There are a number of other factors which can increase the stability of the chelate. The replacement of ammonia molecules by molecules such as ethylenediamine leads to heat changes in solution in the range from 0–5 kcal. In addition, there is a small increase in entropy which can contribute another 0–5 kcal to the stability of the chelate. This is probably caused by an increase in the translational entropy of the complex, which more than compen-

References, p. 273–274

sates for the loss in configurational entropy arising from the formation of a rigid ring.

Ring size is another variable factor, and five-membered rings are normally more stable in solution than those containing six atoms. This is not always true, particularly if π-electron systems can arise, with associated resonance stabilisation. For example, in the acetylacetonates it is possible to write structures of the form shown.

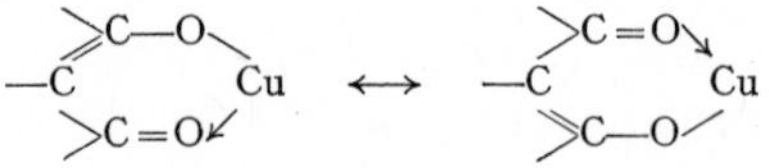

```
  >C—O↘              >C=O↘
—C      Cu   ←→    —C      Cu
  >C=O↙              >C—O↗
```

Alternatively, we can write a completely conjugated six-membered chelate ring in which both a co-ordinate bond and a covalent double bond to the metal are present. There are, however, difficulties about this second type of structure since it does not assume back-co-ordination from the metal, as is usually postulated, and would lead to an increase, rather than a decrease, of negative charge on the metal. The formation of double bonds using *d*-electrons from the metal is also rather implausible since oxygen has no low level orbitals which would permit it to serve as an acceptor without destroying the conjugated double bond system.

When attempts are made to correlate these results with the thermal and chemical stability of chelates in the related polymers, the picture is rather unsatisfactory. Little reliable information exists. It has recently been shown that the thermal stability, both in vacuum and in air, of a number of acetylacetonates is less than that of the ligand itself[41,42]. The decomposition of polymers of tetraacetylethane appeared to follow a similar pattern[43]. In addition, the thermal stability of the dimeric copper phthalocyanine depends on a kinetic effect rather than inherent thermodynamic stability, since breakdown is due to a slow decomposition reaction[44].

These disappointing results are not altogether surprising when it is recalled that metal ions are very powerful catalysts for certain oxidation reactions, and there is reason to suppose that when suitable valency changes are possible, the metal ion in a chelate might assist in the oxidative breakdown of the chelate. That this is by no means always true was shown by experiments[21] with various metal ion derivatives of Schiff's bases where, in certain cases, little oxidative breakdown, if any, occurred when the compound was heated in air instead of nitrogen. These results are all the more surprising because the related derivatives of Schiff's bases and cobalt take up and give off oxygen reversibly[50]. It appears that the available valency states of the metal ion are of importance, and this may be the reason for the high thermal stability possessed by some zinc complexes[45,28], in spite of their unexceptional free energies of formation in solution. It has been shown[21] that in the case of Schiff's bases which contain both donor nitrogen atoms and phenol groups which are involved in chelation, substituents which increase both the electron availability at the donor atom and the acidity of the phenol group also enhance thermal stability. It has been known for some time that these factors lead to the stabilisation of chelates in solution.

Physical properties, such as melting point and plasticity, will depend on the residual forces between the chains and here, too, the available information is very meagre. It has been shown that the structures of copper dimethylglyoxime and nickel dimethylglyoxime are quite different[46]. In the latter case, a lattice is formed in which the nickel atoms are vertically placed, one above the other, and it has been suggested that the marked difference in solubility between the copper and nickel compounds is a result of the formation of a metal–metal bond between the nickel atoms. The strength of this bond has been estimated to be of the order of 10 kcal, which is certainly comparable with the strength of hydrogen bonds found in organic polymers. In the solid state, the molecules of the copper derivatives of salicylaldehyde ethylenediamine are distorted and the separation of the metal atoms is less than the sum of their covalent radii[47].

An indication of the effect of these forces is evident from consideration of measurements on some 8-hydroxyquinoline chelates (Fig. 25)[48]. The chelates of the divalent metal ions have sublimation temperatures which depend on the nature of the metal ion, whereas those of the trivalent ions tend to lie within a relatively narrow range for a given chelate. These observations lend strong support to the idea that appreciable and variable metal–metal bonding may occur

References, p. 273–274

in compounds of the divalent metal ions, whereas in compounds of the trivalent ions, these ions are largely encased in an organic shell and very much weaker forces exist between molecules. The fact that the tris-chelated aluminium isovalerylacetonate is a liquid at room temperature is in accord with such a picture[49].

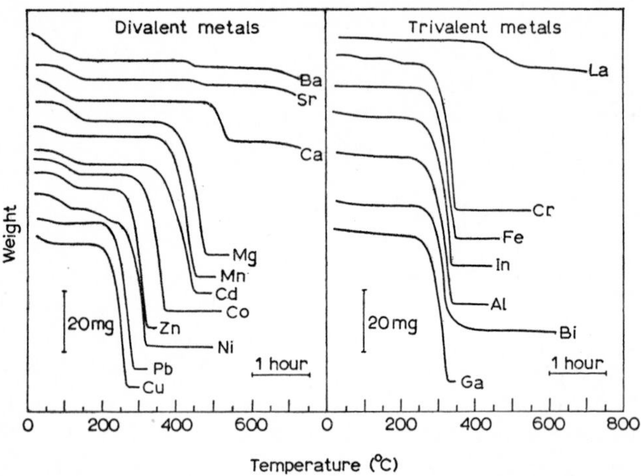

Fig. 25. Weight loss curves for metal 8-hydroxyquinolates *in vacuo*. Fifty-mg samples were used. For clarity, curves are displaced along the ordinate. Reproduced with permission from R. G. Charles and A. Langer, *J. Phys. Chem.*, 63 (1959) 604.

It is clear from the above discussion that the problem of preparing chelate polymers of high molecular weight has not yet been solved, and that the difficulties are much greater than was foreseen. These arise, principally, from their low solubility, which interferes both with the study of properties such as molecular weight and with the attainment of high degrees of polymerisation when using the usual synthetic methods. Although residual forces between molecules are appreciable, it may be possible to control these with suitable plasticisers, and this, together with the opportunities that chelation offers for creating new chain configurations, should lead to materials with unusual mechanical properties. It has been shown that good thermal stability may be associated with chelation, although it is not necessarily conferred by it, and so it is to be hoped that ways will soon be found of preparing a range of metal chelate polymers of high molecular weight.

REFERENCES

1 W. C. FERNELIUS, *W.A.D.C. Technical Report*, 56–203.
2 J. P. WILKINS and E. L. WITTBECKER, *U.S.P.* 2,659,711 (1953).
3 C. N. KENNEY, unpublished work.
4 R. W. KLUIBER and J. W. LEWIS, *J. Am. Chem. Soc.*, 82 (1960) 5777.
5 V. V. KORSHAK, E. S. KRONGAUS and V. E. SHEINA, *Vysokomol. Soedineniya*, 2 (1960) 662.
6 N. A. GLUKHOV, M. M. KOTON and YU. V. MITIN, *Vysokomol. Soedineniya*, 2 (1960) 971.
7 F. W. KNOBLOCH and W. H. RAUSCHER, *J. Polymer Sci.*, 38 (1959) 261.
8 A. L. UNDERWOOD, T. Y. TORIBARA and W. F. NEUMAN, *J. Am. Chem. Soc.*, 72 (1950) 5597.
9 R. L. FRANK, G. R. CLARK and J. N. COKER, *J. Am. Chem. Soc.*, 72 (1950) 1827.
10 S. KANDA and Y. SAITO, *Bull. Chem. Soc. Japan*, 30 (1957) 192.
11 J. R. ELLIOTT, *Thesis*, University of Illinois, 1943.
12 J. C. BAILAR, *W.A.D.C. Technical Report*, 57–657.
13 W. F. AMON and M. W. KANE, *U.S.P.* 2,505,085 (1950).
14 K. A. JENSEN, *Z. anorg. Chem.*, 252 (1944) 227.
15 C. S. MARVEL and J. H. RASSWEILLER, *J. Am. Chem. Soc.*, 80 (1958) 1197.
16 C. S. MARVEL and M. M. MARTIN, *J. Am. Chem. Soc.*, 80 (1958) 6600.
17 W. C. DRINKARD and J. C. BAILAR, *J. Am. Chem. Soc.*, 81 (1959) 4795.
18 F. SCHLENKER, *Kunststoffe*, 47 (1957) 7.
19 *British Patent* 791,325 (1958) (E. I. du Pont de Nemours & Co.).
20 *British Patent* 776,156 (1957) (E. I. du Pont de Nemours & Co.).
21 C. S. MARVEL and N. TARKÖY, *J. Am. Chem. Soc.*, 79 (1957) 6000.
C. S. MARVEL and N. TARKÖY, *J. Am. Chem. Soc.*, 80 (1958) 832.
C. S. MARVEL and P. V. BONSIGNORE, *J. Am. Chem. Soc.*, 81 (1959) 2668.
22 F. LIONS and K. V. MARTIN, *J. Am. Chem. Soc.*, 79 (1957) 2733.
23 E. BAYER, *Chem. Ber.*, 90 (1957) 2785.
24 W. C. DRINKARD and D. N. CHAKRAVARTY, *Conference on High Temperature Polymer and Fluid Research*, Dayton, Ohio, May 1959.
25 C. S. MARVEL and M. M. MARTIN, *J. Am. Chem. Soc.*, 80 (1958) 619.
26 V. KUGLER, *J. Polymer Sci.*, 29 (1958) 637.
27 T. R. PATTERSON, F. J. PAVLIK, A. A. BALDONI and R. L. FRANK, *J. Am. Chem. Soc.*, 81 (1959) 4213.
28 K. V. MARTIN, *J. Am. Chem. Soc.*, 80 (1958) 233.
29 J. A. ELVIDGE and A. B. P. LEVER, *Proc. Chem. Soc.*, (1959) 195.
30 R. D. JOYNER and M. E. KENNEY, *J. Am. Chem. Soc.*, 82 (1960) 5790.
31 G. WILKINSON and F. A. COTTON, *Progress in Inorganic Chemistry*, Ed. F. A. Cotton, Vol. I, Interscience Publishers, New York, 1959, p. 1.

[32] P. L. Pauson, *Quart. Revs.* (*London*), 9 (1955) 391.
[33] F. S. Arimoto and A. C. Haven, *J. Am. Chem. Soc.*, 77 (1955) 6295.
[34] L. E. Coleman and M. D. Rausch, *J. Polymer Sci.*, 28 (1958) 207.
[35] K. L. Rinehart, *Conference on High Temperature Polymer and Fluid Research*, Dayton, Ohio, May 1959.
[36] R. L. Schaaf and P. T. Kan, *Conference on High Temperature Polymer and Fluid Research*, Dayton, Ohio, May 1959.
[37] G. Wilke, *Angew. Chem.*, 72 (1960) 581.
[38] F. A. Cotton, *Acta Chem. Scand.*, 10 (1956) 1520.
[39] L. E. Orgel, *J. Chem. Soc.*, (1952) 4756.
[40] H. Irving and R. J. P. Williams, *J. Chem. Soc.*, (1953) 3192.
[41] R. G. Charles, *J. Phys. Chem.*, 63 (1959) 2084.
[42] M. Mendelsohn, E. M. Arnett and H. Freiser, *J. Phys. Chem.*, 64 (1960) 660.
[43] R. G. Charles, *J. Phys. Chem.*, 64 (1960) 1747.
[44] E. A. Lawton, *J. Phys. Chem.*, 62 (1958) 384.
[45] C. S. Marvel, S. A. Aspey and E. A. Dudley, *J. Am. Chem. Soc.*, 78 (1956) 4905.
[46] C. V. Banks and D. W. Barnum, *J. Am. Chem. Soc.*, 80 (1958) 3579.
[47] K. Packler and M. Stackelberg, *Z. anorg. Chem.*, 305 (1960) 286.
[48] R. G. Charles and A. Langer, *J. Phys. Chem.*, 63 (1959) 603.
[49] R. G. Charles, *J. Inorg. & Nuclear Chem.*, 6 (1958) 42.
[50] See, for example, A. E. Martell and M. Calvin, *Chemistry of the Metal Chelate Compounds*, Prentice Hall, New Jersey, 1952, p. 341.
[51] F. W. Knobloch, *U.S. Library of Congress Card*, No. Mic. 59–3879.

AUTHOR INDEX

There are three types of entries: (i) "x^y" indicates reference no. y on p. x of text; (ii) "(x)" indicates the page on which a list of references is found; (iii "x" indicates page on which author's name is mentioned without a covering reference.]

Abel, E. W., 179[135], 180[135], 182[135], (199)
Adams, M. D., 27[36], (53)
Ajoti, M., 4[4], (18)
Alfrey, T., 230[53], (254)
Amon, W. F., 261[13], (273)
Anderson, R. C., 144[17], (160)
Anderson, R. P., 74[70], (85), 181[91], 184[91], (197)
Andrianov, K. A., 71[62,63,64], (85), 163[16], 164[16,134], 166[16], 167[22], 168[29], 170[41], 171[16,44], 172[44,51,52,55], 174[52], 176[72,75], 177[75], 178[52,79], 181[89], 182[16b], 186[110], 189[16b,130], 193[129,130], 194[130], (195, 196, 197, 198, 199), 201[1,3], 202[4,5,6], 203[1], 204[8], 205[9,10,11,12], 207[13], 208[14], 209[4,5,6,15], 210[15], 214[4,5,6], 215[1,26,27], 219[26], 224[12], 225[1,45,48], 226[59], 231[59], 233[63], 238[72], 239[1], 240[74,77,84], 245[84], 247[84,87,89], 248[84,89], 249[90], 250[90], 251[89,91], 252[88], (252, 253, 254, 255)
Antler, M., 152[43], (160)
Appel, R., 117[24,27], 120[36], 121[36], (136, 137)
Apple, E. F., 59[6], (83)
Arbuzov, B. A., 186[112], (198)
Aries, R. S., 44[99], (56)
Arimoto, F. S., 267[33], (274)
Aristarkhova, G. I., 44[100b], (56)
Arnett, E. M., 270[42], (274)
Arnold, H. R., 71[52], (85)
Aronovich, P. M., 37[78], (55)
Artamonova, T. V., 89[15b], (109)
Artsdalen, E. R. van, 44[102], (56)
Ashby, E. C., 70[42,43], (84)
Asnovich, E. Z., 205[11,12], 215[27], 224[12], 247[87], 252[88], (252, 253, 255)
Aspey, S. A., 271[45], (274)
Astakhin, V. V., 176[72], (197)
Atlas, S. M., 173[58], (196), 211[18], (253)
Aubrey, D. W., 34[70,71], 35[77], 36[77], 37[72], 38[77], 45[70], 46[70,71], 49[77], 50[70,72,77,94e], 52[72,77], (54, 55)
Audrieth, L. F., 87[1], 90[22], (108, 109), 133[59], (137), 163[10], (195), 260

Bach, H., 89[13a], (108)
Bailar, J. C., 261[12], 262[17], 265[12], (273)
Baker, H. R., 146[26], (160)
Balacco, F., 70[45], (84)
Baldoni, A. A., 212[20], (253), 265[27], (273)
Bamford, W. R., 41[93], (55), 63[39], 73[39], (84)
Baney, R. H., 167[26], (195)
Banks, R. E., 9[14], 17[14], (19)
Banks, C. V., 271[46], (274)
Banus, J., 23[14], 29[14], (53)
Barfield, P. A., 46[114], 47[114], (56)
Barnum, D. W., 271[46], (274)
Barry, A. J., 141[7], (160), 240[80,81], 241[81], 243[81], (254, 255)
Bartlett, R. K., 36[33b], 51[33b], (53)
Bartocha, B., 171[49], (196)
Basille, L. J., 27[37], (53)
Bauer, S. H., 23[21a], 45[103,104] (53, 56)
Bayer, E., 263[23], (273)
Beattie, I. R., 194[136], (199)
Becher, H. J., 23[18,19a], 29[55], 34[69], 45[19a,108], 46[69,111], 48[18], (53, 54, 56), 97[31], (109)
Becke-Goehring, M., 91[26], (109), 111[7], 112[10], 113[7,14], 114[18], 115[18,19], 116[7,21], 117[18,23], 127[46], 133[58], 135[63], (136, 137)

Bechi, K., 60[8], (83)
Bedell, R., 75[82], (85)
Bekasova, N. I., 44[100a,100b], (56)
Bendict, H. N., 168[33], 169[33], (196)
Benek, L., 127[47], (137)
Bennett, H., 60[9], (83)
Bennett, O. F., 107[48], (109)
Berlin, A. A., 162[3], (195)
Bezman, I. I., 89[15a], (109)
Bilbo, A. J., 9[15], (19)
Binda, F. J., 60[24], (84)
Binger, A., 187[114], (198)
Birchall, J. M., 9[14], 17[14], (19)
Bissot, T. C., 24[24], 28[24], 29[50], 38[81], (53, 54, 55)
Blau, J. A., 60[29], 61[34], (84)
Bloomfield, P. R., 13[16], (19), 128[52], 129[52], (137)
Blumcke, A., 185[105,106], (198)
Blumenthal, W. B., 164[20], (195)
Bode, H., 89[10,13a,13b,20], 91[13b], (108, 109)
Bolz, A., 23[15,16], 25[26], 27[16,34], 28[16], 29[34], 30[16], 35[34], (53)
Bonsignore, P. V., 263[21], 270[21], 271[21], (273)
Boone, J. L., 23[20c], (53)
Borisov, S. N., 204[7], 236[67], (252, 254)
Boyd, T., 213[23], (253)
Bradford, J. L., 36[67a], 37[67b], 39[67b], (54)
Bradley, D. C., 163[17], 175[68,69], 176[69,74], 177[69,74], 179[68], 190[68,69], 191[69,74], (195, 197), 213[22,25], 215[22], (253)
Braun, J., 71[56], (85)
Braunholtz, W., 89[17], (109)
Bray, P. J., 48[117], (56)
Breitling, G., 58[5], (83)
Breitman, B. M., 240[77], (254)
Brendel, C., 79[99], (86)
Brennan, G. L., 32[65], (54)
Bretschneider, O., 7[11], (19)
Brey, W. S., 46[112], (56)
Brindley, P. B., 70[43a], (84)
Brown, C. A., 23[9,12], 40[87], (52, 55), 174[66], 175[66], 178[66], (197), 249[92], (255)
Brown, E. D., 150[37], (160)
Brown, H. C., 61[32], (84)
Brown, J. F., 23[8], (52), 242[86], 247[86], (255)
Brown, M. P., 163[13], (195), 235[65], (254)
Buchheit, P., 23[15,17], (53)
Buchwald, H., 5[7], (19)
Buist, J. M., 158[64], (161)
Bujwid, Z. J., 41[92], (55)
Burg, A. B., 5[8], (19), 23[14,20c,27], 25[27,28,30], 27[31], 28[46], 29[14], 35[73], (53, 54), 76[87,88], 78[94,95], 79[96,98,99,100], 80[100,101,102,103], 82[106], (86)
Bushmarina, A. N., 89[15b], (109)
Bütow, K., 89[20], (109)

Calvin, M., 271[50], (274)
Campbell, D. H., 29[50], 38[81], (54, 55)
Campbell, G. W., 23[21b], 28[21b], (53)
Campbell, P. G., 107[48], (109)
Carmael, A., 60[22], (84)
Caron, A., 111[5,6], (136)
Carroll, D. F., 92[27], 97[27], (109)
Caserio, F. F., 78[91], 81[104], (86)
Cass, R. C., 99[42], (109)
Cazes, J., 71[46], (84)
Chaigneau, M., 31[61,62], (54)
Chakravarty, D. N., 263[24], (273)
Chamberlain, D. F., 60[14], (84)
Chamberland, B. L., 164[19], 183[97], 185[19,98], (195, 198), 221[37,38], 222[42], 224[37], (253)
Chapman, A. C., 87[3], 90[25], 91[3,25], 98[3], 101, (108, 109)
Charles, R. G., 270[41,43], 271[48], 272[49], (274)
Chugunov, V. S., 168[28], 170[42], (196)
Chukovskaya, E. T., 142[11], (160)
Clark, D., 112[11], (136)
Clark, G. R., 261[9], (273)
Coates, G. E., 23[19b], 48[19b], (53)
Coffin, K. P., 45[104], (56)
Cohen, H. J., 190[124], 193[124], (198)
Coker, J. N., 261[9], (273)
Coleman, L. E., 267[34], (274)
Connor, C. J., 154[48], (161)
Conrad, F., 171[50], (196), 239[73], (254)
Coover, H. W., 129[53], 130[53], 132[57], (137)
Corbridge, D. E. C., 97[32], (109), 121, 124[37], (137)
Cotton, F. A., 266[31], 267[38], 268[38], 269[31], (273, 274)
Cottrell, T. L., 22[5], 44[5], (52)
Coursen, D. L., 45[105], (56)
Cowley, A. H., 173[61], (196)

Craig, D. P., 88[4], 93[4,28,29], 94[28,30], 96[4], 99[30], 105[28,29], 106[45], (108, 109), 110[1], (136)
Craig, R. A., 188[116], (198)
Crain, R. D., 220[32], (253)
Crawford, B. L., 34[69], 46[69], (54)

Daasch, L. W., 89[11], 90[11], 97[33], (108, 109)
Dahl, G. H., 25[25b], 27[25b], 32[65], (53, 54)
Dandegaonker, S. H., 62[35,36], (84)
Danforth, J. D., 176[71], (197)
Daudt, W. H., 167[25], (195), 240[81], 241[81], 243[81], (255)
Davies, D. W., 46[112], (56)
Dawson, J. W., 39[86], 40[86], 41[92], 48[115], (55, 56)
Denault, G. C., 177[76], 178[76], (197), 216[30], (253)
Dennis, N. T. M., 153[45], (161)
Dennoon, C. E., 60[26], (84)
Dessy, R. E., 190[124], 193[124], (198)
Deuel, H., 41[92], (55), 60[19], (84)
Dewar, M. J. S., 21[2], 41[94c], 51[94c], (52, 55), 99[40], (109)
Dewing, J., 23[23], 24[23], 28[23], 42[23], (53)
Diener, W., 28[45], (54)
Dikareva, T. A., 247[87], (255)
Dishon, B., 89[19], (109)
Dmitrieva, N. A., 173[59], (196)
Dolgov, B. N., 173[59], 174[67], 175[67,70], 178[70,77], 179[81], 180[128], 193[128], (196, 197, 198)
Domicone, J. J., 240[81], 241[81], 243[81], (255)
Donohue, J., 111[5,6], 112[9], (136)
Dornberger-Schiff, K., 124[44], (137)
Dornow, A., 49[124], 50[124], (56)
Douglas, C. M., 89[16a], (109)
Dougill, M. W., 97[37], (109)
Doyle, C. D., 144[21], 146[21], (160)
Dudley, E. A., 271[45], (274)
Dulova, V. G., 168[29], 172[52], 174[52], 178[52,79], (196, 197), 202[4], 209[4], 214[4], (252)
Dunnevant, W. R., 43[98b], (56)
Drinkard, W. C., 262[17], 263[24], (273)
Dworkin, A. S., 44[102], (56)

Eaborn, C., 138[4], (160), 167[23], 168[23], 170[23], 188[23], (195), 241[85], (255)
Ebert, F., 7[11], (19)
Edsall, J. T., 34[69], 46[69], (54)
Elliott, J. R., 156[52], (161), 261[11], (273)
Ellis, C., 60[12], (83)
Elvidge, J. A., 266[29], (273)
Emeléus, H. J., 25[29], 28[29,41], (53), 58[4], (83), 162[1], (195)
English, W. D., 50[128], 52[129], (56), 174[65], 179[65], (197)
Erickson, C. E., 43[98b], (55), 71[53], (85)
Eustance, J. W., 242[86], 247[86], (255)
Evers, E. C., 32[63,64a], (54)

Fairbrother, F., 173[61], (196)
Fedotov, N. S., 23[20b], (53)
Fehér, F., 185[105,106,107], 186[107], (198), 232[60], (254)
Fekete, F., 150[40], (160)
Fenske, M. R., 152[42], (160)
Fernelius, W. C., 258[1], (273)
Fertig, J., 187[113], (198)
Fitch, F. T., 144[18], (160)
Fletcher, E. A., 61[32], (84)
Fletcher, H. J., 240[75], (254)
Fleming, R. F., 167[25], (195)
Florin, R. E., 77[89], (86)
Fluck, E., 91[26], (109), 115[19], (136)
Fordham, S., 41[93], (55), 63[39], 73[39], (84), 138[5], (160)
Foss, O., 6[10], (19)
Fowell, R. A., 100[43], (109)
Fraenkel, G. K., 111[4], (136)
Frank, R. L., 212[20], (253), 261[9], 265[27], (273)
Fraser, R. D. B., 34[69], 46[69], (54)
Frazer, M. J., 75[82], (85), 181[88], (197)
Freidlina, R. K., 142[11], (160)
Freiser, H., 270[42], (274)
Freitag, W. O., 32[63,64a], (54)
Frensdorf, H. K., 157[61], (161)
Frick, S., 34[69], 46[69,111], (54, 56)
Fries, G., 117[23], (136)
Frisch, K. C., 182[96], (197), 222[41], (253)
Fritz, G., 162[137], (199)

Gamble, E. L., 76[86], (86)
Ganina, T. N., 172[51], 176[75], 177[75], (196, 197), 205[10], 215[26], 219[26], (252, 253)
Gardner, D. M., 111[4], (136)
Garrett, A. B., 188[116], (198)
Gasselin, V., 60[15], (84)
Gaze, R., 213[25], (253)
Gee, G., 104[44], (109), 111[2], (136)
Gehrt, H. H., 49[124], 50[124], (56)
Gemeinhardt, T. G., 158[65], (161)
George, P. D., 156[52], (161)
Gerber, H., 117[24,27], 118[28], 119[28], (136)
Gerding, H., 163[8,9], (195)
Gerrard, W., 20[3], 24[85b], 29[51], 35[51], 37[51,51a], 39[51], 40[51,90], 41[51,90,92], 48[3], 49[3,122,123], 50[125], (52, 54, 55, 56), 60[29], 61[30,33,34], 62[35,36], 70[43a], 75[82], 76[83], (84, 85), 181[87,88], 187[113], (197, 198)
Gibbs, C. F., 71[61], (85), 172[54], (196)
Gilbert, A.R., 146[25], 147[27], (160)
Gilkey, J. W., 141[7], (160), 240[80,81], 241[81], 243[81], (254, 255)
Gillespie, R. J., 106[46], (109)
Gilman, H., 142[12], (160), 163[15], 168[33], 169[33], (195, 196), 222[40], (253)
Gilmont, R., 99[41], (109)
Gilmont, P., 76[86], (86)
Girardot, P. R., 27[38,39], (53)
Glukhov, N. A., 259[6], (273)
Goehring, M., 113[12], 114[17,18], 117[18,22], 120[36], 121[36], 125[45], 127[47], 128[49], 133[60], (136, 137)
Goldish, E., 111[6], (136)
Goubeau, J., 23[13,17,19a], 33[66], 41[94a], 45[19a,107], (53, 54, 55, 56), 70[41], (84)
Gräbner, H., 33[66], (54)
Graf, R., 117[25,26], (136)
Green, L. Q., 168[27], (195)
Gribova, I. A., 89[15b], (109)
Griffey, P. F., 76[83], (85)
Grobe, J., 162[137], (199)
Groch, F., 81[85], (85)
Groszos, S. J., 51[126], (56)
Grundmann, C., 90[23], (109)
Guenther, F. O., 240[82,83], 242[82], 244[83], (255)
Gulledge, H. C., 216[28], (253)
Gunderloy, F. C., 43[98b], (55), 71[53], (85)
Gutmann, V., 191[125], (198)
Gutowsky, H. S., 159[68], (161)
Guy, J., 31[62], (54)

Haber, C. P., 78[93], (86), 89[13c,16a], (108, 109)
Hackford, J., 171[45], (196)
Hägg, G., 163[7], (195)
Hall, R. A., 149[31], (160)
Hamilton, S. B., 41[94b], (55), 71[47], (84)
Hantzsch, H., 120[35], (137)
Harle, O. L., 60[18], (84)
Harris, J. J., 35[75], 37[80b], 40[89], 41[89], (55)
Hartley, S. B., 99[38], (109)
Hartzfeld, H., 168[33], 169[33], (196)
Harvey, M. C., 171[48], (196)
Haszeldine, R. N., 9[14], 17[14], (19)
Hauser, E., 89[17], (109)
Hauserman, F. B., 237[69], (254)
Haven, A. C., 130[55], (137), 267[33], (274)
Haworth, D. T., 29[53], (54)
Hayter, R. G., 60[17], (84)
Hecht, G., 119[31], (136)
Heidemann, A., 27[59], 31[59], (54)
Heinke, J., 117[22], (136)
Heinze, G., 120[34], (137)
Hellman, M., 9[15], (19)
Henglein, F. A., 71[59,60], (85), 166[21], 181[90], 182[93], 189[123], (195, 197, 198), (220[34], 225[44], 234[64], (253, 254)
Hennecka, H., 119[31], (136)
Hennion, C. F., 70[43], (84)
Herbst, H., 187[113], (198)
Herre, F., 58[5], (83)
Herring, D. L., 89[13c,16b], (108, 109)
Hertwig, K., 23[16,20a], 27[16], 29[54], 30[16], (53, 54)
Hewitt, F., 82[105], (86)
Hickam, W. M., 144[20], (160)
Hizawa, K., 72[76], (85)
Hoard, J. L., 45[105], (56)
Hobbs, E., 97[32], (109)
Hoffman, A. K., 71[49,50,51], (85)
Hohn, F. J., 230[53], (254)
Hohnstedt, L. F., 29[53], 40[88], 41[88], (54, 55)
Holbrock, G. W., 150[37], (160)
Holden, J. R., 89[11], 90[11], (108)
Holl, A., 120[35], (137)
Holle, W., 28[43], (53)

Holliday, A. K., 82[105], (86)
Holmstedt, B., 97[34], (109)
Hook, D. E., 141[7], (160)
Horeld, G., 29[49], (54)
Hornbaker, E. D., 171[50], (196), 239[73], (254)
Hudson, H. R., 37[51a], (54)
Hunter, M. J., 240[15], (254)
Huntress, A. R., 153[45], (161)
Hurd, D. T., 58[3], 74[78], (83, 85), 220[35], (253)
Hurd, R., 158[64], (161)
Hurley, F. R., 128[50], (137)
Hutchinson, J. H., 182[92], (197), 220[31], (253)
Hyde, J. F., 167[25], 170[38,39,40], 173[62,63], (195, 196)
Hyman, M., 60[25], (84)

Iler, R. K., 238[70], (254)
Ingham, R. K., 163[15], (195), 222[40], (253)
Irany, E. P., 60[11], (83)
Irving, H., 269[40], (274)
Ishino, T., 213[24], (253)
Ito, K., 48[116,118,121], (56)
Iverson, M. L., 172[56], 173[57], (196), 211[16,17], (253)

Jacobs, L. E., 46[110], (56)
Jacques, J. K., 99[39], 100[39], (109)
Jaffé, H. H., 93[28], 94[28], 105[28], (109)
Jensen, K. A., 261[14], (273)
Joannis, A., 28[42,44], (53)
Johannson, O. K., 150[37], (160), 167[25], 170[40], (195, 196)
John, K., 91[26], (109)
Johnson, L., 23[21b], 28[21b], (53)
Joyner, R. D., 266[30], (273)

Kallander, L. G., 38[83], (55)
Kan, P. T., 267[36], (274)
Kanazashi, M., 188[120], (198)
Kanda, S., 261[10], (273)
Kane, M. W., 261[13], (273)
Kantor, S. W., 147[27], (160), 169[35], (196)
Kanzler, K., 172[53], (196)
Karateev, D. A., 186[108], (198), 230[54,55,56,57], 231[54,55,56], 233[54,57,61], (254)
Kary, R. M., 182[96], (197), 222[41], (253)
Kashutina, E. A., 189[130], 193[129,130], 194[130], (198), 238[72], (254)
Katchman, A., 242[86], 247[86], (255)
Kautsky, H., 171[49], (196)
Kazakova, A. A., 186[110], (198), 202[5], 209[5,15], 210[15], 214[5], (252, 253)
Keenan, C. W., 28[52], (54)
Keith, J. N., 32[63], (54)
Keller, H., 70[41], (84), 185[105], (198)
Keller, R. N., 39[82], (55)
Kenney, C. N., 259[3], 265[3], 266[3], (273)
Kenney, M. E., 266[30], (273)
Kerr, G. T., 188[117,118], (198)
Ketelaar, J. A. A., 97[35], (109)
Kharitonov, N. P., 179[81], (197)
Khromova, V. I., 233[61], (254)
Khrustaleva, W., 215[26], 219[26], (253)
Khudobin, Yu. I., 179[81], (197)
Kipping, F. S., 166[32], 170[36,37], 171[45], (196)
Kirsanov, A. V., 117[22], 119[32], (136)
Kiseleva, T. M., 221[39], (253)
Kiser, K. M., 242[86], 247[86], (255)
Klaus, E. E., 152[42], (160)
Klement, R., 125[45a], 127[47,48], (137)
Klevens, H. B., 46[110], (56)
Kluiber, R. W., 259[4], (273)
Knobloch, F. W., 259[7], 267[51], (273, 274)
Koch, O., 127[48], (137)
Koch, T. A., 162[5], (195)
Koenig, F. J., 27[36], (53)
Koenig, P. E., 182[92], (197), 220[31,32], (253)
Kohn, E. J., 89[11], 90[11], (108)
Kolesova, V. A., 185[103], 186[103], (198)
Konkle, G. M., 149[29], (160)
Korshak, V. V., 44[100a,100b], (56), 89[15b], (109), 162[4], 163[4], (195), 259[5], (273)
Kostroma, T. V., 37[80a], (55)
Koton, M. M., 221[39], (253), 259[6], (273)
Kovacich, S. A., 152[44], (160)
Kozminskaya, T. K., 37[79], (55)
Krantz, K. W., 242[86], 247[86], (255)
Krebs, H., 162[2], (195)
Kreshkov, A. P., 186[108], (198), 230[54,55,56,57], 231[54,55,56], 233[54,57,61], (254)
Krieble, R. H., 74[77], (85), 180[85], (197)
Kriner, W. A., 32[63,64a], (54)

Krongaus, E. S., 259[5], (273)
Kronrod, N. Y., 71[54], (85)
Krüerke, U., 71[58], (85), 180[84], (197)
Kubba, V. P., 21[2], 41[94c], 51[94c], (52, 55)
Kubo, M., 46[109], 48[116,118,119,121], (56)
Kuchen, W., 5[7], (19)
Kudryavtsev, R. V., 71[64], (85), 225[48], (254)
Kugler, V., 265[26], (273)
Kuhlborsch, G., 185[105], (198)
Kuljian, E. S., 25[28], (53)
Kurasheva, N. A., 168[29], 172[52], 174[52], 178[52], (196), 202[4], 209[4], 214[4], (252)
Kursanov, D. N., 71[64], (85), 225[48], (254)
Kusumoto, H., 159[68], (161)

La Mer, V. K., 61[31], (84)
Lang, R., 71[59,60], (85), 181[90], 182[93], 189[123], (197, 198), 220[34], 225[44], 234[64], (253, 254)
Langer, A., 271[48], 272, (274)
Langer, J., 90[21], (109)
Lappert, M. F., 20[3], 23[10a,10b], 24[85a,85b], 32[64b,101], 33[67,68], 34[68,70,71,72], 35[10b,77], 36[10b,77,101], 37[68,72], 38[77], 39[84,85a], 41[92], 44[64b,67,101], 45[70], 46[68,70,71,101,114], 47[114], 48[3], 49[3,77,121,122], 50[10a,10b,70,77,94e,101,125], 52[68,72,77], (52, 54, 55, 56), 60[29], 61[33,34], 62[35,36], 70[40a,43a], (84)
Larsson, L., 97[34], (109)
Laubengayer, A. W., 27[33], 30[33], 36[33], (53), 60[17], (84)
Laudenslager, H. B., 167[25], (195)
Lawrenson, I. J., 159[68], (161)
Lawton, E. A., 89[13c], (108), 270[44], (274)
Lazier, W. A., 60[27], (84)
Lee, J., 46[114], 47[114], (56)
Leffler, A., 81[85], (85)
Lehr, W., 135[58], (137)
Leigh, G. J., 194[136], (199)
Lennarz, W. J., 71[48], (84)
Letsinger, R. L., 41[94b], (55), 63[37], 71[47], (84)
Lever, A. B. P., 266[29], (273)
Lewis, C. W., 144[22,23], (160)
Lewis, F. M., 138[3], (159)
Lewis, J. W., 259[4], (273)
Leznov, N. S., 226[59], 231[59], 233[63], (254)
Liebau, F., 124[44], (137)
Liebig, J. von, 88[5], (108)
Liehr, W., 194[133], (199)
Lienau, G., 89[20], (109)
Lindqvist, I., 3[2], (18)
Lindvig, P. E., 162[5], (195)
Lions, F., 263[22], (273)
Lippert, K., 185[105,107], 186[107], (198), 232[60], (254)
Lippincott, W. T., 38[83], (55)
Lipscomb, W. N., 4[4], (18), 24[2], (53), 57[1], (83)
Lisner, A., 179[83], (197)
Livingstone, J. G., 23[19b], 48[19b], (53)
Lloyd, L. L., 168[32], (196)
Loeffler, M. H., 144[20], (160)
Loew, G., 158[66], (161)
Longuet-Higgins, H. L., 34[69], 46[69], (54)
Lonsdale, K., 45[105], 48[120], (56)
Lowe, A., 158[64], (161)
Lucken, E. A. C., 99[40], (109)
Lund, E. W., 112[9], (136)
Lund, L. G., 88[7], 102[7], (108)
Lynds, L., 58[7], (83)

McCall, M. A., 132[57], (137)
McCloskey, A. L., 50[128], 52[129], (56)
Maccoll, A., 93[28], 94[28], 105[28], (109)
McConnell, R. L., 129[53], 130[53], 132[57], (137)
McCusker, P. A., 70[42,43], (84), 180[86] (197)
MacDiarmid, A. G., 32[63,64a], (54), 164[19], 183[97], 185[19,98], (195, 198), 221[37,38], 222[42], 224[37], (253)
McDonald, W. S., 36[33b], 51[33b], (53)
McDowell, W. J., 28[52], (54)
McGeachin, H. McD., 97[36], 103[36], (109)
MacGillavry, C. H., 121[37a], (137)
McGregor, R. R., 74[71,76], (85), 138[2], (159), 227[49,50], (254)
McHard, J. A., 149[29], (160)
Machus, F. F., 170[43], (196)
Magnusson, E. A., 93[29], 105[29], 106[46], (109)
Mahler, W., 5[8], (19)

Majumdar, M. K., 23[10a,10b], 35[10b], 36[10b], 50[10a,10b,94e], (52, 55)
Makowski, H. S., 70[42], (84)
Malatesta, L., 186[111], (198)
Malmberg, P. R., 60[20], (84)
Malowan, J. E., 128[50,51], (137)
Malz, H., 117[22], (136)
Mann, T., 135[62], (137)
Mark, H. F., 173[58], (196), 211[18], 230[53], (253, 254)
Martell, A. E., 271[50], (274)
Martin, F. S., 227[51], (254)
Martin, K. V., 263[22], 266[28], 271[28], (273)
Martin, M. M., 262[16], 264[25], (273)
Martini, H., 25[25a], 27[25a], (53)
Marvel, C. S., 60[26], (84), 262[15,16], 263[21], 264[25], 270[21], 271[21,45], (273, 274)
Mattiello, J. J., 60[13], (83)
Ma Zhui-Zhan, 44[100a], (56)
Meads, J. A., 170[36], (196)
Meals, R. N., 138[3], (159)
Meller, A., 191[125], (198)
Mendelsohn, M., 270[42], (274)
Messner, J., 114[18], 115[18], 117[18], (136)
Metlesics, W., 163[14], (195), 236[66], (254)
Meuwsen, A., 120[34], (137)
Meyer, G., 75[82a], (85)
Michel, A., 163[11], 164[11], (195)
Mikhailov, B. M., 20[3], 23[20b], 26[47b], 27[47b], 37[78,79,80a], 48[3,47b], 49[3], (52, 53, 54, 55)
Minami, S., 213[24], (253)
Mitin, Yu. V., 259[6], (273)
Moerman, N. F., 163[8], (195)
Moews, P. C., 27[33], 30[33], 36[33], (53)
Mohler, F. L., 77[89], (86)
Mooney, E. F., 37[51a], (54), 61[30], (84)
Morgan, W. L., 42[96], (55), 60[23], (84)
Mortimer, C. T., 100[43], (109)
Mountfield, B. A., 24[85b], (55), 61[33,34], (84)
Mozgova, K. K., 162[4], 163[4], (195)
Muetterties, E. L., 41[92], (55)
Mulliken, R. S., 46[112], (56)
Murphy, C. M., 144[19], (160)
Musgrave, O. C., 23[11], 24[22], (52, 53), 63[38,40], 65[38], (84)
Muthmann, W., 116[20], (136)

Nakagawa, T., 46[109], (56)
Nametkin, N. S., 170[43], (196)
Narisada, M., 46[109], (56)
Nebergall, W. H., 171[48], (196)
Nesmeyanov, A. N., 176[73], (197)
Newman, M. S., 188[116], (198)
Newsom, H. C., 52[129], (56)
Neuman, W. F., 261[8], (273)
New, N., 149[30,31], (160)
Nicklas, A., 25[25a], 27[25a], (53)
Niedenzu, K., 39[86], 40[86], 41[92], 48[115], (55, 56), 127[47], 128[49], (137)
Nielsen, M. L., 113[13], 130[54], (136, 137)
Nijimoto, E., 73[68], (85)
Nitzskhe, S., 229[52], (254)
Nogina, O. V., 176[73], (197)
Nojimoto, E., 72[67], (85)
Normant, H., 71[56], (85)
Nöth, H., 50[94d], (55)
Nyholm, R. S., 93[28], 94[28], 105[28], 106[46], (109)

O'Brien, J. F., 182[94], (197), 221[36], (253)
Ogle, P. R., 38[83], (55)
Olin, A. D., 43[98b], (55)
Orgel, L. E., 93[28], 94[28], 105[28], (109), 268[39], (274)
Orlov, N. F., 173[60], 174[67], 175[67,70], 178[70,77], 180[128], 189[122], 193[128], (196, 197, 198)
Ostdick, T., 180[86], (197)
Osthoff, R. C., 23[9,12], (52)
Otto, R. J. A., 90[22,24], (109)

Packer, E. A., 157[62], (161)
Packler, K., 271[47], (274)
Paddock, N. L., 87[1,3], 88[47], 90, 91[3], 93[4], 94, 95, 96[4], 98[3], 99[38], 101, 102[7], (108, 109)
Paine, D. H., 87[3], 90[25], 91[3,25], 98[3], 101, (108, 109)
Pantsios, A. A., 128[49,51], (137)
Paquin, A. M., 119[30], (136)
Parini, V. P., 162[3], (115)
Park, J. C., 71[61], (85), 172[54], (196)
Park T. O., 63[38], 65[38], (84)
Parry, R. W., 24[24], 27[35,38,39], 28[24], 29[50], 38[81], (53, 54, 55)
Parsons, T. D., 71[55], (85)

Patnode, W. I., 74[74], (85), 118[119], 193[119], (198), 238[71], (254)
Patterson, T. R., 212[20], (253), 265[27], (273)
Pavlick, F. J., 212[20], (253), 265[27], (273)
Pavlov, S. A., 205[9], (252)
Pauson, P. L., 266[32], (274)
Peake, J. S., 171[48], (196)
Pearce, C. A., 50[125], (56)
Pease, R. S., 30[56], 45[56], (54)
Pecjak, F. A., 60[20], (84)
Peeler, R. L., 152[44], (160)
Pellicciotto, A. M., 40[88], 41[88], (55)
Petrashko, A. I., 207[13], (252)
Petree, H. E., 173[64], 174[64], (197)
Pettit, R., 21[2], 41[94c], 51[94c], (52, 55)
Pflugmacher, A., 28[45], (54)
Pierce, O. R., 150[37], (160)
Pietrusza, E. W., 167[24], 168[24], 188[117], (195, 198), 201[2], (252)
Pike, R. A., 150[40], (160)
Platt, J. R., 46[110,111], (56)
Plieth, K., 124[44], (137)
Pohland, E., 27[32], 28[32], 30[32], (53)
Polmanteer, K. E., 149[29], (160)
Pompa, F., 97[27], (109)
Ponomarenko, V. A., 236[67], (254)
Popp, R., 125[45a], (137)
Porter, R. F., 27[33], 30[33], 36[33], (53)
Post, H. W., 240[76], (254)
Power, D. B., 153[45], (161)
Powles, J. G., 159[69], (161)
Price, F. P., 188[115], (198)
Price, W. C., 34[69], 46[69], (54)
Prins, J. A., 6[9], (19)
Prober, M., 156[52], (161)
Proctor, J. E., 88[7,8], 89[8], 102[7], (108)
Prokai, B., 32[64b], 44[64b], (54)
Prosen, E. J., 99[41], (109)
Pudovik, A. N., 186[112], (198)
Pummer, W. J., 9[15], (19)
Pyszora, H., 32[101], 33[67], 34[70,71], 36[101], 44[67,101], 45[70], 46[70,71,101], 50[70,101], (54, 56), 61[34], (84)

Quill, L. L., 38[83], (55)
Quinn, E., 77[89], (86)

Raistrick, B., 97[32], (109)
Ramaswamy, K. L., 48[119], (56)
Randolph, C. L., 23[27], 25[27], (53)
Rassweiller, J. H., 262[15], (273)
Rätz, R., 90[23], (109), 122[39b], (137)
Rausch, M. D., 267[34], (274)
Rauscher, W. H., 259[7], (273)
Rector, C. W., 46[111], (56)
Rice, R. G., 89[11], 90[11], (108)
Richter, H., 58[5], (83)
Rinehart, K. L. 267[35], (274)
Ripamonti, A., 97[27], (109)
Rippere, R. E., 61[31], (84)
Ritter, D. M., 27[31], 35[73], (53, 54), 71[55], (85)
Robinson, R., 170[37], (196)
Robinson, T. S., 34[69], 46[69], (54)
Roche, M. P., 167[25], (195)
Rochow, E. G., 74[75], (85), 88[9], (108), 138[1], (159), 163[13], 168[31], 182[30], 192[30], (195, 196), 220[33], 235[65], (253, 254)
Römer, G., 88[6], (108)
Roos, G., 117[22], (136)
Roothaan, C. C. J., 46[112], (56)
Rosenberg, S. D., 163[15], (195), 222[40], (253)
Rossini, F. D., 99[41], (109)
Rudner, B., 40[89], 41[89], (55)
Rüdorff, G., 7[13], (19)
Rüdorff, W., 7[12,13], (19)
Ruff, O., 7[11], (19)
Ruigh, W. L., 43[98b], 51[127], (55, 56), 71[53], (85)
Rust, J. B., 42[95], (56), 177[76], 178[76], 182[95], (197), 211[19,93], 216[19,29,30], 217[29], 218[29], 221[29], (253, 255)
Rutkowski, A. J., 70[43], (84)
Rutovsky, B. N., 186[110], (198)
Ryschkewitsch, G. E., 35[75], 46[112], (55, 56)

Sabun, L. A., 226[59], 231[59], 233[63], (254)
Saffer, C. M., 171[47], (196)
Safford, M. M., 60[21], 74[78,79], (84, 85)
Saito, Y., 261[10], (273)
Saji, A., 46[112], (56)
Saliba, S., 113[14], (136)
Salzberg, P. L., 60[27,28], (84)
Sambeth, J., 125[45], 127[46], (137)
Sass, R. L., 112[9], (136)
Sauer, R. O., 171[46], 185[100], (196, 198)
Saunders, C. E., 144[19], (160)

Saunders, J. H., 158[65], (161)
Saylor, J. C., 150[37], (160)
Sazanova, V. A., 71[54], (85)
Scala, L. E., 144[20], (160)
Schaaf, R. L., 267[36], (274)
Schaeffer, G. W., 27[36,37], 35[76], 46[110,111], (53, 55, 56)
Schaeffer, R., 25[25b], 27[25b], 32[65], 35[76], (53, 54, 55)
Schafer, H. G., 179[83], (197)
Schechter, W. H., 70[44], (84)
Scheinost, K., 71[59,60], (85), 181[90], 189[123], (197, 198), 225[44], 234[64], (253, 254)
Schenck, R., 88[6], (108)
Schenk, J., 6[9], (19)
Schenk, P. W., 111[3], 113[15], (136)
Schiff, H., 60[8], (83)
Schlenker, F., 263[18], (273)
Schlesinger, H. I., 27[31], 28[40], 35[73,76], 36, (53, 54, 55)
Schmack, L., 182[93], (197), 220[34], (253)
Schmidbaur, H., 185[99], 186[99], 187[114], 188[121], 192[126,127], 194[131,132], (198, 199), 224[43], 233[62], 237[68a], (253, 254)
Schmidt, F. C., 188[119], 193[119], (198), 238[71], (254)
Schmidt, M., 185[99], 186[99], 187[114], 188[121], 192[126,127], 194[131,132], (198, 199), 224[43], 233[62], 237[68a], (253, 254)
Schoeller, K., 186[109], (198)
Schmulder, P., 166[21], (195)
Schultz, D. R., 27[39], (54)
Schulze, J., 135[63], (137)
Schumb, W. C., 171[47], (196)
Schupp, L. J., 40[87], (55)
Schuster, K., 22[6,7], 23[6,7], (52)
Schwarz, R., 114[18], 115[18], 117[18], (136), 186[109], (198)
Scott, F. L., 119[29], 120[29], (136)
Scott, N., 173[61], (196)
Searle, H. T., 87[1,3], 88[7], 89[12], 90[25], 91[3,12,25], 92[12], 99[38], 101, 102[7], (108, 109)
Sedlak, M., 43[98b], (55), 71[53], (85)
Seel, F., 90[21], 97[31], (109)
Segal, C. L., 182[95], (197), 211[19,93], 216[19,29], 217[29], 218[29], 221[29], (253, 255)
Seitter, E., 116[20], (136)
Seyferth, D., 75[81], (85)
Shaw, R. A., 89[14], 91[14], (108)
Shearer, N. H., 129[53], 130[53], (137)
Sheina, V. E., 259[5], (273)
Sheldon, J. C., 26[47a], 27[47a], 45[47a], 49[47a], (54)
Shepp, A., 23[21a], (53)
Shkapenko, G., 71[61], (85), 172[54], (196)
Shore, S. G., 27[35,38], (53)
Signaigo, F. K., 60[28], (84)
Sillén, L. G., 163[12], (195)
Silver, A. H., 48[117], (56)
Silverman, M. B., 71[55], (85)
Simmler, W., 240[78], 242[78], (254)
Singh, A., 179[135], 180[135], 182[135], (199)
Singleterry, C. R., 146[26], (160)
Sisler, H. H., 35[75], (55)
Skinner, H. A., 22[4a,4b], 44[4a,4b], (52)
Skoog, I., 63[37], (84)
Skorik, Yu. L., 185[104], 187[104], (198)
Sleddon, G. J., 144[17], (160)
Slonimskii, G. L., 247[87], (255)
Slota, P. J., 78[94,95], 80[101], (86)
Smalley, J. H., 35[74], (54), 89[15a], (109)
Smith, A. R., 153[45], (161)
Smith, B. C., 26[47a], 27[47a], 45[47a], 48[47a], (54), 60[17], (84)
Smith, D. C., 144[19], (160)
Smith, D. R., 87[3], 90[25], 91[3,25], 98[3], 101, (108, 109)
Smith, H. O., 119[29], 120[29], (136)
Smith, N. B., 22[4a,4b], 44[4a,4b], (52)
Snyder, H. R., 71[48], (84)
Solms, J., 41[92], (55), 60[19], (84)
Sommer, L. H., 107[48], (109), 167[24], 168[24,27], 174[65], 179[65], 188[117,118], (195, 197, 198), 201[2], (252)
Sowerby, D. B., 163[10], (195), 260
Spasskii, S. S., 178[78], (197)
Spiess, W., 114[18], 115[18], 117[18], (136)
Springall, H. D., 99[42], (109)
Sprung, M. M., 74[70], (85), 181[91], 184[91], (197), 240[82,83], 242[82], 244[83], (255)
Stackelberg, M., 271[47], (274)
Stafiej, S. F., 35[74], 51[136], (54, 56)
Staudinger, H., 89[17], (109)
Stavitskii, I. K., 204[7], 236[67], (252, 254)
Steger, E., 135[61], (137)
Steinberg, H., 50[128], (56)
Steindler, M. J., 28[40], (54)
Steinman, R., 87[1], (108)

Stern, D. R., 58[7], 78[92], (83, 86)
Stewart, R. D., 78[92], (86)
Stock, A., 25[25a], 27[25a,32], 28[32,43], 30[32], 45[106], (53, 56)
Stokes, H. N., 88[2], 89[18], 91[2], (108, 109), 133[58a], (137)
Stone, B. D., 113[13], (136)
Stone, F. G. A., 28[41], 30[57], (53, 54), 57[2], 58[4], 82[106], (83, 86)
Stout, L. E., 60[14], (84)
Stratton, C., 89[14], 91[14], (108)
Strickson, J. A., 181[87,88], (197)
Strother, C. O., 142[8], (160)
Sturm, W., 83[107], (86)
Sujishi, S., 32[63], (54)
Sun, K. H., 60[20], (84)
Sutton, L. E., 93[28], 94[28], 105[28], (109)
Suvorov, A. L., 178[78], (197)
Svendsen, S. R., 112[9], (136)
Sviridova, N. G., 236[67], (254)

Takimoto, H. H., 177[76], 178[76], 182[95], (197), 211[19,93], 216[19,29,30], 217[29], 218[29], 221[29], (253, 255)
Tamborski, C., 240[76], (254)
Tarköy, N., 263[21], 270[21], 271[21], (273)
Tatlock, W. S., 168[30,31], 182[30], 193[30], (196), 220[33], (253)
Teach, E., 81[85], (85)
Tesi, G., 89[16a], (109)
Tewkesbury, E. J., 152[42], (160)
Thamer, R., 89[13b], 91[13b], (108)
Thilo, E., 122[39,39a,39b], 123[40,41], 124[42,44], 127[40], (137)
Thomas, I. M., 175[68,69], 176[69,74], 177[69,74], 179[68], 190[68,69], 191[69,74], (197)
Thomas, J. R., 60[18], (84)
Thomas, L. H., 60[16], (83)
Thomas, W. M., 71[49,50,51], (85)
Thompson, J. M. C., 24[22], (53)
Thümmler, K., 111[3], (136)
Tilley, B. P., 24[85a], 39[85a], (55)
Toor, E. W., 48[120], (56)
Toribara, T. Y., 261[8], (273)
Topchiev, A. V., 170[43], (196)
Toy, A. D. F., 87[1], (108)
Traube, W., 120[34], (137)
Trefonas, L. M., 23[21c], (53)
Tromans, F. R., 97[36], (109)
Truhlar, J., 128[49,51], (137)
Tsao, I., 142[11], (160)
Tucker, H., 71[61], (85), 172[54], (196)
Turner, H. S., 26[33a,48], 36[33b,48], 51[33a,33b,48], (53, 54)
Tyler, L. J., 169[34], (196), 240[79], (254)

Ulmschneider, O., 41[94a], (55)
Underwood, A. L., 261[8], (273)
Upson, R. W., 42[97], 43[98a], 44[97], (55), 72[66], (85)

Vale, R. L., 74[69], (85)
Van Artsdalen, E. R., 44[102], (56)
Van Wazer, J. R., 5[6], (18), 122[38], 124[43], (137), 164[18], (195)
Vogl, O., 162[6], (195)
Vogt, L. H., 242[86], 247[86], (255)
Voigt, D., 113[12], (136)
Voigt, G., 114[17], (136)
Volkova, L. M., 71[63], (85), 181[89], (197), 225[45], (254)
Voronkov, M. G., 71[65], (85), 173[59], 178[77], 179[82,128], 185[101,102,103,104], 186[101,102,103], 187[104], 189[122], 193[128], (196, 197, 198), 225[46], 226[46], 230[58], 231[58], (254)
Vries, T. A. de, 97[35], (109)

Wachters, L. H. J., 6[9], (19)
Wade, K., 25[29], 28[29], (53)
Wagner, G. H., 142[8,10], (160)
Wagner, R. I., 36[67a], 37[67b], 39[67b], (54), 76[87,88], 78[90,91], 79[96,97], 81[97,104], (86)
Wall, L. A., 77[89], (86)
Wallis, J. W., 49[123], (56)
Walther, H. A., 120[33], (136)
Wannagat, U., 194[133], (199)
Wardlaw, W., 213[25], (253)
Warne, R. J., 26[33a], 36[33b], 51[33a,33b], (53)
Warrick, E. L., 74[71,76], (85), 227[49], (254)
Wartik, T., 59[6], (83)
Watanabe, H., 46[109], 48[116,118,119,121], (56)
Watt, J. A. C., 153[46,47], (161)
Watt, W. J., 60[17], (84)
Wazer, J. R. van, 5[6], (18), 122[38], 124[43], (137), 164[18], (195)
Weiss J., 112[8], (136)
Wells, A. F., 2[1], 3[2,3], 4[5], (18)

Wentorf, R. H., 27[58,60], 30[8], 31[58,60], (54)
West, C. D., 60[25], (84)
West, R., 167[26], (195)
Westrick, R., 121[37a], (137)
Weyenberg, D. R., 107[48], (109)
White, R. F. M., 90[25], 91[25], 106[47], (109)
White, T. R., 99[42], (109)
Whitehead, M. A., 99[40], (109)
Whitehead, W. G., 142[10], (160)
Whitehouse, D. B., 140[6], (160)
Whitmore, F. C., 167[24], 168[24,27], 188[117,118], (195, 198), 201[2], (252)
Wiberg, E., 20[1], 22[6,7], 23[6,7,13,15,16,17], 23[20a], 25[25a,26], 27[16,25a,34], 28[16], 29[34,49,54], 30[16], 35[34], (52, 53, 54), 71[58], 83[107], (85, 86), 172[53], 180[84], (196, 197), 240[78], 242[78], (254)
Wick, M., 74[80], (85), 151[41], (160), 225[47], 227[47], 228[47], 229[52], 250[47], (254)
Wieker, W., 123[40], 127[40], (137)
Wierl, R., 45[106], (56)
Wilke, G., 267[37], (274)
Wilkins, J. P., 258[2], 259[2], (273)
Wilkinson, G., 266[31], 269[31], (273)
Williams, R. J. P., 269[40], (274)
Williams, T. C., 150[40], (160)
Wilson, A., 92[27], 97[27], (109)
Wilson, C. O., 78[93], (86)
Wittbecker, E. L., 258[2], 259[2], (273)
Woggon, H., 122[39b], (137)
Wood, J. F., 157[62], (161)
Woods, W. G., 52[129], (56), 172[56], 173[57], (196), 211[16,17], (253)
Wright, H. R., 131[56], (137)
Wright, J. G. E., 74[72], (85)
Wurster, C. W., 124[44], (137)

Yolles, S., 78[84], (85)
Young, M. A., 36[33b], 51[33b], (53)

Zamyatina, V. A., 44[100a,100b], (56)
Zappel, A., 150[34], (160)
Zeiss, H., 163[14], (195), 236[66], (254)
Zeitler, V. A., 174[66], 175[66], 168[66], (197), 249[92], (255)
Zenftman, H., 131[56], (137)
Zgonnik, V. N., 71[65], (85), 179[82], 180[82], 185[102,103], 186[102,103], (197, 198), 225[46], 226[46], 230[58], 231[58], (254)
Zhdanov, A. A., 164[134], 168[29], 170[41], 172[52], 174[52], 178[52], 189[130], 193[129,130], 194[130], (196, 198, 199), 202[4,5,6], 204[8], 205[9,10,11,12], 208[14], 209[4,5,6,15], 210[15], 214[4,5,6], 224[12], 238[72], 249[90], 250[90], 251[91], (252, 253, 254, 255)
Zolotov, Yu. M., 119[32], (136)
Zuech, E. A., 142[12], (160)
Zueva, G. Ya., 236[67], (254)

INDEX OF COMPOUNDS

Compounds are classified under 6 main headings: (i) boron compounds; (ii) phosphorus compounds; (iii) silicon compounds; (iv) sulphur compounds; (v) compounds of other elements; and (vi) metal chelate polymers and related compounds (classified according to ligand).

Boron Compounds

B 57
B_2Al 4

Boranes and Haloboranes

B_2H_6 25, 27, 28, 30, 57, 78, 79, 81, 82, 83
B_4H_{10} 57
B_5H_9 23, 28, 57, 79, 80, 81
B_5H_{11} 57
B_6H_{10} 57
$B_{10}H_{14}$ 57
$BH_2(CHRCH_2O)_nH$ 58
BBr_3 70
BCl_3 70
B_2Hal_4 4
B_4Cl_4 4, 58
BF_3 70
$BHCl_2$ 58, 59
$(BBr)_n$ 28

Alkyl- and Aryl-Boranes and -Haloboranes

BMe_3, 35, 70
$B(C_2H_2Ph)_4K$, 71
BMe_2Br, 77
BPh_nCl_{3-n} 44
$BPhCl_2$ 62, 75
$B(C_6H_4OMe)Cl_2$ 62
$B(C_6H_4NH_2)Cl_2$ 41
$(BCl_2CH_2)_2$ 58, 59
$(BCl_2CH)_2$ 58
$BPhF_2$ 73

Borinic esters

$B(C_6H_4OMe)ClOC_6H_4BCl_2$ 62
$BPh(OAr)Cl$ 62
$BR(OR)Cl$ 70
$B(OR)Cl_2$ 70

Boronic Acids and Esters

$B(OH)_2R$ 60
$B(OH)_2C_2H_3$ 71
$B(OH)_2CH_2CHCH_2$ 71
$B(OH)_2CHCHCl$ 71
$BPh(OH)_2$ 64, 75
$B(OH)_2C_6H_4C_2H_3$ 70, 71
$B(OH)_2C_6H_4Et$ 71
$BH(OEt)_2$ 58
$BH(OCHMe_2)_2$ 58
$BPh(OCH_2)_2$ 63
$BPh(OCH_2)_2CMe_2$ 64
$BPh(OCH.CMe_3)_2$ 63
$BPh(OCH_2CH_2)_2NH$ 63, 64, 65
$BPh(OCHC_5H_4N)_2$ 64
$BC_6H_4X(OCH_2CH_2)_2NH$ 65
$X = Me, Br, OMe, NO_2$
$B(OR)_2Cl$ 70
$BClOC_6H_4O$ 39, 61
$(—BC_6H_4O)_nMeCl_2$ 62
$[B(OH)_2]_2R$ 72
$[B(OH)_2]_2(CH_2)_2$ 73, 74
$[B(OH)_2]_2(CH_2)_4$ 41
$[B(OH)_2]_2(CH_2)_n$ 63, 64
$[B(OH_2)_2]_2C_6H_4$ 41, 63, 64, 73, 74

$[B(OR)_2]_2(CH_2)_4$ 65, 66
[R = C_2H_4, CHMeCHMe, $CHMeCH_2$, C_2Me_4, C_2Ph_4, C_3H_6CHMe, $CH_2CMe_2CH_2$ $CH_2CPh_2CH_2$, $CH_2CMe_2CH(CHMe_2)$, $CH_2C(CH_2Cl)_2CH_2$, $(CH_2)_2C(CH_2O)_2CH_2$, $C_2H_4NHC_2H_4$]
$[B(OCHRCH_2)_2NCH_2CHROH]_2X$ 66, 68, 69
R = H, X = $(CH_2)_4$
R = H, X = p-C_6H_4
R = Me, X = $(CH_2)_4$
$[B(OR)_2]_2C_6H_4$ 65, 67
[R = C_2H_4, $CHMeCH_2$, C_2H_4CHMe, CHMeCHMe, C_2Me_4, $CH_2CMe_2CH(CHMe_2)$, o-C_6H_4, $C_2H_4NHC_2H_4$, $C_2H_4NMeC_2H_4$, $CH_2CMe_2CH_2$, $CH_2C(CH_2Cl)_2CH_2$]
$[B(OCH_2)_2CEtCH_2OH]_2C_6H_4$ 69, 70
$[B(OCH_2)_2R(CH_2O)_2BX]_n$ 68, 69
R = C, X = $(CH_2)_4$
R = C, X = p-C_6H_4
R = CH_2—CH_2 , X = $(CH_2)_4$ or p-C_6H_4
)C C(
CO
$[(CH_2)_nN(CH_2CHRO)_2BXB(OCHRCH_2)_2N]_n$ 65, 66, 67, 68
[n = 6, R = H, X = $(CH_2)_4$
n = 6, R = H, X = p-C_6H_4
n = 2, R = Me, X = $(CH_2)_4$
n = 2, R = Me, X = p-C_6H_4]

Oxides, Boric Acids and Esters

$(B_2O_2)_n$ 59
$B_2(OH)_4$ 59
$[BOCH_2CH(OH)CH_2O]_2O$ 61
$B(OCH_2CH_2)_3N$ 63
$[B(OC_6H_4O)]_2OC_6H_4O$ 61
$[B(OCH_2)_2OCH_2]_2$ 60, 61
$(BOBu^n)_n$ 70
$(BO_2C_6H_3O)_n$ 62

Boroxoles

$(BOR)_3$ 70
$(BOBu^n)_3$ 70
$(BOPh)_3$ 43
$(BOC_6H_4C_2H_3)_3$ 71
$(BOC_6H_4Et)_3$ 71
$(BOC_6H_4CHBrCH_3)_3$ 71
$(BOBr)_3$ 70
$(BOCl)_3$ 70
$(BOF)_3$ 70
$[BO(OR)]_3$ 39
$[BO(OMe)]_3$ 38
$(BONHMe)_3$ 38
$(BONMe_2)_3$ 38, 70
$[B_3O_3(OR)pyO]_n$ 39
$[B_3O_3(OMe)_2]_2NPh$ 39
$[B_3O_3(OMe)NPh]_n$ 39
$[B_3O_3(NMe)_{1.5}]_n$ 38, 52

BORON-NITROGEN COMPOUNDS

Aminoboranes and Three-Coordinate Boron Derivatives

$B(NH_2)_3$ 15, 28
$B(NHR)_3$ 45, 46, 50
$B(NHPr^i)_3$ 50
$B(NR_2)_3$ 45, 46, 50
$B(NMe_2)_3$ 44, 45, 70
$B(NEt_2)_3$ 50
$B(NBu_2)_3$ 50
$B(NHAr)_3$ 45, 46
$B(NHPh)_3$ 44
$B(NHC_6H_2Br_3)_3$ 49
$B(NRAr)_3$ 45, 46, 49
$B(NMePh)_3$ 49, 51
$B(NHBu^t)(NPr^i_2)_2$ 50
$BPh(NMe_2)_2$ 47
$B(NMe_2)_2Cl$ 44
$B(NPr^i_2)_2Cl$ 50
$BX[NPh(C{:}O.Y)_2]$ 44
$BMe_2.NMe_2$ 45, 48
$BPh_2.NMe_2$ 48
$BPhCl.NMe_2$ 46, 47
$BCl_2.NMe_2$ 44
$BF_2.NMe_2$ 23, 29
$BMe_2.NMePh$ 46
$BPh_2.NPh_2$ 48
$BCl_2.N(SiH_3)_2$ 25
$BH.NH(C_6H_4)_2$ 21
$(BH_2.NMe)_2$ 24, 28
$B_2(NH)_3$ 27, 28
$[(BO_2C_6H_4)NH]_2SO_2$ 39
$(B_2NH)_n$ 28

$[BCl(C_6H_4).NH.C_6H_4]_n$ 41
$[B(Ph)NH.CO.NH(CH_2)_6NH.CO.NH]_n$ 42
$[BH(NMe_2)_2]_n$ 25, 26
$[(B(NH)_2C_6H_3)_2X]_n$ 42, 50
$(BO_2C_6H_4.NRR')_n$ 22, 24

Mononuclear Boron Pseudohalides and Autocomplexes

$B(CN)_3$ 31
$BCN.O_2C_6H_4$ 32
$B(NCS)_nHal_{3-n}$ 33
$(BH_2.CN)_n$ 32
$(BBu^n{}_2.CN)_n$ 32
$(BPh_2.CN)_n$ 32
$[B(NCO)_2.O)Bu^n]_n$ 33
$(BMe_2.NCO)_n$ 32
$(BPh_2.NCO)_n$ 33
$[B(NMe_2)_2.NCO]_n$ 33
$[B(OBu^n)_2.NCO]_n$ 33
$[BNCO.O_2C_6H_4]_n$ 33

Borazans and Addition Polymers of Borazens

$BH_3.NH_2Me$ 28
$BH_3.NMe_3$ 28
$BH_3.NH_2OMe$ 29
$BH_3.NOHRR'$ 38
$BH_3.NCSiH_3$ 32
$BH_3.NCSiMe_3$ 32
$BH_3.NCR$ 25, 26, 28, 32
$BCl_3.NH_2R$ 26
$BCl_3.py$ 49
$BCl_3.NCR$ 49
$BPh_2(CN).py$ 32
$(BH_3.NH_3)_2$ 27, 30
$B_2H_6.2NH_3$ 76
$(BH_3.NHMe)_2$ 28
$B_2H_5.NH_2$ 27
$(BH_2.NH_2)_3$ 25
$(BH_2.NHMe)_3$ 24, 25, 28
$(BH_2.NMe_2)_3$ 23, 28
$(BHCl.NH_2)_3$ 25
$(BH.NH)_3.3MeOH$ 29
$(BH_2.NH_2)_n$ 24, 26, 27, 28, 30
$(BH_2.NR_2)_n$ 22, 23
$(BH_2.NMe_2)_n$ 23, 24, 25, 28
$[BH_2.N(SiH_3)_2]_n$ 25
$(BH_2.N:CHR)_n$ 26
$(BH_2.N:CHCH_3)_n$ 25
$(BH_2.NRR'.O)_n$ 38
$(BHMe.NMe_2)_n$ 22, 23
$[BH.N(SiH_3)_2]_2$ 25
$(BR_2.NH_2)_n$ 22, 23
$(BMe_2.NH_2)_n$ 23
$(BPh_2.NH_2)_n$ 23
$(BR_2.NHMe)_n$ 22, 23
$(BMe_2.NHMe)_n$ 23
$(BPh_2.NHMe)_n$ 23
$(BXX'.NYY')_n$ 22
$(BHal_2.NR_2)_n$ 22, 23
$(BBr_2.NMe_2)_n$ 23
$(BCl_2.NMe_2)_n$ 22, 23

Borazoles

$(BX.NY)_3$ 20, 21, 26, 51
$(BH.NH)_3$ 26, 27, 35, 45, 48
$(BH.NMe)_3$ 35, 45
$(BX.NAr)_3$ 36, 37, 50
$(BH.NPh)_3$ 35
$B_3MeH_2.N_3H_3$ 35
$B_3RH_2.N_3Me_3$ 35
$B_3RH_2.N_3Ph_3$ 35
$B_3Me_2H.N_3H_3$ 35
$B_3R_2H.N_3Me_3$ 35
$B_3R_2H.N_3Ph_3$ 35
$B_3MeEtH.N_3Ph_3$ 35
$(BR.NR')_3$ 37
$(BMe.NH)_3$ 35
$(BMe.NMe)_3$ 52
$(BMe.NPh)_3$ 29, 51, 52
$B_3Me_3.N_3Me_2Li$ 37
$(BCH_2CHCl.NH)_3$ 51
$B_3Me_2Bu.N_3Ph_3$ 35
$B_3Pr^nEtMe.N_3Ph_3$ 35
$(BPh.NH)_3$ 51, 52
$(BPh.NMe)_3$ 51, 52
$(BAr.NR)_3$ 37
$(BAr.NAr')_3$ 37
$(BPh.NPh)_3$ 52
$B_3N_3(C_6H_4X)_3$ 41
$B_3R_2Hal.N_3Me_3$ 35
$BMe_2Cl.N_3Me_3$ 35, 39
$B_3RHal_2.N_3Me_3$ 35
$(BHal.NH)_3$ 15
$(BCl.NH)_3$ 15, 32, 35, 36, 44
$(BCl.NR)_3$ 26, 36
$(BCl.NPh)_3$ 41
$B_3(NCO)Cl_2.N_3H_3$ 36

$B_3(NCO)_2Cl.N_3H_3$ 36
$(BNCO.NH)_3$ 33
$(BCN.NH)_3$ 32
$(BNH_2.NH)_3$ 35
$(BNHR.NH)_3$ 15
$(BNHBu^n.NH)_3$ 35
$(BNHR.NR')_3$ 33, 34, 35, 36
$B_3(NR_2)(NHR')_2.N_3R_3''$ 36
$B_3(NR_2)_2(NHR').N_3R_3''$ 36
$(BNEt_2.NH)_3$ 37
$[B(NHCONR'R'').NR]_3$ 43
$B_3(NR_2)_3.N_3R_3'$ 36
$B_3(OR)(HNR')_2.N_3R_3''$ 35
$B_3(OR)_2(HNR').N_3R''_3$ 35
$(BOMe.NH)_3$ 29
$(BOBu^n.NEt)_3$ 37
$[BO(:O)P(OR)_2.NH]_3$ 40
$[BO(:O)P(OR)_2.NR]_3$ 40
$[BCl.NH.O:P(OR)_3]_3$ 39
$[B_3(NHR)_2NR_3]_2NR$ 34, 35
$(B_3X_2.NEt_3)_2NEt$ 36, 37
$(B_3Me_2.NMe_3]_2O$ 39
$B_5N_5H_8$ 27, 30
$B_6N_6H_{10}$ 27, 30, 36, 37
$(BN)_n$ 21, 27, 28, 29, 30, 31, 45, 48, 52
$(B.NH)_n$ 27, 30
$(B_3NHR)NR.N_3R_3)_n$ 33, 34
$[B_3(NR)_{1.5}N_3R_3]_n$ 33, 34
$[B_3NEt)_{1.5}N_3Et_3]_n$ 33, 34
$[B_3Cl_3.N_3(C_6H_4)_{1.5}]_n$ 40
$[B_3(NHR)NR.N_3H_3]_n$ 15

Borazocines

$(BX.NY)_4$ 26, 51
$(BH.NR)_4$ 28
$(BCl.NBu^t)_4$ 26, 27, 28
$(BNCS.NBu^t)_4$ 26, 27

Polyborazens

$(BH.NR)_5$ 28
$(BX.NY)_n$ 26
$(BH.NH)_n$ 27, 29
$(BH.NOMe)_n$ 29
$(BPh.NBu^n)_n$ 16, 29, 37
$(BPh.NBu^i)_n$ 37
$(BF.NMe)_n$ 28

Miscellaneous Boron-Nitrogen Compounds

$(B_4H_4.NMe_3)_n$ 28
$[(BCl_2^-)_2N^+(CH_2)_4N^+]_n$ 24
$(BCl_2.NH.C_6H_4.NH_3)^+BCl_4^-$ 40

ARSENIC-BORON COMPOUNDS

$AsH_2Me.BH_3$ 82
$AsHMe_2.BH_3$ 82
$(AsMe_2BH_2)_3$ 82
$(AsMe_2BH_2)_4$ 82
$(AsH_4B)_n$ 82
$(AsH_3BMe)_n$ 82
$(AsMe_2BH_2)_n$ 82

PHOSPHORUS-BORON COMPOUNDS

$PH_2.BMe_2$ 77
$(PH_2.BMe_2)_n$ 77
$(PHMe.BH_2)_n$ 76, 82
$PR_2.BH_2$ 78
$(PMe_2.BH_2)_3$ 16, 76, 77, 78, 80, 81
$(PMe_2.BH_2)_4$ 76, 77, 80, 81
$[(PMe_2.BH_2)_2]_2PMe.BH$ 78
$(PMe_2.BH_2)_n(NR_3)_2$ 81
$(PMe_2.BR_2)_n$ 79
$(PMe_2.BMe_2)_3$ 77, 79
$(PMe_2.BHal_2)_3$ 78
$(PMe_2.BF_2)_3$ 78
$(PMeEt.BH_2)_n$ 81, 82
$(PMePr.BH_2)_n$ 82
$(PEt_2.BH_2)_n$ 82
$[P(C_6H_{11})_2.BH_2]_3$ 79
$[P(CF_3)_2.BH_2]_3$ 16, 79
$(PH_3)_2B_2H_6$ 76
$PH_2Me.BH_3$ 76
$PHMe_2.BH_3$ 16, 76, 81
$PHMe_2.BHMe_2$ 77
$PHR_2.BHal_3$ 78
$P_2Me_4.BH_3$ 80
$P_2Me_4.2BH_3$ 80
$P(O)H(OR)_2.BCl_3$ 75
$P(O)(OR)_3.BCl_3$ 76
$P(O)H(OR)OBCl_2$ 75
$[P(O)H(OBCl_2)O]_2BCl$ 75
$[(P_4Me_2)_4B_{10}H_9]_n$ 80
$[(PMe_2)_2(B_9H_8)(NMe_2)]_n$ 80
$[(PMe_2)_2N_4B_{15}H_9]_n$ 81

$(PBH_{3.75})_n$ 76
$(PBO_4)_n$ 75, 76
$(PHO_3BPh)_n$ 75
$[P(O)OBN]_n$ 129

For other boron compounds containing SILICON and SULPHUR, see under the appropriate elements (pp. 294 and 298, respectively)

Phosphorus Compounds

P_4 5

Phosphines, Phosphorus Halides, Complex Halides and Pseudo-halides

P_2H_4 5
PCl_4^+ 132
PCl_6^- 132
$[PCl_6]NH_4$ 89
PF_6^- 110
P_2Hal_4 5
P_2Cl_6 135
P_2Cl_{10} 132, 133

Phosphorus Alkyls and Aryls

PH_2Ph 5
$PH(CF_3)_2$ 5, 79
PMe_3 77
P_2Me_4 80
$P_2(CF_3)_4$ 5
$(PCF_3)_4$ 5
$(PPh)_4$ 5
$(PCF_3)_5$ 5
$(PHCHMeCH_2)_nPH_3$ 81

Alkyl- and Aryl-Phosphorus Halides

PR_2Hal 78
PR_2N_3 89
$PPhCl_2$ 5
PCF_3I_2 5
PH_2R_2Hal 78
PPh_2Cl_3 89

Phosphorus Oxides, Oxyacids, and Oxyanions

P_4O_{10} 2, 123, 126, 127
$P_2O_7H_2$ 126, 127
$(PO_3^-)_3$ 122
$(PO_3^-)_4$ 123
$P_4O_{13}^{6-}$ 122
$(PO_3^-)_n$ 110, 122, 125
$(P_nO_{3n+1})^{(n+2)-}$ 122
$(P_nO_{3n+1}H_2)^{n-}$ 122
$(PO_3NH_4)_n$ 124, 125
$(P_2O_6^{2-}.enH_2^{2+})_n$ 125
PO_4H_2Na 123
$P_2O_7H_2Na_2$ 123
$(PO_3Na)_3$ 123
$(PO_3Na)_n$ 123

Amino- and Aminohalo-Phosphines, and Derivatives

$P(NEt_2)_3$ 100
$PMe_2.NMe_2$ 80
$PNMe_2(C_4H_8)$ 80
PNR_2Cl_2 135
$(PMe_2)_2NH$ 81
$[PNH_2NH]_n$ 135
$(PNR_2NH)_n$ 135
$(PN)_n$ 135

Phosphonitrilic Derivatives

$(PNMe_2)_3$ 89, 92, 98
$(PNPh_2)_3$ 89, 90
$(PNBr_2)_3$ 89, 98
$P_3N_3Br_4Cl_2$ 89
$P_3N_3Br_2Cl_4$ 89
$P_3N_3BrCl_5$ 89, 90, 91
$(PNCl_2)_3$ 12, 87, 88, 89, 90, 91, 97, 98, 99, 100, 102, 106, 107, 133
$P_3N_3Cl_4F_2$ 90, 91, 107
$(PNClF)_3$ 91
$P_3N_3Cl_2F_4$ 107
$(PNF_2)_3$ 90, 92, 97, 98, 99, 101, 102, 103
$(PNClNMe_2)_3$ 91, 107
$[PN(NMe_2)_2]_3$ 98
$(PNpip_2)_3$ 90
$[PN(OH)_2]_3$ 90
$[PN(OMe)_2]_3$ 90

$(PNMe_2)_4$ 89, 91, 97
$(PNPh_2)_4$ 89
$(PNPhCl)_4$ 89, 91
$(PNBr_2)_4$ 89
$(PNCl_2)_4$ 88, 97, 99, 102, 106, 134
$(PNF_2)_4$ 97, 98, 99, 101, 102, 103
$(PNCl_2)_5$ 88
$(PNF_2)_5$ 98, 99, 101, 102, 103
$(PNCl_2)_6$ 88
$(PNF_2)_6$ 91, 98, 99, 101, 102, 103
$(PNCl_2)_7$ 88
$(PNF_2)_7$ 98, 99, 101, 102, 103
$(PNF_2)_8$ 98, 99, 101, 102, 103
$(PNF_2)_9$ 98, 99, 101, 102, 103
$(PNF_2)_{10}$ 98, 99, 101, 102, 103
$(PNF_2)_{11}$ 98, 99, 101, 102, 103
$(PNF_2)_{14}$ 98
$[PN(CF_3)_2]_n$ 89
$(PNHal_2)_n$ 5, 12, 13
$(PNBr_2)_n$ 13
$(PNCl_2)_n$ 12, 13, 14, 87, 88, 90, 92, 101, 106, 132, 133
$(PNF_2)_n$ 13, 98, 99, 101, 102, 103, 104, 105, 108
$(PNCl_2)_nPCl_5$ 12, 88
$(PNNH)_n$ 133, 134
$[PN(NH_2)_2]_n$ 133, 134
$P_9N_7Cl_9$ 91

Phosphoryl Derivatives

$POCl_3$ 131
$P(O)(NCO)_3$ 100
$P(O)CH_2ClCl_2$ 130
$P(O)PhCl_2$ 130, 132
$P(O)R_2Hal$ 78
$P(O)OPhCl_2$ 131
$P(O)(OH)_2NH_2$ 124
$P(O)OH(NH_2)_2$ 126
$P(O)(NH_2)_3$ 127, 128
$P(O)Ph(NH_2)_2$ 129
$P(O)(OH)(NH_2)O^-$ 97
$[P(O)(NH_2)_2]_2O$ 127, 128
$[P(O)(NH_2)_2]_2NH$ 128
$[P(O)(OEt)O]_4$ 122, 123
$[P(O)RO]_n$ 127
$[P(O)RO.R'.O]_n$ 131
$[P(O)PhO.C_6H_4.O]_n$ 131
$[P(O)(OR)O.R'.O]_n$ 131
$[P(O)RNH.R'.NH]_n$ 130
$[P(O)PhNH(CH_2)_6NH]_n$ 130
$[P(O)(OR)NH.R'.NH]_n$ 130
$[P(O)(OPh)NH.R'.NH]_n$ 130, 131
$[P(O)(CH_2Cl)NHCONH]_n$ 130
$[P(O)PhNHCONH]_n$ 130
$[P(O)(NH)O^{-+}NH_4]_n$ 126
$[P(O)RNH)_n$ 127, 129, 130
$[P(O)PhNH]_n$ 129
$[P(O)RNR']_nR'NH_2$ 14
$[P(O)(NH_2)O]_n$ 127
$[P(O)(NH_2)NH]_n$ 127, 135
$[P(O)(NH_2)NH]_nNH_3$ 128
$(PON)_n$ 13, 129
$(P_2O_2N_3H_3)_n$ 128, 129
$(P_2O_5NH^{2-})_n$ 126

Miscellaneous Phosphorus Compounds

PN_2H 132
$PCl_3:NH$ 89
P_3NCl_{12} 132
$[P(NH)NSO_2NH]_n$ 135

For phosphorus compounds containing BORON and SILICON see under these elements (pp. 289 and 295, respectively)

Silicon Compounds

Si_n 4, 139
Si_2Ca 4

Silanes, Halosilanes and Complex Halides

Si_6H_{14} 4, 162
$(SiH_2)_n$ 4
$SiCl_4$ 4, 11, 14, 139
$Si_{10}Cl_{22}$ 4, 162
SiF_4 144
SiF_6^{2-} 110
Si_2I_6 4
$(SiI)_n$ 4
$SiHCl_3$ 11, 141, 142

Alkyl- and Aryl-silanes

$SiPhH_3$ 143, 171

$SiRPhH_2$ 143, 171
$SiRR'PhH$ 143
$SiEt(Am^i)_2H$ 179
$SiPh_3H$ 143
$Si(Me)_4$ 144
$SiPh_4$ 145, 169, 171
$SiMe_3CHCH_2$ 188
$SiRR'R''Ph$ 143

Alkyl- and Aryl-Halosilanes

SiR_2HCl 143, 186
$SiRHCl_2$ 151
$SiMe_3Br$ 180
$SiEt_3Br$ 179, 180, 186
SiR_3Cl 143, 173, 178, 180, 186, 204
$SiMe_3Cl$ 11, 179, 185, 186, 187, 188, 192, 194, 224
$SiEt_3Cl$ 179, 194
$SiPh_3Cl$ 183, 184, 185, 196
SiR_2Cl_2 139, 140, 143, 146, 205, 212, 215, 235
$SiMe_2Cl_2$ 10, 11, 88, 183, 188, 194, 204, 219, 226, 227, 233, 236
$SiEt_2Cl_2$ 219, 230
$SiAr_2Cl_2$ 139
$SiPh_2Cl_2$, 73, 183, 184, 222
$SiR[(CH_2)_nCF_3]Cl_2$ 151
$SiR[(CH_2)_nCN]Cl_2$ 151
$SiRCl_3$ 143, 205, 215, 241
$SiMeCl_3$ 11, 183, 233
$SiEtCl_3$ 206
$Si(CF_2CHF_2)Cl_3$ 11
$Si(CH_2CH_2CF_3)Cl_3$ 11
$SiPhCl_3$ 141, 142, 183, 205, 224, 242
$Si(Tol)Cl_3$ 141
$Si(C_6H_4Ph)Cl_3$ 141
$Si_2R_4Cl_2$ 143

Silyl Perchlorates

$SiR_3(ClO_4)$ 194
$SiEt_3(ClO_4)$ 194
$SiAr_3(ClO_4)$ 194
$SiPh_3(ClO_4)$ 195

Silica and Silicates

SiO_4^{4-} 2
$Si_2O_7^{6-}$ 2
$Si_3O_9^{6-}$ 2
$(SiO_2)_n$ 2
$(SiO_3^{2-})_n$ 110

Silanols

$Si(OH)_3R$ 169, 208, 215
$Si(OH)_3Et$ 204
$Si(OH)_3Ph$ 169, 204, 205
$Si(OH)_2R_2$ 139, 146, 169, 219
$Si(OH)_2Me_2$ 10, 11, 169
$Si(OH)_2Et_2$ 202, 233
$Si(OH)_2Ph_2$ 72, 171, 175, 184, 185, 224, 239
$Si(OH)R_3$ 167, 169, 187, 189, 190, 194
$Si(OH)Me_3$ 167, 168, 171, 174, 175, 176, 180, 190, 191, 193, 214, 238
$Si(OH)Et_3$ 168, 172, 176, 179, 186, 188, 190, 194, 201, 202, 203
$Si(OH)Ar_3$ 167
$Si(OH)Ph_3$ 167, 168, 171, 175, 182, 183

Alkoxysilanes

$Si(OR)_4$ 231
$Si(OMe)_4$ 226
$Si(OPr^n)_4$ 176
$Si(OBu^n)_4$ 181
$Si(OBu^s)_4$ 181
$Si(OCHPhMe)_4$ 181
$Si(OR)_3R'$ 231
$Si(OEt)_3Et$ 231, 232
$Si(OEt)_3Ph$ 243
$Si(OR)_2H_2$ 73
$Si(OR)_2R'_2$ 72, 212, 221, 225
$Si(OMe)_2Ph_2$ 73, 74
$Si(OEt)_2Me_2$ 73, 74, 203, 220, 221, 226, 234
$Si(OEt)_2Et_2$ 231, 232, 233
$Si(OEt)_2MePh$ 73
$Si(OBu)_2Me_2$ 181
$Si(OR')R_3$ 185
$Si(OMe)Me_3$ 180
$Si(OMe)MeEt_2$ 186
$Si(OMe)Et_3$ 180
$Si(OEt)Me_3$ 189
$Si(OEt)Et_3$ 188
$Si(OPr^i)Me_3$ 173
$Si[OCH(Me)Ph]Me_3$ 187
$Si(OCHPh_2)Me_3$ 187

Alkoxyhalosilanes

$Si(OBu^n)_3Cl$ 181
$Si(OBu^s)Cl_3$ 181

Acetoxysilanes

$Si(OAc)_2R_2$ 211, 221, 225
$Si(OAc)_2Me_2$ 181, 189, 190, 211, 216, 217, 234
$Si(OAc)_2Et_2$ 213, 226
$Si(OAc)_2Ph_2$ 217
$Si(OAc)Me_3$ 172, 176, 177, 191, 216
$Si(OAc)Et_3$ 191
$Si(OAc)Ph_3$ 170

Disiloxanes

$(SiR_3)_2O$ 173, 178, 180, 187, 188, 209
$(SiMe_3)_2O$ 168, 169, 173, 175, 177, 180, 185, 187, 188, 191, 192, 194, 195, 214, 225, 228
$(SiEt_3)_2O$ 180, 209, 210
$(SiPhH_2)_2O$ 171
$(SiMe_2Ph)_2O$ 169
$(SiPh_3)_2O$ 169
$[Si(OH)Me_2]_2O$ 74
$[Si(OH)Et_2]_2O$ 201, 202
$SiEt_3OSiEt_2Cl$ 186
$(SiBr_3)_2O$ 171
$(SiCl_3)_2O$ 171

Trisiloxanes

$(SiOR_2)_3$ 145
$(SiOMe_2)_3$ 181
$(SiOEt_2)_3$ 173, 181
$(SiOPh_2)_3$ 223

Tetrasiloxanes

$(SiOR_2)_4$ 147, 173, 204
$(SiOMe_2)_4$ 147, 149, 174, 181, 188, 235
$(SiOEt_2)_4$ 181

Tetrasilyl Orthocarbonate

$[SiO(CH_2Ph)_3]_4C$ 170

Tetrasiloxysiloxane

$Si(OSiPh_3)_4$ 192

Hexasilsesquioxanes

$(SiO_{1.5}Ph)_6$ 240, 241, 245

Octasilsesquioxanes

$(SiO_{1.5}Et)_8$ 240, 241
$(SiO_{1.5}Pr^n)_8$ 240, 241
$(SiO_{1.5}Bu^n)_8$ 240, 241
$(SiO_{1.5}Ph)_8$ 243, 245

Dodecasilsesquioxanes

$(SiO_{1.5}Me)_{12}$ 240, 241
$(SiO_{1.5}Ph)_{12}$ 243

Polysilsesquioxanes

$(SiO_{1.5}R)_n$ 204, 215
$(SiO_{1.5}CH_2CH_2CF_3)_n$ 11
$(SiO_{1.5}Ph)_n$ 171, 242

Polyalkyl- and Polydialkyl-siloxanes (Silicones)

$(SiOMeH)_n$ 153
$(SiOR_2)_n$ 139, 144, 145, 146, 147, 152, 180, 240
$(SiOMe_2)_n$ 88, 92, 104, 105, 144, 145, 146, 154, 158, 171, 189, 207, 233, 236, 237
$(SiOEt_2)_n$ 232, 233, 234

Polyarylsiloxanes (Silicones)

$(SiOMePh)_n$ 145, 146
$(SiOAr_2)_n$ 138, 145, 146, 152
$(SiOPh_2)_n$ 146, 171

Polydisiloxysiloxanes

$[SiO(OSiR_3)_2]_n$ 166, 217
$[SiO(OSiMe_3)_2]_n$ 217
$[SiO(OSiPh_3)_2]_n$ 217
$SiMe_3O(SiOMe_2)_n$ Me 238
$(SiEt_3)_2O(SiEt_2O)_n$ 232
$Si(OH)Et_2O(SiOEt_2)_nSi(OH)Et_2$ 234
$SiMe_2Cl(SiOMe_2)_3Cl$ 74
$SiEt_2Cl(SiOEt_2)_nCl$ 173

ALUMINIUM–OXYGEN–SILICON COMPOUNDS

Siloxyalanes

$Al(OSiR_3)_3$ 204, 209
$Al(OSiMe_3)_3$ 172, 173
$Al(OSiEt_3)_3$ 172, 202, 203, 209, 210, 251
$Al(OSiAr_3)_3$ 204
$Al(OSiPh_3)_3$ 172
$Al[OSi(OH)_2R]_3$ 204
$Al[OSi(OH)_2Ph]_3$ 204, 205
$Al(OSiEt_2OSiEt_2OH)_3$ 202
$Al[OSi(OH)_2Ph]_2[OSi(OH)Ph]_2OH$ 205
$Al(OSiEt_3)_2OH$ 202
$AlMe_2OSiMe_3$ 174
$AlEt_2(OSiMe_2)_4Et$ 174
$AlR_2(OSiR'_2)_nR''$ 173
$Al(OR)_{3-n}(OSiR_3)_n$ 211
$Al(OPr^i)_2OSiMe_3$ 173, 211, 212
$Al(OPr^i)_2OSiPh_3$ 172, 211

Siloxyhaloalanes

$Al(OSiEt_3)Br_2$ 173
$Al(OSiR_3)Cl_2$ 173
$Al(OSiMe_3)Cl_2$ 173

Siloxyaluminoxanes

$[Al(OSiEt_3)_2]_2O$ 202
$(AlOSiR_3O)_n$ 166
$[AlOSiMe_3O]_n(OPr^i)(Ac)$ 212
$Al(OSiEt_3)_2O[Al(OSiEt_3)O]_nAl(OSiEt_3)_2$ 202

Polyaluminosiloxanes

$[Al(OR)OSiR'_2O]_n$ 211
$[Al(OCMeCHCOMe)OSiPh_2O]_n$ 213
$[Al(OSiMe_3)OSiMe_2O]_n$ 211
$(AlCl.OSiEt_2O)_2$ 173
$[Al(SiO_{1.5}Ph)_3]_n$ 204, 205
$[Al_{0.5}O(SiMe_2O)_{1.5n}]_x$ 207

Phosphorus-Containing Polyaluminosiloxanes

$[AlOSiR_3OP(O)OSiR_3O]_n(SiR_3)(OSiR_3)$ 209
$[Al(OSiEt_3)_2O]_2P(O)OSiEt_3$ 210

ANTIMONY(III)–OXYGEN–SILICON COMPOUNDS

$Sb(OSiR_3)_3$ 189
$Sb(OSiMe_3)_3$ 189
$Sb_2(OSiMe_2O)_3$ 190, 235

ARSENIC(III)–OXYGEN–SILICON COMPOUNDS

$As(OSiPh_3)_3$ 183, 184
$AsPh(OSiPh_3)_2$ 185
$As_2(OSiPh_2O)_3$ 184, 223
$(AsPh)_2(OSiPh_2O)_2$ 185, 224
$As_2(OSiPh_2OSiPh_2O)_3$ 184, 223
$[AsPhOSiPh_2O]_n$ 224
$[AsO_{1.5}H(SiPhO_{1.5})_8]_n$ 224

ARSENIC(V)–OXYGEN–SILICON COMPOUNDS

$As(O)(OSiMe_3)_3$ 185, 224
$As(O)(OSiPh_3)_3$ 183, 184, 185
$As(O)Ph(OSiPh_3)_2$ 183
$As(O)Me(OSiMe_2Cl)_2$ 182, 183, 222
$As(O)Ph(OSiPh_2Cl)_2$ 183
$As(O)Me(OSiMeCl_2)_2$ 182, 183, 222
$As(O)Ph(OSiPhCl_2)_2$ 183, 222
$As(O)(OH)_2OSiPh_3$ 184
$[As(O)OSiMe_3O]_n$ 224
$[As(O)(OH)OSiPh_2O]_n$ 223
$As(O)(OH)_2[OSiPh_2OAs(O)OH]_nOH$ 222

BORON–OXYGEN–SILICON COMPOUNDS

Siloxyboranes

$B(OSiR_3)_3$ 182
$B(OSiMe_3)_3$ 74, 179, 180
$B(OSiEt_3)_3$ 179, 180
$B(OSiEtAm^i_2)_3$ 178
$B(OSiMe_2OEt)_3$ 227
$B(OSiR_2Cl)_3$ 180
$B(OSiCl_3)_3$ 181
$BMe(OSiEt_3)_2$ 180
$BBr(OSiEt_3)_2$ 180
$BPh(OSiEt_3)_2$ 179
$B(OEt)_2OSiMe_2OAc$ 181
$B(OAc)_2OSiMe_2OBu$ 181

Siloxyhaloboranes

BBr_2OSiMe_3 180
BCl_2OSiR_2Cl 180

Siloxybisboranes

$B_2(OSiPh_2O)_3$ 181

Silyl Metaborates

$[BO(OSiR_3)]_3$ 182

Polyborosiloxanes

$(BR'OSiR_2O)_n$ 72
$B(OR)_2(OSiR_2OB–)_nOSiR_2OAc$ 225
$B(OAc)_2(OSiR_2OB–)_nOSiR_2OR$ 225
$(B_2O_3.3SiMe_2O)_n$ 227

Polyborocarbosiloxanes

$[B(Bu)CH_2SiMe_2OSiMe_2CH_2]_n$ 75

CARBON–OXYGEN–SILICON COMPOUNDS (CARBOSILOXANES)

$(SiMe_2OCH_2O)_n$ 166

CHROMIUM(VI)–OXYGEN–SILICON COMPOUNDS [SILYL CHROMATES(VI)]

$CrO_2(OSiMe_3)_2$ 192
$(CrO_4OSiMe_2)_n$ 237

GERMANIUM(IV)–OXYGEN–SILICON COMPOUNDS

$Ge(OSiPh_3)_4$ 191, 192

HAFNIUM(IV)–OXYGEN–SILICON COMPOUNDS

$Hf(OSiPh_3)_4$ 191, 192

LEAD–OXYGEN–SILICON COMPOUNDS

$Pb(OSiMe_3)_2$ 193
$Pb[(OSiMe_2)_xSiMe_3]$
$[(OSiMe_2)_ySiMe_3]$ 238
$Pb(OH)_2.2Pb(OSiEt_3)_2$ 194

LITHIUM–OXYGEN–SILICON COMPOUNDS

$LiOSiMe_3$ 168
$LiOSiPh_3$ 169

MAGNESIUM–OXYGEN–SILICON COMPOUNDS

$MgHalOSiH_2Ph$ 171
$MgHalOSiHRPh$ 171
$MgBrOSiPh_3$ 171
$MgIOSiMe_3$ 171

MERCURY(II)–OXYGEN–SILICON COMPOUNDS

$Hg(OSiMe_3)_2$ 193

MOLYBDENUM–OXYGEN–SILICON COMPOUNDS

$Mo(OSiPh_3)_3$ 190
$MoO_2(OSiPh_3)_2$ 190

NIOBIUM(V)–OXYGEN–SILICON COMPOUNDS

$Nb(OSiMe_3)_5$ 190
$[Nb(OSiMe_3)_4]_2O$ 190

NITROGEN–OXYGEN–SILICON COMPOUNDS (NITRATOSILANES)

$(NO_3)_4Si.2py$ 194
$(NO_3)_2SiMe_2$ 194
NO_3SiMe_3 194

PHOSPHORUS(III)–OXYGEN–SILICON COMPOUNDS

$P(OSiR_3)_3$ 187
$PR_4OSi(OH)Me_2$ 147
$(PR_4OSiMe_2)_2O$ 147

PHOSPHORUS(V)–OXYGEN–SILICON COMPOUNDS

Silylphosphates

$P(O)(OSiR_3)_3$ 185, 186, 209
$P(O)(OSiMe_3)_3$ 185, 186, 187, 210

$P(O)(OSiEt_3)_3$ 186, 210
$P(O)(OR)(OSiHR_2)_2$ 186
$P(O)(OEt)(OSiEt_2H)_2$ 232
$P(O)(OEt)(OSiEt_2Cl)_2$ 232
$P(O)(OH)_2OSiR_3$ 209
$P(O)(OH)_2OSiMe_3$ 186, 210
$P(O)(OH)_2OSiEt_3$ 186, 209, 210
$P(O)(OR)_2OSiHR_2$ 186
$P(O)(OEt)_2OSiHEt_2$ 186
$P(O)(OEt)_2OSiEt_2OSiEt_3$ 186

Silyl Phosphonates

$P(O)H(OSiMe_3)_2$ 186
$P(O)H(OSiMeEt_2)_2$ 186
$P(O)Et(OEt)OSiEt_3$ 186

Silyl Phosphorochloridates

$P(O)(OSiMe_3)Cl_2$ 187

Phosphatopolysiloxanes

$[P(O)(OEt)_2]_2O(SiEt_2O)_n$ 231

Poly(Silyl Phosphates)

$P(O)[OSiEt_2OP(O)(OEt)_2]_2OEt$ 232
$[P(O)(OEt)OSiEt_2O]_n$ 231
$[P(O)OSi(OR)_2R'O]_n$ 231

POTASSIUM–OXYGEN–SILICON COMPOUNDS

$KOSiMe_3$ 182
$K(SiOR_2)_4OH$ 147

RHENIUM(VII)–OXYGEN–SILICON COMPOUNDS

$ReO_3(OSiMe_3)$ 194

SODIUM–OXYGEN–SILICON COMPOUNDS

Sodium Silanolates

$NaOSiR(OH)_2$ 204, 208
$NaOSiEt(OH)_2$ 170, 204
$NaOSiPh(OH)_2$ 170, 204, 205
$NaOSiR_3$ 175, 193, 204
$NaOSiMe_3$ 167, 168, 169, 172, 178, 182, 193
$NaOSiEt_3$ 168, 180, 189
$NaOSiPhMe_2$ 169
$NaOSiPh_3$ 168, 169, 170, 172, 183, 185, 190, 191, 193

Disodium Silanediolates

$(NaO)_2SiR_2$ 220
$(NaO)_2SiPh_2$ 212, 213, 239

Disodium Siloxane Derivatives

$(NaOSiR_2)_2O$ 204
$(NaOSiMe_2)_2O$ 170
$(NaOSiPhEt)_2O$ 170
$Na_2O(SiOMe_2)_n$ 207
$Na_2O(SiOMePh)_3$ 170, 204

Trisodium Silanetriolates

$(NaO)_3SiPh$ 170

Poly(Sodium Siloxanes)

$[(NaO)SiMeO]_n$ 170
$[(NaO)SiCH_2PhO]_n$ 170
$[(NaO)SiPhO]_n$ 170

Poly(Sodium Aluminosiloxanes)

$NaO[SiMe_2OAl(ONa)O]_2Na.7H_2O$ 204
$Na[OSiMe_2OAl(ONa)]_2SiMe_2ONa.8H_2O$ 203

SULPHUR(VI)–OXYGEN–SILICON COMPOUNDS

Silyl Bisulphates

SO_4HSiR_3 188
SO_4HSiEt_3 188
$(SO_4H)_2SiMe_2$ 188
$SO_2(OH)O(SiEt_2O)_nSiEt_2OH$ 234

Silyl Sulphates

$SO_4(SiMe_3)_2$ 188, 233
$(SO_4SiMe_2)_2$ 188, 233

$[(SO_4)_3SiMe_2)_n$ 233
$SO_2(OSiMe_3)O(SiMe_2OSO_2O)_nSiMe_3$ 233

TANTALUM(V)–OXYGEN–SILICON COMPOUNDS

$Ta(OSiMe_3)_5$ 190, 191
$Ta(OSiMe_2Et)_5$ 191
$Ta(OSiMeEt_2)_5$ 191
$Ta(OSiEt_3)_5$ 191

TIN(II)–OXYGEN–SILICON COMPOUNDS

$Sn(OSiMe_3)_2$ 182
$(SnOSiMe_2O)_n$ 220

TIN(IV)–OXYGEN–SILICON COMPOUNDS

$Sn(OSiMe_3)_4$ 182
$Sn(OSiEt_3)_4$ 251
$Sn(OSiPh_3)_4$ 191
$Sn(OSiMe_3)_2Me_2$ 182
$Sn(OSiPh_3)_2Me_2$ 182
$[SnO(OSiR_3)_2]_n$ 166
$(SnR_2OSiR'_2O)_n$ 220, 221
$(SnBu^i_2OSiMe_2O)_n$ 221
$(SnR_2O)_m(SiR'_2O)_n$ 219
$(SnEt_2O)_mO(SiR_2O)_n$ 219

TITANIUM(IV)–OXYGEN–SILICON COMPOUNDS

Siloxytitanes

$Ti(OSiR_3)_4$ 175
$Ti(OSiMe_3)_4$ 174, 175, 176, 177, 178, 179, 214
$Ti(OSiMe_2Et)_4$ 191
$Ti(OSiMeEt_2)_4$ 191
$Ti(OSiEt_3)_4$ 175, 178, 191, 194, 251
$Ti(OSiPh_3)_4$ 175, 178, 192
$Ti[OSi(OH)_2R]_4$ 215
$TiO_2[(OSiPh_2)_4]_2$ 175
$Ti(OH)(OSiMe_3)_3$ 214
$Ti(OR)_{4-n}(OSiEt_3)_n$ 176
$Ti(OPr^i)(OSiMe_3)_3$ 178, 216
$Ti(OBu)(OSiEt_3)_3$ 176
$Ti(OPr^i)_2(OSiMe_3)_2$ 176, 178, 216, 217
$Ti(OPr)_2(OSiEt_3)_2$ 176
$Ti(OBu)_2(OSiEt_3)_2$ 176
$Ti(OPr^i)_2(OSiPh_3)_2$ 217
$Ti(OPr^i)_3OSiMe_3$ 176, 178, 216
$Ti(OPr^n)_3OSi(OPr^n)_3$ 176
$Ti(OSiMe_3)_n(OAc)_{4-n}$ 177
$Ti(OPr^i)(OSiMe_3)_2OAc$ 217

Siloxyhalotitanes

$Ti(OSiMe_3)_3Cl$ 178
$Ti(OSiR_3)_2Hal_2$ 178
$Ti(OSiMe_3)_2Cl_2$ 178
$Ti(OSiR_3)Hal_3$ 178
$Ti(OSiMe_3)Cl_3$ 178

Siloxytitanoxanes

$[Ti(OSiMe_3)_3]_2O$ 214
$[Ti(OAc)_2O]_3Ti(OAc)O.OSiMe_3$ 177
$[TiO(OSiR_3)_2]_n$ 166
$[Ti(OSiMe_3)_2O]_n$ 217
$[Ti(OSiMe_3)_2O]_n(OSiMe_3)SiMe_3$ 214

Poly(Titanosiloxanes)

$[Ti(OPr^n)_3O]_2Si(OPr^n)_2$ 176
$[Ti(OSiMe_3)_2OSiMe_2O]_n$ 216
$[Ti(OSiPh_3)_2OSiPh_2O]_n$ 217
$[Ti(OBu)_2O]_mO[SiR_2O]_n$ 215
$[Ti(OSiRO_{0.5})_4H_2O]_n$ 215
$[Ti(OSiMeO_{0.5})_4H_2O]_n$ 215
$[Ti(OSiEtO_{0.5})_4H_2O]_n$ 215

VANADIUM(IV)–OXYGEN–SILICON COMPOUNDS

$V(OSiPh_3)_4$ 193

VANADIUM(V)–OXYGEN–SILICON COMPOUNDS

$V(O)(OSiR_3)_3$ 192
$V(O)(OSiMe_3)_3$ 192
$V(O)(OSiEt_3)_3$ 194
$V(O)(OSiMe_3)_2Cl$ 192
$V(O)(OSiMe_3)Cl_2$ 192

ZIRCONIUM(IV)–OXYGEN–SILICON COMPOUNDS

$Zr(OSiMe_3)_4$ 190, 191
$Zr(OSiMe_2Et)_4$ 191
$Zr(OSiEt_3)_4$ 191
$Zr(OSiPh_3)_4$ 191, 192

Sulphur Compounds

S_8 6, 111
Sα 6, 111
Sβ 6, 111
Sλ 111
Sπ 111
Sρ 111

Sulphur Halides

S_2Cl_2 112
SCl_2 112, 113
SF_6 110

SULPHUR–OXYGEN COMPOUNDS

Thionyl Halides, Imides, and Derivatives

$SOCl_2$ 113
SOF_2 114
$SOFNR_2$ 114
$SOFNH_2$ 114
$SOFNC_5H_{10}$ 114
$(SOFNH_2)_n$ 114
$[S(OH)FNH]_n$ 114
SONR 114
SONH 113, 114, 115
$(SONH)_4$ 115
$(SONH)_n$ 113, 114, 115

Sulphanuric Halides

$(SOClN)_3$ 116, 117
$(SOFN)_n$ 116, 117

Sulphuryl Derivatives

$SO_2(NCO)_2$ 117, 118, 119
SO_2NH_2NCO 118
$SO_2(NH_2)_2$ 39, 117, 118, 119
$SO_2(OH)NH_2$ 120
$SO_2(NH)_3(CNH)_2$ 120
SO_2NNH_4 120
$(SO_2)_2NH(NH_2)_2$ 119
$(SO_2)_2(CH_2)_4N_4$ 119
$S_2O_5(NCO)_2$ 117
$(SO_2NH)_3$ 120, 121
$S_3O_{10}(NH_4)_2$ 121
$(SO_2NH)_4$ 120, 121
$(SO_3)_n$ 110, 117, 121, 124, 163
$(SO_2NH)_n$ 120
$SO_3H(SO_2NH)_nOH$ 121
$(SO_2NHCOOC_2H_4O)_n$ 118
$[SO_2NHC(O)NH]_n$ 118
$[SO_2.(CH_2)_2N_2]_n$ 119

SULPHUR–NITROGEN COMPOUNDS

Sulphur Nitrides, Imides, and Derivatives

S_2N_2 17, 113
S_4N_4 17, 112, 113, 115
$(SN)_n$ 17, 113
$S_4(NH)_4$ 17, 112, 113, 115
$S_6(NH)_2$ 111, 112
S_7NH 6, 17, 111, 112
$(SNCl)_3$ 17, 115
$(SNNH_2)_3$ 116
$(SNH)_n$ 113
$(SNMe)_n$ 113
$[S_4(NH)_2N_2C_2(CN)_2]_n$ 113

SULPHUR–BORON COMPOUNDS

$(SBH)_3$ 83
$(SBOMe)_3$ 83
$(SBNMe_2)_3$ 83
$(SMeBH_2)_n$ 83
For silicon sulphates, see under SILICON (p. 296)

Compounds of Other Elements

Antimony

Sb_2O_3 2

Arsenic

AsH_3 82

Beryllium

$Be_4O(RCOO)_6$ 264, 265
$Be_4O(CH_3COO)_6$ 264

Carbon

CF_3NO 17
CONH 114, 115
C_2F_3NO 18
$C_2N_2(NH_2)_2$ 120
$(CNH_2N)_3$ 115
$C_2(CN)_4$ 113
$C_6F_4H_2$ 9
$C_6F_4I_2$ 9
$[CH_2N(CH_2CH.OHMe)_2]_2$ 66
$(C)_n$ 4, 7, 8, 21, 30
$(CF)_n$ 6, 7
$(CFN)_n$ 18
$(CF_2)_n$ 6, 8, 9
$(CONH)_n$ 114, 115
$(CF_2CClF)_n$ 6, 8
$(CH_2CF_2)_n$ 9
$(NCF.OCF_2)_n$ 18
$(C_2F_4ONCF_3)_n$ 17
$(C_4F)_n$ 8
$[(CF_2)_3CFCF_3]_n$ 8
$(C_6F_4)_n$ 9
$(C_6F_5.CFCF_2)_n$ 10

Germanium

$(GeOR_2)_n$ 235
$(GeOMe_2)_3$ 236
$(GeOMe_2)_4$ 235
$(GeOMe_2)_n$ 163
$(GeOPh_2)_3$ 236
$(GeOPh_2)_4$ 236
$(GeOPh_2)_n$ 163, 236

Gold

$(AuR_2CN)_n$ 257

Lead

Pb_2R_6 4

Nickel

$[Ni(CN)_2]_n$ 257

Palladium

$(PdCl_2)_n$ 2, 3

Selenium

Se_8 6
Seα 6
Seβ 6

Silver

$(AgSCN)_n$ 2, 3

Titanium

$Ti_2O(OR)_6$ 12
$Ti_3O_2(OR)_8$ 12
$Ti(OR)_3O[Ti(OR)_2O]_nTi(OR)_3$ 213

Tin

Sn_2R_6 4
$(SnOR_2)_n$ 219
$(SnOMe_2)_n$ 163

Metal Chelate Polymers and Related Compounds

(Classified according to ligand)

Ammonia

$M(NH_3)_6^{2+}$ 268, 269
M = Ca,Co,Cr,Fe,Mn,Ni,Ti,V

Bis(α-Aminoacids)

Bis(α-aminoacids) 260
Metal(Co)polymers derived from 261
Terephthalic acid-β-hydroxyethylglycine nickel derivative and polycondensate of 265

β-Diketones

Acetylacetone 258, 269
Aluminium derivatives, 212, 213, 265, 272

Metal acetylacetonates 257, 258, 270
–, chelate polymers from 258
Titanium derivatives 218
1,1,1-Trifluoroacetone 269

Glyoximes

Bisglyoximes 260
Dimethylglyoxime-copper 271
Dimethylglyoxime-nickel 271

o-Hydroxy-aldehydes, -ketones, and Quinones

Bis(*o*-hydroxy)aldehydes 260
Bis(8-hydroxyquinolates) 271, 272
2,5-Dihydroxybenzoquinone, polymers derived from 261
1,6-Dihydroxyphenazine, polymers derived from 261
4-Hydroxy-5-formyl-salicylaldehyde, polymers derived from 261

Phthalocyanines

Copper phthalocyanine dimer 270
Chlorophenoxygermanium phthalocyanines 266
Metal phthalocyanines, general 261, 270
Siloxygermanium phthalocyanines 266
Tetracarboxydiphenyl ether, polymers derived from 262
Tetracyanodiphenyl ether, polymers derived from 262

π-Complexes

1,1′-Bischloroformylferrocene, and polymers derived from 267
trans-Cinnamoylferrocene, copolymers from 267
Ferrocene 267
Ferrocenes 266
Lithio-dimethylferrocene, and polymers derived from 267
Lithio-ferrocene, and polymers derived from 267
Nickel cyclooctatetraene, and polymers derived from 267
Poly(vinylferrocene) 267
Siloxanylferrocenes, and polymers derived from 267
Vinylferrocene 267
–, copolymers from 267

Poly(Allylacetoacetate)

Chelate polymers derived from 263

Rubeanic Acid

Copper derivative 261
Nickel derivative 261

Schiff's Bases

Schiff's bases 260
Chelate polymers derived from (Co,Cu,Fe) 263, 265, 271
Chelate polymers derived from glyoxal-aminophenols 263
Chelate polymers derived from pyridine dialdehyde-ethylenediamine 263
Chelate polymers derived from salicylaldehyde-ethylenediamine 271

Sebacoyl Diacetophenone

Sebacoyl diacetophenone 258
Chelate polymers derived from (Al,Be,Co,Cu,Fe,Ni,Zn) 259

Tetraketones

Tetraketones 258, 259, 260, 270
Chelate polymers derived from 270

Water

$M(H_2O)_6^{2+}$ 268, 269
M = Ca,Co,Cr,Fe,Mn,Ni,Ti,V

Miscellaneous Ligands and Polymers

Basic beryllium carboxylates, polymeric 264
Bis(dithiocarbamates) 260
Bis(8-hydroxyquinolines) 260
Bis(iminoacetic acid)-metal polymers 261
Bis(nitrosophenols) 260
Bis(xanthates) 260
Dialdehydes or diketones-semicarbazones, chelate polymers derived from 263
1,8-Diamino-3,6-dithio-octane-acetylacetone, chelate polymers derived from 263
Dimercaptals, metal polymers derived from 263
β-Hydroxyethylethylenediamine, cobalt derivative 265
Naphthazarin, beryllium-containing polymers derived from 261
Pentaerythrityl tetraacetate, chelate polymers derived from 263
Thiopicolinamide-metal polymers 266

SUBJECT INDEX

Catenation

In boron compounds 4, 21
In carbon compounds 3, 4, 6
In germanium compounds 4, 5
In phosphorus compounds 5
In selenium compounds 6
In silicon compounds 4, 162, 163
In sulphur compounds 6
In tellurium compounds 6

Materials

Autocomplexes 2, 3, 31–33
Bischelates, polymer formation from 259–261
Bifunctional monomers
–, boron-containing 35, 36, 52, 58, 59
–, sulphur-containing 117–120
Borazon 21, 30
"Bouncing putty", 74, 227, 228, 250
Carbon-functional silicones 141, 156–159
Carbosiloxanes 166, 167
Condensed anions 163
Condensed cations 2, 110, 122–127, 163
Elastomers 9, 11, 34, 74, 87, 148–151, 157, 235, 236
Fluoro-alkyl nitroso compounds 17, 18
Fluoro-alkyl silicones 11
Fluorocarbons 6, 8–10, 18
Fluorophosphines 79
Homoatomic polymers 3, 57
Isocyanates
–, boron-containing 32, 33, 44
–, organic, addition reactions of 43, 44, 68, 69, 157
–, sulphur-containing 117, 118
Phospham 132
Phosphinoboranes 79
Stereoregular (syndiotactic) polymers 242, 243
Vinyl derivatives
– of boron compounds 71
– of silicon compounds 155

Properties of Polymers and Model Monomers

Applications, technological 6, 9–11, 42, 58, 60, 70, 74, 75, 110, 126, 128, 130–132, 140, 148–158, 179, 213, 215, 222, 228, 229, 233, 237, 238, 252
Base strengths
– of phosphonitrilic derivatives 106
– of silanols 167, 168
Bond properties
–, aromatic character
–, – in borazoles 44–49
–, – in phosphonitrilic compounds 92–108
Bond properties, bond strengths
–, – B—B 57
–, – B—C 57
–, – B—O 57
–, – B—N 22, 44, 45, 47
–, – C—H 267
–, – C—N 268
–, – co-ordinate bonds in metal complexes 267
–, – hydrogen bonds 256, 271
–, – metal-metal 271
–, – P—N 98–100
–, – Si—O and Ti—O 249

Bond properties
–, π-bonding, $d\pi$ — $p\pi$
–, – in phosphinoboranes 16, 77
–, – in phosphorus compounds 110
–, – in P—N 13, 93–96, 105, 106
–, – in P—O 125
–, – in P—P 125
–, – in Si—O 167
–, – in sulphur compounds 110
–, – in S—S 5
–, – in thiophen 106
–, π-bonding, $p\pi$ — $p\pi$
–, – in B—N 21, 22, 44–49
–, – Si—O 162
–, – Ti—O 176
Effect of metal ions
– on degradation of polysiloxanes 144–146, 249–251
– on oxidative stability of metal chelate polymers 270, 271
Geometrical isomerism
– in aminoboranes 48
– in phosphonitrilic derivatives 91
Hindered rotation in aminoboranes 46–48
Irradiation of polymers 74
Miscellaneous properties of polymers
–, adhesive 74, 131, 140, 141, 153, 238
–, dielectric 140, 141
–, electrical conductivity 7, 8, 30, 31, 229
–, flame resistance 130, 132
–, flexibility 9, 82, 102–106, 108
–, ion-exchange 41, 60
–, lubricity 152
–, mechanical 80, 108, 205, 207, 247, 263, 272
–, semiconductance 113
–, solvent solubility 1, 3, 6, 8, 9, 12, 15, 18, 24, 34, 36, 38, 40, 42, 52, 59, 69, 72, 73, 118, 125, 128–131, 134, 192, 203, 205–207, 210, 213–216, 218, 220, 224, 226, 235, 237, 242, 244, 247, 257, 262, 266, 272
Miscellaneous properties of polymers
–, surface activity 140, 141, 159, 238
–, viscosity 8, 9, 34, 37, 38, 73, 74, 79–82, 103–105, 118, 139, 203, 207, 210, 214, 218, 224, 230, 236, 259, 271
–, water-repellency 3, 74, 92, 140, 141, 154, 179
Stability
–, chemical 1, 6–11, 14, 17, 18, 31, 34, 49, 52, 57, 58, 76, 108, 132, 140, 270
–, hydrolytic 4, 11, 14, 17, 22, 24, 32, 34, 36, 38, 40–42, 49–52, 57, 62, 64, 66–68, 70, 73–77, 79, 87, 89, 116–118, 121, 134, 144, 179, 182–184, 191–194, 202, 203, 211, 213, 214, 220–223, 227, 233, 235, 251, 252
–, oxidative 1, 8, 14, 31, 57, 63, 70, 71, 73, 76, 79, 140, 247–249, 267, 270, 271
–, thermal 1, 5, 6, 8, 9–11, 14, 15, 17, 21, 24, 34, 38, 40, 41, 51, 57, 59, 66–69, 71, 73, 77–83, 87, 92, 100–102, 107, 140, 141, 144–146, 172, 179, 184, 191, 200, 201, 203, 206, 207, 217, 236, 245, 247–249, 258, 259, 261–267, 270–273
–, thermodynamic 269
Thermodynamic properties
–, aminoboranes 23, 44, 45
–, borazoles 44
–, energy of dissociation
–, – of $M(H_2O)_6^{2+}$ 269
–, – of $M(NH_3)_6^{2+}$ 267, 269
–, heats of formation of phosphonitrilic derivatives 99
–, heats of polymerisation of phosphonitrilic derivatives 99, 103
–, π-electron energies in phosphonitrilic derivatives 96, 100
–, phosphinoboranes 81
–, ligand field stabilisation in complex ions 267, 268

Reaction Mechanisms

Addition polymerisation 22
Alkylchlorosilane rearrangements 143
Boron acetate–tetramethoxysilane interaction 226
Boron compounds, displacement in 3-co-ordinate 49–51
Boron trichloride–alkoxysilane interactions 181

Chelate stability, influence of ring size on 270
Co-ordination number, influence on polymer properties 249–251
Degree of polymerisation, control of 3, 10, 14, 18, 51, 78, 88, 128, 147, 203, 272
Disulphuryl isocyanate, hydrolysis of 118
High pressure polymerisation 21, 24, 27, 28, 30, 42
Phosphonitrilic derivatives
–, formation of 89, 132, 133
–, nucleophilic substitution in 90, 91, 107
Polysilsesquioxanes, formation of 240–245
Silicone formation, transient catalysts for 147, 148
Siloxanes
–, redistribution reactions in 146, 241, 243
–, thermal degradation of 144–146
Steric effects in selected reactions 16, 22–24, 26, 35–37, 47, 49–51, 142
Sulphur–nitrogen compounds, hydrolysis of 116, 117
Trichlorosilane–benzene interaction 142
Trimethyl borate–diethylsilyl diacetate interaction 226
Tris(triphenylsiloxy)aluminium, thermal degradation of 172

Spectral and Structural Data

Bond moments in phosphonitrilic derivatives 105
Diamagnetic anisotropy in borazoles 48
Dipole moments
–, of aminoboranes 23, 48
–, of borazocines 27
–, of borazoles 48
–, of thiophen 105
Electron diffraction of borazoles 45
Infrared spectra
–, of aminoboranes 23, 45, 46
–, of $B_5N_5H_8$ 25
–, of borazoles 36, 41, 46
–, of cyanoboranes 31, 32
–, of diethanolamine boronic esters 64
–, of fluorocarbons 7, 8
–, of isocyanatoboranes 33
–, of nitrile-borane adducts 25
–, of $Pb(OH)_2.2Pb(OSiEt_3)_2$ 194
–, of P-H-containing compounds 75
–, of phenylsilsesquioxanes 243
–, of phosphonitrilic derivatives 97–99, 101–103
–, of polyborazoles 34
–, of polyboroxoles 38
–, of polydimethylaluminosiloxanes 207
–, of polyethyltitanosiloxanes 215, 216
–, of polymethylaluminosiloxanes 246
–, of polymethyltitanosilanes 215, 216, 246
–, of polyphenylarseno(III)siloxanes 224
–, of silanols 167
–, of triethylsilyl vanadate 194
Mass spectra
–, of borazocines 26
–, of $B_5N_5H_8$ 30
–, of tris(triphenylsiloxy)aluminium 172
Nuclear magnetic resonance spectra
–, of aminoboranes 23, 46–48
–, of borazocines 26
–, of borazoles 48
–, of boron nitride 4
–, of phosphonitrilic derivatives 106
Raman spectra
–, of aminoboranes 23, 45
–, of phosphonitrilic derivatives 97
Ultraviolet spectra
–, of 9-aza-10-boraphenanthrene 21, 51
–, of borazoles 46
X-ray structural data
–, on antimony trioxide 2
–, on $B_5N_5H_8$ 30
–, on borazoles 45

X-ray structural data
–, on borides, metallic 4
–, on boron nitrides 30, 45
–, on carbon monofluoride 7
–, on *N,N*-dimethylaminoborane 23, 24
–, graphite 4
–, on heptasulphur penta-imide 6, 112
–, on hexasulphur di-imide 112
–, on *N*-methylaminoborane 24
–, on palladium(II) chloride 2, 3
–, on phenylsilsesquioxanes 243
–, on phosphides, metallic 5
–, on phosphonitrilic derivatives 12, 92, 97, 103, 106
X-ray structural data
–, on phosphoro-amidate ion 97
–, on phosphorus 5
–, on phosphorus pentoxide 2
–, on polymetaphosphate ion 124
–, on polyphenylsiloxanes, 206
–, on polysulphides 6
–, on selenium 6
–, on silicates 2
–, on silicides, metallic, 4
–, on silver thiocyanate 2,3
–, on sulphur 6, 111, 112
–, on sulphur trioxide 121
–, on tetrasulphur tetranitride 112
–, on tetrasulphur tetra-imide 112